DEVELOPMENTS IN SEDIMENTOLOGY 6

THE IDENTIFICATION OF DETRITAL FELDSPARS

FURTHER TITLES IN THIS SERIES

1. *L. M. J. U. VAN STRAATEN, Editor*
DELTAIC AND SHALLOW MARINE DEPOSITS

2. *G. C. AMSTUTZ, Editor*
SEDIMENTOLOGY AND ORE GENESIS

3. *A. H. BOUMA and A. BROUWER, Editors*
TURBIDITES

4. *F. G. TICKELL*
THE TECHNIQUES OF SEDIMENTARY MINERALOGY

5. *J. C. INGLE Jr.*
THE MOVEMENT OF BEACH SAND

7. *S. DZULYNSKI and E. K. WALTON*
SEDIMENTARY FEATURES OF FLYSCH AND GREYWACKES

8. *G. LARSEN and G. V. CHILINGAR, Editors*
DIAGENESIS IN SEDIMENTS

9-10, *G. V. CHILINGAR, H. J. BISSELL and R. W. FAIRBRIDGE, Editors*
CARBONATE ROCKS

DEVELOPMENTS IN SEDIMENTOLOGY 6

THE IDENTIFICATION OF DETRITAL FELDSPARS

BY

L. VAN DER PLAS

Geology and Mineralogy Department
Agricultural State University, Wageningen, The Netherlands

ELSEVIER PUBLISHING COMPANY Amsterdam London New York 1966

ELSEVIER PUBLISHING COMPANY
335 JAN VAN GALENSTRAAT, P.O. BOX 211, AMSTERDAM

AMERICAN ELSEVIER PUBLISHING COMPANY, INC.
52 VANDERBILT AVENUE, NEW YORK, N.Y. 10017

ELSEVIER PUBLISHING COMPANY LIMITED
RIPPLESIDE COMMERCIAL ESTATE
BARKING, ESSEX

LIBRARY OF CONGRESS CATALOG CARD NUMBER 65-13883

WITH 66 ILLUSTRATIONS AND 40 TABLES

PRINTED IN THE NETHERLANDS

PREFACE

The present text was originally prepared to inform the members of a research team about the numerous feldspar-identification methods that have been developed in the course of time. The members of the team, developing routine methods for the quantitative mineralogical analysis of sedimentary rocks and soils, felt the need for a comprehensive text on feldspar-identification methods. This text had to cover the properties of feldspars as a group of minerals, as a number of chemical compounds and as a family of rather comparable crystalline phases. Moreover, the text had to contain the available information on concentration techniques and determination procedures. The manual which meets with these requirements, grew to the present book.

Upon surveyance of the available identification techniques, it becomes apparent that they are in most cases suitable only for the analysis of feldspars present in igneous or metamorphic rocks. This will soon be explained. Currently used feldspar-identification techniques have been developed to a large extent by petrographers dealing almost exclusively with igneous or metamorphic rocks. Such methods start with the implicit assumption that the measurements carried out on a small number of crystals of one mineral specimen may be generalized to a large extent to all the crystals of this mineral present in the sample. That such an assumption may be made is due to the fact that samples of igneous or metamorphic rocks may be more or less regarded as an equilibrium assemblage of minerals in the thermodynamical sense. As soon as these methods are applied to samples of sediments, the objections against such implicit assumptions are clearly felt. Sedimentologists, soil scientists and a number of other specialists expect any feldspar concentrate to be an assemblage of an unknown number of unknown feldspars from an unknown number of unknown source rocks. In this text the above aspects of the sample and the consequences this has for the identification method receive all the interest such a characteristic deserves.

Sedimentologists, soil scientists and others are often faced with the problem of how to make a quantitative mineralogical analysis of samples containing both fine and coarse particles. Identification techniques for fractions smaller than $2\ \mu$ are entirely different from those applicable to fractions having a $200\text{-}\mu$ particle size. Still, the mineralogical composition must be expressed in such a way that it accounts for the whole sample. This implies, for instance, that the result of X-ray powder analyses and those of optical analyses must be described in as much the same way as possible. The present book will give some suggestions as to the solution of this rather difficult problem. In addition, it will show that investigators, working exclusively with X-ray methods, speak a language entirely different from the one used by microscopists. Microscopists have developed a rather large "arsenal" of terms and names, whereas the X-ray worker can distinguish only between monoclinic and triclinic phases of varying chemical composition and of varying obliquity. This calls for a standardized nomenclature for the description of feldspars, at least for those feldspars found in sediments.

In the last decades ideas about feldspars have changed radically. A large number of research workers are trying to unravel the complex relationships between structure, chemical composition, twinning pattern, physical circumstances of genesis, and exsolution phenomena that have been observed in the crystalline phases of the system $KAlSi_3O_8$–$NaAlSi_3O_8$–$CaAl_2Si_2O_8$. Numerous papers have been published in addition to the increasing number of collected lectures held during feldspar-symposia. The results of such a vast effort in this fascinating field of mineralogy and crystallography are of the greatest importance to the sedimentologist, the petrographer and the soil scientist. For this reason the purely analytical aspects of a specific identification procedure need to be discussed against the background just mentioned.

One of the most important aspects of the quantitative mineralogical analysis of sediments and soils is the concentration of a certain mineral or a group of minerals for better and more efficient study. Consequently, an important part of the text is devoted to concentration techniques of feldspars. Both the specific-gravity concentration, as well as flotation methods, are treated. Handpicking feldspars from stained samples is also a fast moving process. Staining techniques are treated in detail.

THE LEVEL OF DISCUSSION

Upon writing this treatise on feldspar identification I found it rather difficult to determine the level of discussion. The following considerations helped to reach a compromising decision.

The petrographic microscope is a routine instrument for sedimentologists and all of them are assumed to be familiar with the various determination techniques of minerals in thin sections. Most soil scientists are in any event familiar with, if not experts on, X-ray powder methods because they need these in a rather specialized way for the analysis of clay minerals. Finally, a large number of excellent handbooks are available in practically every language which give an elementary course on X-ray powder work, as well as optical crystallography. Therefore, the present book begins with the assumption that the reader is familiar with the elementary aspects of X-ray powder work and with the use of a petrographic microscope. The text provides the reader with a more or less complete inventory of currently used identification techniques. In discussing the practical aspects of the various procedures it takes into account the numerous limitations experienced by the workers who study sediments and soils.

ACKNOWLEDGEMENTS

In this preface, I feel obliged to acknowledge the stimulating discussions and good advice received from friends and colleagues. The critical remarks of my wife concerning the wording of the presented ideas may have led to a more understandable text.

I wish to thank all those who contributed to this book in its embryonic, its preliminary and its final stage. Especially my colleague, the leader of our research team, Dr. J. Ch. L. Favejee deserves words of gratitude for his invaluable criticism and stimulating advice. The head of our department Professor Dr. D. J. Doeglas made valuable comments on the preliminary text. Furthermore, I thank Dr. P. Hartman, Dr. A. C. Tobi and Dr. A. H. van der Veen for the meticulous care they showed in commenting on parts of the manuscript. Moreover, Dr. Van der Veen helped me a great deal by critically reading the whole text in its final shape.

The workers of the ore-dressing department of the Technical University, Delft, The Netherlands, kindly introduced me into flotation methods and Mr. R. van Ginkel M.I. assisted in conceiving the section on this subject. Great help was received from the people of the Mathematical Centre of the Agricultural University of Wageningen in doing all sorts of calculations with their mechanical equipment. Miss A. M. G. Bakker and Mr. R. Schoorl are gratefully mentioned for their enthousiastic collaboration in optical work and in preparing and evaluating numerous X-ray powder patterns. Moreover, Mr. Schoorl kindly assisted in preparing the indexes. Last but not least I wish to thank Mr. S. Slager A.I. for really helping me to start the work presented here.

In conclusion it must be stated that the material in this text is the fruit of agreeable teamwork and numerous discussions. Consequently, some of the reported ideas sprang just spontaneously from these discussions and it is hard to trace their parentage. The personnel of the Mineralogical Laboratory and of other branches of our Earth Science Department co-operated in every way possible. The drawings, for instance, have been expertly made by Mr. G. Buurman and Mr. W. F. Andriessen. The flow sheets in the final chapter have been devised and drawn by Mr. J. Bult. Mr. Z. van Druuten carefully prepared the photographs.

Thanks are also due to the authors whose diagrams, with their kind permission, were used to complete this text, while at the same time I am indebted to the many publishers who gave permission to use such material.

Although a book like this one could not possibly have been written without making ample use of the results of other workers in the field, the writer wishes to state that he alone is responsible for the way in which such results have been reported here. Moreover, he will be grateful for any criticism on the present text as well as for any suggestion towards the development of better methods for the identification of detrital feldspars.

Ede (The Netherlands)   L. VAN DER PLAS

CONTENTS

PREFACE V

CHAPTER 1. INTRODUCTION 1
Feldspars exposed to terrestrial influences 3
Feldspars in a marine environment 5
Feldspars in sediments 6
    Information concerning the source area of a sediment, 6 – Feldspars as a stratigraphic
    guide, 7 – Feldspars as a source of information on the environment of a sedimentary
    deposit, 8 – Feldspars as an indication of the history of a sediment after deposition, 8
Feldspars in soils 9
    Minerals as a store of macro elements, 11 – Minerals as a store of micro elements, 12 –
    The mineralogical composition as a soil-forming factor, 12 – The behaviour of minerals
    under soil conditions, 13 – Experiments with feldspars in soil science, 13
Final remarks 16

CHAPTER 2. THE NATURE OF FELDSPARS 19
Feldspars 19
    The order–disorder relation, 20
Classification of feldspars 23
Alkali feldspars 25
The chemical composition of alkali feldspars 33
Plagioclase feldspars 34
    Albite, 34 – Anorthite, 35 – Intermediate plagioclase feldspars, 36
The chemical composition of plagioclases 38

CHAPTER 3. PERTHITES, MESOPERTHITES, ANTIPERTHITES AND
PERISTERITES 41
Introduction 41
Perthites 42
Mesoperthites and antiperthites 44
Peristerites 45

CHAPTER 4. IDENTIFICATION PROCEDURES BASED ON CHEMICAL
METHODS 47
Introduction and review 47
Staining methods 49

Methods for staining feldspars 50

Staining samples of feldspar grains with cobaltinitrite, 50 – Staining samples of feldspar grains with hemateine, 51 – Staining rock slabs or thin sections with cobaltinitrite, 51 – Staining rock slabs or thin sections with hemateine, 52 – Staining rock slabs or thin sections with bariumrhodizonate, 52

CHAPTER 5. IDENTIFICATION PROCEDURES BASED ON PHYSICAL
METHODS, AN INTRODUCTION 53

Introduction 53

Physical properties of crystals, 54 – Concentration methods, 54 – Identification methods, 55

Summary 56

CHAPTER 6. CONCENTRATION OF FELDSPARS BASED ON SPECIFIC GRAVITY
AND ON FLOTATION 57

The specific gravity of feldspars 57

Specific-gravity limits for concentrating purposes, 59 – Alkali feldspars, 62 – Plagioclase feldspars, 63

Flotation of feldspars 66

The physico-chemical aspects of flotation, 66 – The procedure of flotation, 69 – The efficiency of flotation, 72 – Practical aspects of flotation on an industrial scale, 72 – Final remarks, 73

CHAPTER 7. THE INDICES OF REFRACTION AND THE AXIAL ANGLE OF
FELDSPARS 75

The indices of refraction of feldspars 75

Introduction, 75 – Alkali feldspars, 75 – Plagioclase feldspars, 80

The axial angle of feldspars 90

Introduction, 90 – Alkali feldspars, 93 – Plagioclase feldspars, 95

CHAPTER 8. THE ORIENTATION OF THE INDICATRIX OF FELDSPARS . . . 99

Introduction 99

The use of Euler angles 100

Alkali feldspars 105

Plagioclase feldspars 106

Universal stage methods, 108

The zone method; procedures and remarks 115

Mounting of the thin section, 115 – The measurement procedure, 117 – Determination of the structural state, 128

Methods requiring a petrographic microscope only 132

Conclusions 143

CHAPTER 9. TWINNING OF FELDSPARS 145

Introduction 145

Classification of feldspar twins 145

The occurrence of feldspar twins 149

Alkali feldspars, 150 – Plagioclase feldspars, 153

The identification of feldspar twins 156
    Plagioclase twins, 156 – Alkali-feldspar twins, 165

CHAPTER 10. THE X-RAY POWDER PATTERNS OF FELDSPARS 169
Introduction. 169
X-ray powder methods 170
    The Debye-Scherrer arrangement, 170 – Focussing arrangements, 172 – Calibration, 174 –
    Comments on the type of target of the X-ray tube, 175 – Comments on sample preparation,
    176 – Summary, 177
Space groups and unit-cell parameters of feldspars 178
Powder patterns of alkali feldspars 180
    Disordered monoclinic phases, 180 – Partly ordered or completely ordered homogeneous
    triclinic phases, 184 – The concept "obliquity", 190 – Powder patterns of perthites, 191
Powder patterns of plagioclase feldspars 195
    Plagioclases with less than 20% An, 197 – Plagioclases with more than 20% An, but less
    than 40% An, 199 – Plagioclases with more than 40% An, 200
Concluding remarks 202
Concerning the tables. 203

CHAPTER 11. ON THE IDENTIFICATION OF FELDSPARS IN CLASTIC ROCKS;
A CRITICAL DISCUSSION 227
Introduction. 227
Aspects of a quantitative detrital feldspar analysis 229
    Quartz- and feldspar-rich arenaceous sediments and soils, 230 – Argillaceous sediments
    and clay-rich soils, 240 – Carbonate sediments and soils, 245 – Miscellaneous sediments
    and soils, 250
A flow sheet for the study of detrital feldspars 254
    Introduction, 254 – The sample, 255 – The pre-treatment, 256 – Oxidation of organic
    compounds, 256 – Removal of carbonates, 256 – Removal of gypsum, 258 – Removal of
    iron oxide, 259 – Sieving and the preparation of size fractions, 260 – The separation of
    heavy and light minerals, 261 – Flotation of the light fraction, 262 – Staining of feldspars,
    263 – Some remarks about counting methods, 263 – The reliability of counting results,
    264 – A discussion of the flow sheet of Fig.65, 265
Aspects of a qualitative detrital feldspar analysis 271
    Quartz- and feldspar-rich arenaceous sediments and soils, 271 – Argillaceous sediments
    and clay-rich soils, 274 – Carbonate sediments and soils, 275 – Final remarks, 276

REFERENCES 277

INDEX TO PROCEDURES 289

GENERAL INDEX 291

Chapter 1

INTRODUCTION

Feldspars constitute a group of minerals with varying amounts of sodium, potassium and/or calcium in a comparable aluminium-silicium-oxyde structure. The potassium, sodium and calcium ions are situated in large spaces within this framework.

The potassium- and sodium-rich members of the group with a negligible amount of calcium are known as alkali feldspars. These crystalline phases may still have a rather varying chemical composition. Moreover, the structure of phases with an identical chemical composition is not necessarily the same. The various modifications of feldspars rich in potassium are known as sanidine, orthoclase, microcline and adularia. If the amount of sodium surpasses the potassium content, the phase is sometimes described as anorthoclase. Lamellar aggregates consisting of potassium-rich and sodium-rich feldspars, caused by exsolution, are known as perthites.

Members of this group of minerals rich in calcium and/or sodium, but with a negligible amount of potassium, are known as plagioclases. The plagioclases are named according to their chemical composition, notwithstanding the fact that different modifications exist. The pure or rather pure sodium feldspars are known as albites. Conventionally, albite must have less than 10 molecule percentage of the pure calcium-feldspar composition. The following chemical boundaries, also described in the next chapter, are used for the other categories. From 10 to 30% the phase is known as oligoclase, from 30 to 50% as andesine, the next 20% range is termed labradorite and the following bytownite. Anorthite is at least a 90% pure calcium feldspar. For an insight into the chemical composition see Fig.1.

As the next chapter deals with a more detailed description of the nature of feldspars, we can leave this subject now and turn to the reasons for studying feldspars. Sedimentologists and soil scientists faced with the identification of feldspars may still wonder why the identification of these minerals receives special treatment. They may even wonder why attention should be payed to these minerals at all; the reasons will be considered here.

Textbooks on geology and petrography leave no doubt as to the fact that the crust of the earth comprises large amounts of these minerals. Igneous rocks are estimated to contain on the average more than 60 volume percentages of feldspars. Another important group of rocks, the metamorphic rocks, are known to

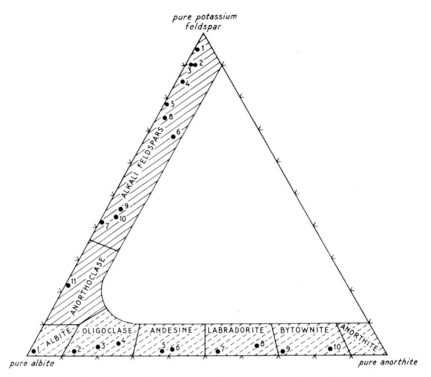

Fig.1. A triangular diagram illustrating the chemical composition of feldspars in terms of end members. The nomenclature of the feldspar series is also shown. The numbered dots represent the chemical analyses of specific feldspars listed with the same numbers in Tables I and II.

be composed of, among other minerals, large amounts of feldspars. In this case these minerals are either brought about by the recrystallization of the original material, or as a result of such a recrystallization with the additional introduction of potassium and/or sodium from elsewhere. The last mentioned process, so important in metamorphism, is known as potassium and/or sodium metasomatism.

In the light of the foregoing discussion about the importance of feldspars in igneous and metamorphic rocks, we may state without further proof that feldspars must play a role in the composition of sediments and soils. They play this role either as feldspar fragments or as the alteration products of these minerals. This statement may be made irrespective of the fact that large amounts of sediments came into being through a re-sedimentation of the erosion products of other sediments.

Numerous papers, a few of which will be discussed later on, elucidate the foregoing thesis. Feldspars are found in virtually every sample of a sediment or a soil. It goes without saying that the quantity may vary. Moreover, the afore-mentioned papers also provide evidence for the occurrence of feldspar fragments in the whole range of possible particle sizes. Fractions even smaller than 2μ may contain feldspars. On the other hand, feldspars have been found in sand fractions of more than 500 μ. This feature is familiar to those who deal frequently with X-ray diffraction patterns of the clay fractions of such samples, or to those dealing exclusively with sand fractions.

FELDSPARS EXPOSED TO TERRESTRIAL INFLUENCES

The behaviour of feldspars in sediments and soils can be explained by some thermodynamical properties of these crystalline phases. Studies have shown that feldspars are stable in a surrounding characterized by relatively high temperatures and pressures. Both pressure and temperature are much higher than the values they show at the earth's surface. It seems that specific amounts of the substance H_2O favours also the origin of feldspars under certain physical circumstances. On the other hand, there is enough evidence that feldspars can grow in an environment characterized by pressures and temperatures very similar to those found on the surface of the earth. In the latter case, the concentration of specific ions in the all-pervading lye is exceptional. We are not quite certain as yet whether such feldspars grow as stable or as metastable crystalline phases.

Experiments have shown that feldspar fragments behave rather differently under leaching conditions. Their behaviour in this case depends on numerous conditions. Some of these are enumerated here:

(1) the pH of the surrounding liquid phase,
(2) the nature of the ions in the liquid phase,
(3) the concentration of ions in the liquid phase,
(4) the temperature of the liquid phase,
(5) the particle size of the feldspar fragments,
(6) the chemical composition of the feldspar fragments,
(7) the modification of the feldspar fragments,
(8) the presence of exsolution phenomena such as perthites.

A comparable behaviour has been demonstrated to exist through the study of feldspar fragments in soils under the influence of different climates. It is known, for instance, that the fine fraction present in some soils from arctic regions is still rather rich in feldspars. Soils of about the same age found in humid tropical regions have fine fractions that are devoid of feldspars, even if the parent material contains this mineral in large quantities.

The analysis of these and comparable examples gives an important insight into the aspects of feldspar alteration during the weathering of rocks, sediments or the parent material of soils. It has been established that slight differences in the physical circumstances, i.e., in climate, play an important role. It is self-evident that the time factor may not be neglected. In general, we can state that feldspars are rather susceptible to alteration under the influence of the factors found frequently in humid tropical climates. The alteration of feldspars in moderate climates or even in arctic environments depends on numerous factors. The amount of water percolating through the soil profile is a variable property; the pH of this percolating water may be either low or high. The soil may well be frozen for a large part of the year. The type of vegetation, whether a forest or a tundra vegetation, is also of influence. Soil scientists will grasp the reason for the reluctance of definite statements immediately. One may simply not say, for instance, that "feldspars only fragmentate in arctic soils". First of all, arctic soils do not exist as such. The different soils found in arctic surroundings may even have properties similar to those found in the humid tropical regions. This is due to the differences observed in the digesting of organic material found in some of such soils.

If the surface conditions are such that the feldspars are severely attacked, the sodium, potassium and calcium ions are rather rapidly washed away, whereas the silicon- and aluminium-rich compounds tend to remain in situ for some time. The resulting residue is therefore enriched in such compounds as silica, aluminium silicates, silicium hydroxide and aluminium hydroxide. For example, the genesis of some bauxite deposits on granites, basalts or comparable rocks is thought to be favoured by such or similar processes.

Sedimentologists may wonder why the soil-forming processes and the degradation of feldspars in the parent material of soils has been emphasized. The answer is simple. At present, mineral fragments of sand or silt size are formed by mechanical and thermal weathering in only subordinate amounts. As examples we may take the formation of such fragments by the mechanical action of glaciers or by the nocturnal chilling of rock surfaces in desert regions. It is assumed that the greatest amount of sand, silt and clay particles is presently formed by the influence of a vegetation. Subsequent erosion of these soils or debris will produce a considerable load of small particles in the gullies, in the small rivers and in the larger rivers in such an area. The irregular supply of water, due to seasonal variations, often leads to floods in the lower plains with all the consequences a sedimentologist can envisage. The effects of wind erosion after the retreat of glaciers or after the harvesting of large areas producing cereals must also be considered. A third aspect is the accelerated erosion, one of the consequences of turning primeval landscapes into arable land. Enormous amounts of sand and clay have been made available in the last few thousand years through soil erosion. It is only recently that man has organized his struggle against this type of erosion. In order to stress not only the role of vegetation in the formation of sedimentary rocks, but also the influence of such a vegetation on feldspars as well, soil-forming processes have been considered here in some detail.

As soon as soils are washed down by rain and are transported by rivers or by the wind, the resulting sediment may have a feldspar content different from the parent material of the original soil. The alteration of feldspars in such soils before erosion started may explain this. One step further, we may envisage a granite or some other igneous rock as the source of the parent material of a soil. Such a rock may be found in different regions of the earth. The parent material is subjected to various influences dependent on the type of climate. We may enumerate a number of such influences: (*1*) the amount of rainfall; (*2*) the average temperature as well as the maximum and the minimum temperature; (*3*) the pH of the percolating soil solution; (*4*) the duration of a frost period. As a result we can imagine the development of rather different soils on one and the same type of rock. As soon as such soils are washed down and transported, we will find a number of sediments with differing mineralogical compositions, although the parent material of these soils in question is derived from the same or a similar igneous rock.

Until now one factor, though not neglected, has not been treated with special attention. Time is an important agent in the degradation of silicates and thus of feldspars. The time during which a feldspar is exposed to atmospheric influences and the related soil forming processes determine the degree of alteration. It is well-known that frequently reworked sediments tend to have a rather poor mineral assemblage, whereas young sediments and soils may be comparatively rich. This poor and rich element is also reflected in the feldspar contents of such samples. For example, Miocene glass sands occurring in the southern part of The Netherlands and in the adjacent parts of Belgium and Germany have less than 0.2% of feldspars. These are dune sands, overlayed by a formation of lignite and brown coal. It is assumed that the acid-soil solutions leached the underlying sand, resulting in a residue of practically pure quartz. If such sands are afterwards distributed over other areas by the action of wind or water, the resulting product is necessarily poor in feldspars too.

FELDSPARS IN A MARINE ENVIRONMENT

The behaviour of feldspars has been considered under the influences of terrestrial circumstances. Feldspars in marine sediments are exposed to quite a number of different influences.

The temperature of the sea floor is fairly constant and more or less the same as the average temperature of a moderate climate. Moreover, this temperature is never below zero degrees centigrade. The pressure, on the other hand, is always higher than in a terrestrial environment. Such pressures can even become rather extreme in deep-sea areas. Finally, feldspars in marine sediments are continuously exposed to a liquid phase containing a number of important ions. These ions are known to be the main constituents of feldspars also, i.e., the ions of sodium, potassium and calcium. In this liquid surrounding, one may expect a kind of equilibrium between the transport of ions from the liquid phase towards the surface of the feldspar crystal and the transport of ions in the other direction. Observational evidence shows that feldspars, isolated from some recently developed marine sediments, may have formed a new rim surrounding the older detrital grains. This indicates that under specific circumstances feldspars may be formed on the sea floor. The question concerning the whereabouts of the silicon and the aluminium, necessary for this newly formed feldspar material in the case under investigation, will not be considered here.

This brief record of the behaviour of feldspars in sediments and soils under atmospheric or marine influences may give some idea about the information sedimentologists and soil scientists can obtain by studying the feldspars in the various fractions of their samples. In the two following sections we will treat some details of this study separately for sedimentologists and for soil scientists.

FELDSPARS IN SEDIMENTS

An account of the reasons why sedimentologists should study feldspars must draw attention to the properties of the feldspars themselves. Feldspars show a diversity of structures. They are characterized by a variety of chemical compositions. They are sometimes unmixed, showing different types of exsolution phenomena known as perthites or peristerites. Finally, they may show a large number of characteristic twinning patterns. If all these properties are compiled one can see that a large number of combinatory possibilities exist. These combinations may function as useful criteria for sedimentological purposes. As an example of such purposes one may point to the information that may be obtained on the source area of such a sediment. In other cases the feldspars may furnish a lithostratigraphical characterization of a sedimentary formation. Others may use these minerals in order to get information on the changing geomorphology of the terrestrial areas surrounding a sedimentary basin during a certain period of the earth's history. Without trying to arrive at a complete enumeration, let us consider some of these aspects in more detail.

Information concerning the source area of a sediment

Sedimentologists reach interesting conclusions about the source area of their samples through an extensive study of the mineralogical composition of such samples. A study of the feldspars may not only be expected to give additional information, but in some cases the crucial arguments can be expected from a study of these crystalline phases. The morphology of the feldspar particles may tell something about the means of transport and the probable distance from site of deposition to source area. The chemical composition of the plagioclases can reveal information about the type of rock in which these minerals originally grew. It is known now that the chemical composition of a plagioclase is not only dependent on the available ions at the period of formation, but also on the physical circumstances, the temperature and pressure during their genesis. The various twinning types observed in both alkali feldspars and plagioclases may lead to interesting conclusions about the origin of these crystal fragments. Metamorphic rocks are characterized by quite another type of feldspar twinning and quite another twinning pattern than igneous rocks. Volcanic rocks again may show their own characteristic set of feldspar twins. The structural state of feldspars that is only slightly reflected in the more currently measured optical properties, also depends on the physical circumstances that governed this genesis. Because structural state is an important aspect of feldspars, it must be studied with X-ray powder methods in order to get the necessary information quickly. Finally, the type of exsolution pattern observed is in some cases also determined by rather special circumstances during its origin. Such exsolution patterns, in this case, may provide additional information.

In order to illustrate what can be done, for a simple example we may turn to the feldspar composition of the sands deposited by the two main rivers in The Netherlands. One of these, the river Rhine, meets rather young volcanic deposits in its recent course, before entering the border. The presence of sanidine from these volcanic deposits in the Rhine sediments has been ascertained in numerous cases. The river Meuse cuts through a large area of Devonian, Carboniferous and Cretaceous sandstones and limestones in Belgium. The feldspar content of these sediments is generally rather low, and volcanic feldspars constitute only a fraction of the total feldspar content. Hence, we may not expect sanidines to occur frequently in the alkali-feldspar fractions of recent Meuse sands. In fact, such alkali feldspars are only seldom encountered. On the other hand, the Devonian sediments just mentioned contain a specific type of perthite, a so-called mesoperthite. The special characteristics of this perthite will be discussed in the chapter on perthites. The presence of a fragment of such a mesoperthite will settle a dispute on the origin of unknown sands in the course of these two rivers immediately. There are certainly more and better examples to be found. Such examples will be discussed further in this book. After reading these pages the sedimentologist may get an idea about the various possibilities in this particular field of detrital feldspar study.

Feldspars as a stratigraphic guide

In certain cases, even if it is not possible to determine the source area of a sediment, the composition of the mineral assemblage may be rather characteristic. The same often holds for the feldspar fraction alone. Two aspects demand our attention. The characteristic property may be found with the amount of total feldspars in the sample, whether small or large. It may also, however, be found among the feldspar phases or among the types of twins. In a study of the feldspar fraction of the Devonian sedimentary rocks of eastern Belgium, J. MICHOT (1963) found that especially the rocks of the Famennian were characterized by large amounts of feldspar. The other rocks of this stratigraphic unit were either devoid of feldspars or contained them in minor amounts. If for a lack of fossils the rocks of a small outcrop cannot be assigned to a specific formation, the high feldspar content of such sandstones in this region of Belgium makes it plausible that we are dealing with Famennian rocks.

Feldspars as a source of information on the environment of a sedimentary deposit

As an example of an investigation giving ample information on the environment of sedimentary deposits, we have in mind the work of PETERSON and GOLDBERG (1962). These authors were interested in the available geological aspects of a part of the bottom of the southern Pacific. They studied a large number of samples from this vast area. It goes without saying that such additional information as is available in a geological survey of a terrestrial region is lacking in this case. The authors had to combine their information on sample composition with the traces of a precision depth recorder.

In their study, discussed in some detail in Chapter 11, they found that the feldspars derived from volcanic activity are rather stable in a marine environment. They were able to give rough outlines of differing sediment-petrographical provinces within the area under study. In short, the study of the mineralogical composition of only a limited number of samples enabled the above-mentioned investigators to draw a rough picture of that part of the ocean floor under study, complete with the nature of its submarine volcanoes.

Feldspars as an indication of the history of a sediment after deposition

High pressure and temperature such as exist during metamorphic processes or during the consolidation and cooling of a magma, are by no means necessary for the production of feldspars in rocks. Still, the majority of the existing feldspars were produced by these processes. From a large number of papers it is evident that feldspars may come into existence during physical circumstances of rather low temperature and pressure. Such feldspars are called authigenic feldspars. They are known, for instance, from the Famennian sediments in Belgium. In these rocks the minerals are found together with a much larger number of detrital feldspars. As examples of other sources of these authigenic feldspars we may enumerate the following rocks: (*1*) the Upper Cretaceous of Hannover in Germany; (*2*) various calcareous rocks in the southwestern part of Switzerland; (*3*) the Silver Peak region in western Nevada, U.S.A. It is generally accepted that the formation of feldspars at near-surface conditions requires rather high ratios of alkali ions to hydrogen ions in the liquid phase. The idea that by leaching of alkali-rich material the ground water can become rich in alkaline and consequently promotes the growth of such minerals, is at variance with current ideas in soil science.

Evidence appears to exist for the thesis that the formation of authigenic albite may be promoted by the presence of high concentrations of calcium ions. These minerals are for a large part found in calcareous rocks. Finally, there is evidence for the formation of authigenic feldspars on the sea floor under certain circumstances. Our knowledge about these circumstances is still rather limited. Whatever the reason for their genesis may be, the presence of authigenic feldspars in a sediment provides information about an important part of the processes that influenced this sediment after its deposition.

From the above discussion it may be clear that a study of detrital feldspars may lead to some interesting conclusions on the provenance, the genetical history and the environment of a sedimentary formation. Moreover, detrital feldspars, just as heavy minerals, may function as a characteristic of a sedimentary formation. A combination of a study of heavy and light minerals also may give important results, but this has been known, or should have been known, since RETGERS published his mineralogical analysis of a dune sand from Scheveningen in 1891.

FELDSPARS IN SOILS

Feldspars grow in igneous and metamorphic rocks. The amount of feldspars originated in other environments is negligible. Igneous rocks are assumed to be the initial source of the ions now found in sediments, whether in the form of silicates or as other compounds. This implies that the minerals present in igneous rocks are the source of the important elements in the soil, irrespective of whether an igneous rock or a sediment is in fact the source of the parent material of such a soil. A survey of the important minerals in igneous rocks makes it clear that at least potassium and sodium are, for a large part, to be found in feldspars and micas. Calcium, though an important constituent of amphiboles and pyroxenes, is thought to have been stored for a large part in feldspars too. This is clear from the consideration that igneous rocks are made up of feldspars for more than 60% on the average. Consequently, we must assume that nearly all the potassium and sodium ions that are now found in chlorides and clay minerals were once stored in feldspars. The same holds for the calcium ions now found in carbonates and sulfates.

The process of weathering, soil formation and subsequent erosion liberated the ions from the original minerals. Afterwards they were taken in solution, transported by water and brought into the sea or in large lakes. The evaporation of the water filling such lakes, or the closed marine basins, caused these ions again to find place in a crystal lattice. Now the minerals in which they found place are various types of rock salt, gypsum, anhydrite or calcite. In this way large concentrates are formed of such important ions as potassium, sodium and calcium. The well-known salt deposits, the large gypsum deposits and the extensive formations of calcareous rocks are there to witness the importance of this concentration process. The ions on which our attention has been focussed are important for soil scientists, because they are the main nutrient elements of all types of vegetation.

The sequence weathering, soil formation, erosion, has been shown to produce a concentration of certain elements in some areas. The counterpart of this concentration in one place is a residue in another place. These residues, the depleted soils in old agricultural areas, the bauxite deposits, the areas covered with almost pure quartz sand, the residual kaolinite deposits and numerous other formations can testify to the importance of such an impoverishment of the original surface rocks.

As long as the residue constitutes an economically important formation such as a bauxite deposit, geologists are inclined to talk about the importance of such a "concentration". As soon as the residue is an area of poor soils, created by ages of cultivation, soil scientists are inclined to speak about the "impoverishment" of the soil by certain farming methods. In fact, however, we are dealing with residues in both cases. Examples of the desastrous effects of some traditional farming methods are too numerous. Especially those methods where the total crop is consumed by man and beast, and the farmyard manure is not turned to the soil but used as fuel instead. This treatment left behind soils with an extremely low traditional fertility, hardly rich enough to protect the farmers from starvation.

Although farmers have always tried to restore the cycle of ion transport by applying some or other kind of fertilization, this process has only recently become important. By a large-scale exploitation of salt deposits, calcareous formations and gypsum mines it has become possible to produce the raw materials for the modern chemical industry involved in the production of fertilizers. Application of such fertilizers to depleted soils is nothing else than a redistribution of ions, as K. J. Hoeksema pointed out quite recently in a lecture.

Besides the role of feldspars as the initial stores of rather important macro elements, a few other considerations may lead one to study the feldspar content of a soil and its parent material. Four such reasons will be considered shortly. Before entering this discussion it is necessary to treat in more detail the aspects of soil fertility.

Soil fertility is a rather complex conception. A fertile soil may not show mechanical resistance to root development. The amount of moisture must be such, that the crop neither has too much, nor too little water. The soil must provide a number of ions for the plant. These ions must be readily available at the time they are needed. If they are available too early they tend to be washed away. Such properties determine soil fertility. The concept may also be treated in another way.

We described the concentration process by the sequence weathering, soil formation and erosion. If, however, the surface is covered by a vegetation such as observed in primeval deciduous forests, the ions liberated from the minerals are generally not washed away. On the contrary, they are taking part in the vegetation cycle. Such a vegetation does not constitute an impoverishment of the soil. Burning down such woods in order to produce arable land leaves behind a soil with an excellent structure, rich in ions fit for a crop. The fertility of such an area is often called the *initial fertility*. The fertility that remains after a long period of agriculture depends to a large extent on the farming methods of our ancestors. Such a fertility will be called the *traditional fertility*. Because of the application of unsatisfactory farming methods, soils with a high initial fertility may become extremely poor. The sad results of such types of agriculture are found on large areas of this planet.

Aside from these two types of soil fertility we know of soils on extremely rich parent material such as recent river plains or volcanic ash deposits. The fertility of such soils depends to a large extent on the rapid weathering of the minerals in the parent material. This fertility, different from the two foregoing types, is often designated by the term *natural fertility*. It goes without saying that the traditional fertility of a soil has come about partly through weathering of minerals. Traditional fertility may for this reason be described as the sum of the influences of traditional farming methods and the natural fertility of the soil.

Soil scientists studying the mineralogical composition of a soil may expect to obtain information on its natural fertility. Therefore, the study of feldspars may help with an insight into a number of aspects of soil fertility. Let us turn now to the reasons which cause a soil scientist to study the mineralogical composition.

Minerals as a store of macro elements

The application of the results of mineralogical investigations has been hampered to some extent by the fact that "artificial" fertilizers are comparatively cheap. This is at least the situation in countries with an advanced economy. Still, large areas exist where the population has to depend on what is present in the soil or in its immediate surroundings in order to raise their crops. They are not in a position to be able to apply man-made fertilizers. By improving such farming through better farming methods, we can expect to get better results. Furthermore, a selection of those soils with a high natural fertility will provide better yields. It often suffices to bring water by man-made constructions to areas with soils of a high natural fertility. In selecting these soils, the knowledge of the macro elements stored in the specific minerals is of importance. By a mineralogical analysis of the light fraction and the clay fraction we may get an insight into the potential natural fertility. If other factors cooperate or can be made to cooperate, there are areas where even a rather poor farmer can produce a good crop. Moreover, he can do this on his own and does not need to run from one office to the other in search of funds. Especially this last factor may be more stimulating to this man than anything modern agriculture has to offer him.

Minerals as a store of micro elements

It is well-known that agricultural crops cannot live from potassium and nitrogen alone. A number of other elements in extremely small quantities are also necessary for good results. For this reason a soil scientist must be interested in the source of these micro elements. It is firmly believed that micro elements are found in heavy minerals alone. Notable examples of this concept are the mineral tourmaline, assumed to be a source of borium, and amphiboles and pyroxenes as a possible source of magnesium. A study of trace elements present in micas and feldspars clearly indicates that these minerals too are stores of numerous elements. Copper, for instance, is found in every feldspar, which always contains iron, magnesium, rubidium and lead. A discussion of the trace elements in feldspars is given in Chapter 2. A calculation will often show that only 50 p.p.m. of a certain element in about 10% of feldspars is much more important than even 1% of the same element in a heavy mineral that occurs only once in about 10,000 particles. A number of trace elements or minor elements in a soil are still of unknown parentage, so that the amount of phosphorus is never successfully explained by the amount of apatite in a soil.

A study of the mineralogical composition with special regard to minor elements is still very useful. This is even true for regions where fertilizers are comparatively cheap. The ideas about the importance of the role of heavy minerals as a store of micro elements are in sore need of a revision. At present little is known about the trace elements in clay minerals, in mica, in quartz and in feldspars isolated from real soil samples. About the trace-element content of feldspars from igneous and metamorphic rocks quite a great deal is known at present. This knowledge can be used to the advantage of soil science.

The mineralogical composition as a soil-forming factor

Studies carried out in The Netherlands, among other places, have taught that the "soil type" is correlated with the mineralogical composition of the parent material. All other soil-forming factors being the same, different soils may be found on parent material with a different mineralogical composition. This becomes clear at once if clay-rich parent material is compared to a sandy parent material. It also holds true for soils on two sandy materials with only slightly differing mineralogical compositions.

Consequently, soil scientists interested in soil-forming processes simply must analyse the mineralogical composition of their samples, and not only the composition of the heavy mineral fraction and the clay fraction. Above all the fraction containing the bulk of minerals, the light fraction in which quartz, mica and feldspars are found, must be analysed.

The behaviour of minerals under soil conditions

The fourth reason is of a fundamental nature. Soils are for the most part made up of minerals, i.e., of crystalline phases. It is only logical to study these minerals if one wants to understand a soil's origin, being and decay. Feldspars are found in virtually every soil; if they are not found the chance is big that they have not been looked for in the proper way. The quantity of these feldspars may vary. They may constitute only less than 1 weight percentage, they may represent moderate quantities and they can even be present as the most important minerals.

It will be shown in the next chapter that there are feldspars, and feldspars. A sanidine may have exactly the same chemical composition as a microcline. Still both feldspars are expected to behave quite differently under soil conditions. The structure of these phases is rather different. Consequently, their thermodynamical properties are different. This explains why sanidine, a high-temperature phase, breaks down rather rapidly, whereas microcline, a low-temperature phase, is rather resistent. Such properties are of interest to those studying samples from different soils. On the other hand, the investigators experimenting with such minerals in a laboratory must be familiar with these properties. If they ignore them, their ingenious experimental set-ups simulating soil processes are of little use. As far as my knowledge goes, I never have read of pot experiments with synthetic or natural sands of an accurately determined grain size and an accurately determined mineralogical composition *and also with* an accurately determined number of feldspar modifications. The leaching experiments performed by COR-RENS (1962) are carried out on adularia of unknown structure. Older experiments carried out with "orthoclase", whatever that might have been, never state whether this material is perthitic or not. With feldspars such properties are of great importance.

Soil scientists, interested in the degradation of minerals and the subsequent provision of ions to the vegetation, applied two main approaches. One group began to grow selected plants in selected minerals in pot experiments. Others studied the behaviour of minerals under carefully controlled laboratory conditions. In the following paragraph we ask your attention for the results obtained through such experiments.

Experiments with feldspars in soil science

Numerous experiments have been carried out in order to establish the influence of minerals on the system soil–plant. Such experiments are of interest in various ways. They stress the importance of certain minerals as stores of important elements. On the other hand, they try to evaluate the production of important secondary minerals as soil constituents. Finally, such experiments throw light on the relation between mineralogical composition and soil fertility. To begin with, the results of pot experiments and of experiments using minerals or ground rocks as fertilizers, will be treated in some detail. Later, comments will be made on the laboratory experiments carried out over the last 50 years. Finally, considerations of a theoretical nature concerning the breakdown of feldspars will be adduced.

Experiments with feldspars in growing plants

The experiments with feldspars in pot experiments and with feldspars or feldspar-rich rocks as fertilizers before 1929 have been summarized in Blanck's *Handbuch der Bodenlehre*. From this work it can be seen that in the twenties fertilization experiments with phonolite flour gave cause for enthusiasm in agriculture. The increase of yields on "Odersand" with phonolite flour is compared to those of K_2SO_4. As a result, the increase with phonolite flour is 40% as compared to K_2SO_4, 100%. In both cases equal amounts of K_2O were used, viz., 1,000 g. With 2,000 g of K_2O in the form of both substances the yields were again 49% increased. Other experiments showed that the plants used only 9.4% of the available potassium from the phonolite and 56.1% of the available potassium of K_2SO_4. Experiments with clover showed that feldspars give less potassium to the plant than kainite in the same period of time. Blanck showed that the potassium from micas is more rapidly used by plants than the potassium from feldspars. Moreover, it turned out that "orthoclase" broke down more quickly than microcline in these experiments.

In 1948 LEWIS and EISENMENGER investigated the relationship of plant development to the capacity to utilize potassium from alkali feldspar. Twenty-two seed plants of varying degrees of development were grown in soil in three series. One was free of potassium addition; in the other, potassium was found as a chloride; the third obtained feldspar in a quantity equivalent in potassium content to the second series. In practically all plants the increase of potassium was higher for the potassium-chloride series than for the feldspar series. For instance, the analyses show that rye extracted 0.76% from the control series, 1.00% from the feldspar series and 1.16% from the potassium-chloride experiment. As a conclusion, the authors state that the uptake of potassium from a feldspar depends among others on the order of development of the species.

More recently VAN DER MAREL (1950) made experiments with plants in Mitscherlich pots filled with several Dutch sands of different mineralogical composition. It was proved that the yields were correlated with the mineralogical composition.

Laboratory experiments with feldspars

Soil scientists studied the behaviour of minerals under carefully controlled conditions in the laboratory. To start with, we call the reader's attention to the work of Mohr. While working in the former Dutch East Indies, MOHR (1909) made experiments with basalts. The rocks were ground and put in funnels. The funnels with the basalt particles were percolated with natural rain water.

The ions liberated by this process were collected and measured. The behaviour of plagioclase received his special interest in this study. Correns began similar experiments when pioneering in the field of the degradation of minerals. Feldspars drew his attention. In order to get results comparable to natural circumstances, Correns designed special apparatus for his leaching experiments. The percolating solutions were also carefully selected. He could prove, among other things, the importance of such properties as grain size and the concentration of ions in the soil solution. In a recent paper Correns reviewed the experimental results (CORRENS, 1962).

Others such as MOREY and CHEN (1955), PEDRO (1961) and MARSHALL (1962) studied the experimental breakdown of minerals, especially of feldspars, with other methods and apparatus. Aside from important results, these investigators were proof that at least a number of soil scientists is still interested in the particular aspects of the alteration of feldspars under weathering conditions.

Theoretical considerations

The fact that feldspars break down under soil conditions is due to the specific thermodynamical properties of these crystalline phases. A description of the breakdown of minerals centred around the hydrolyzing properties of water is only a detour and less fundamental. Feldspars are thermodynamically unstable under atmospherical conditions. This implies, for instance, that if a mixture of the necessary ions in the right proportions is brought into solution, this solution will not leave a feldspar crystal behind if the liquid is evaporated. In other words one might say that the sum of the entropies of the products of alteration of a feldspar is larger than the entropy of the crystalline feldspar phase under atmospherical conditions. Matters are complicated to a large extent by the presence of more than one modification with the same chemical composition. Sanidine, for instance, will have another entropy value than a microcline, even if they have exactly the same chemical composition. Consequently, we can expect them to behave differently under similar soil conditions. In general the low-temperature phases, such as microcline, are more stable than the high-temperature modifications such as sanidine.

From a number of investigations it can be concluded that substances with high amounts of potassium are again more stable than similar substances with a low-potassium and, for instance, a higher sodium content. Therefore, the contribution of ions to the liquid phase present in a soil is different for various feldspars. Soil scientists may for this reason be interested in an inventory of the various feldspars in a specific soil. In this way they are able to estimate to a certain extent not only the nutrient element reserves stored in these minerals, but also the expected rate of provision of these stored elements. Although we are still far from formulating practical rules for such estimates, fundamental research along these lines of thought may, in due time, give a better insight into such processes.

FINAL REMARKS

Although the author feels inclined to elaborate on this fascinating subject for some time, an introduction to identification methods for detrital feldspars has been illustrated sufficiently. An account of the reasons has been given. We have seen that at least a number of sedimentologists and soil scientists are interested in feldspars. Furthermore, a large number can be expected to get interested in these minerals. The question remains how to study feldspars. Although numerous methods have been developed by petrographers and mineralogists, these methods are for a large part not well adapted to the special problems a sedimentologist or a soil scientist has to face.

The currently used methods have one general basis. They start from the assumption that the rock under study represents an equilibrium assemblage of minerals. Consequently, the premise that after a few determinations of crystals of one mineral species, for instance plagioclase, the other crystals of the same species may be assumed to give comparable results after measurement. This approach to problems of mineral determinations in rocks is due to the characteristic properties of metamorphic or igneous rocks. Such equilibrium assemblages are caused by rather constant physical conditions during the recrystallization of metamorphic rocks or during the consolidation of a magma. According to Gibbs' Law, an equilibrium assemblage, also one of crystalline phases, has a limited number of such phases. The limitation is determined by the number of components, in other words, by the number of oxides present in such a rock. The number of important oxides being about ten, igneous or metamorphic rocks are assumed to contain not more than about eight to ten mineral types. Consequently, we may expect no more than two feldspar types with one specific structure and one specific chemical composition. In short, the petrographer generally expects his sample to contain no more than two feldspars, one specific plagioclase and one specific alkali feldspar.

The situation in sediments and soils is quite different. If such aggregates of crystalline phases reach an equilibrium state, feldspars may not be present at all. They do not belong to this temperature and pressure region. But sediments and soils seldom attain an equilibrium assemblage of minerals. They are principally aggregates of minerals that are not at equilibrium. This implies that the investigator expects his material, whether a soil or a sediment, to contain the debris of *an unknown number of unknown rocks*. Consequently, he is inclined to expect every mineral fragment to be different from one another. If one applies this to the feldspar group, with its different structures, different chemical composition and different exsolution phenomena, one may become disencouraged. The remainder of this book is devoted to an escape from this chaotic state of affairs, but not by concealing the difficulties. The line of approach is chosen as a result of two assumptions. First it is assumed that by a modification of current methods a set of procedures can be devised that is better adapted to the special problem at hand. Secondly it is thought in such a study of feldspars in soils and sediments efficiency can be largely increased by a concentration of these minerals. The more so because the study of the mineralogical composition of sediments and soils is often a matter of statistics. As an illustration we point to the heavy mineral analysis, based on counts of 100, 250 or even 300 grains. Concentration of the feldspars in one or a few fractions avoids wasting time on other minerals. Some experience with this approach has shown at least that good results can be obtained and better results may certainly be expected.

Chapter 2

THE NATURE OF FELDSPARS

FELDSPARS

On beginning this review of feldspars and feldspar identification, we may perhaps best first describe what is meant by the term feldspar itself. When rummaging through textbooks for a definition, one immediately notices that some differences of opinion exist about its aspects, although the authors have the same group of things in mind. Some of these authors concentrate exclusively on the structural aspects of feldspars, while others are more interested in their chemical composition. Starting with the chemical composition of feldspars, a brief treatment of both aspects will be given below.

It is frequently observed that the various members of groups of minerals with comparable structural characteristics are brought about by what is called diadochy. Diadochy describes the replacement or replaceability of one atom or ion in a crystal lattice by another (see the A. G. I. GLOSSARY, 1957, p.80). It is known, for example, that in certain micas Fe^{2+} can be replaced by Mg^{2+}; in other minerals Al^{3+} can be replaced by Fe^{3+} or by Fe^{2+}. In amphiboles and pyroxenes the substitution of Si by Al, linked with the substitution or addition of ions that can restore electrostatic neutrality, is a well-known aspect of these mineral groups. In diadochy it is important that the size of the replacing ion fits the site in which it will be accepted; the valency of the ion is of secondary importance.

For an insight into the chemical composition of feldspars, it is helpful to begin with the composition of the mineral quartz SiO_2. Applying the above "rules" to $4(SiO_2)$ or Si_4O_8, imagine one of these Si ions to be replaced by an Al ion, for this ion fits the Si-site in the oxygen tetrahedron perfectly. The resulting formula, $AlSi_3O_8^-$, lacks one valency. In order to restore electrostatical neutrality, the Si–Al substitution may be balanced by the addition of a large monovalent cation, namely K or Na. The resulting compound is: $KAlSi_3O_8$ or $NaAlSi_3O_8$.

If two out of four Si ions are replaced by two Al ions, a divalent cation can account for the lacking valency, namely Ca. The resulting compound is: $CaAl_2Si_2O_8$.

There are large ranges of solid solutions besides the ideal composition in which only one kind of cation such as K, Na or Ca is present. When these involve ions of different valencies, as in the combination Na–Ca, there is a corresponding change in the Si/Al ratio too in order to maintain electric neutrality, see Fig.1.

The structure of feldspars is a three-dimensional framework of oxygen

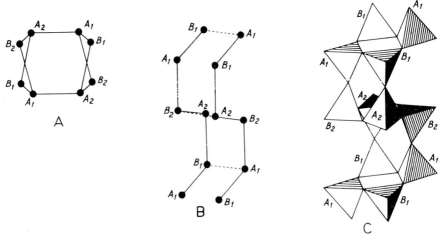

A

B

C

Fig.2. The structure of the $AlSi_3O_8$ framework in detail.
    A. A part of the stripped chain given in B, showing for instance the important four-membered ring of Si and Al, $B_1-A_1-A_2-B_2$.
    B. The stripped chain of C showing the positions of Si and Al.
    C. Chain of tetrahedrons forming part of the $AlSi_3O_8$ framework.

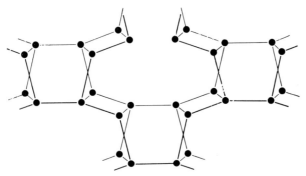

Fig.3. Projection of the Al/Si positions of the $AlSi_3O_8$ framework on the plane (001), after LAVES (1960). See Fig.2 for the position of the four-membered rings.

tetrahedrons in which an Si or Al ion is situated (TAYLOR, 1933). Every oxygen is again linked to two of these Si or Al ions. In the building up of this framework, four-membered rings of tetrahedrons play an important role (Fig.2). These four-membered rings are linked in such a way as to form a kind of honeycomb, as pictured in Fig.3. The large open spaces are filled by the large low-valent cations Na, K, Ca or Ba.

The order–disorder relation

In a paper on the aspects of polymorphic phenomena in crystal structures, BARTH (1934) discussed the various possibilities for a variation in the structural characteristics of a crystalline substance while retaining its chemical composition. One of these possibilities is used to explain the different properties of the members of the alkali-feldspar family. Barth concluded that "the various polymorphic changes in potash feldspar correspond to distortions of the lattice or to a partial rearrangement of the constituent atoms". Using Taylor's structural model, it is further argued that the three Si ions and the one Al ion must be spread over the four available sites in such a way as to account for the different structural properties. Barth ventured the suggestion that the available positions may either be divided statistically by three Si ions and one Al ion, or that Al may have a certain preference for specific sites. If Si and Al occur as variate atoms, i.e., with no preference for positions, the resulting symmetry will be monoclinic. If the Al ions concentrate at special positions, however, a triclinic structure will result. In Fig.4 and 5, this is explained schematically by the use of an illustration technique adopted from Laves (1960) and Laves and Goldsmith (1961). Barth's suggestion was accepted by a large number of mineralogists and crystallographers, and is now referred to as the "*order–disorder*" relation. The ordered structure is that in which the Al has a certain preference for specific positions, and forms a triclinic structure such as in microcline. The term "disordered" conveys the aspects of a statistical spread of Si and Al over the available positions. Thus, if the arrangement of the Al ions is highly systematic, the feldspars are called *ordered feldspars*. If the arrangement of Al is more or less random over the available sites, the feldspars in question are known as *disordered feldspars*. It may cause confusion to note that the highly ordered feldspars have "low" symmetry, i.e., triclinic symmetry, whereas disordered feldspars may well be monoclinic in a number of cases, e.g., sanidine. A study of the structure of feldspars makes it clear that this confusion is due only to the conventional terminology.

It may be worth while to note that the Cambridge group (Taylor and his co-workers) has certain doubts as to whether the characteristics of the stability

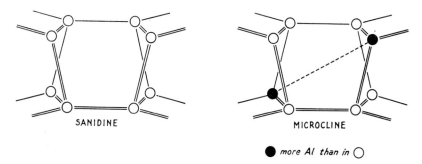

SANIDINE   MICROCLINE

● *more Al than in* ○

Fig.4. The preference of Al for specific sites. In sanidine there is no preference; the sites are of equal probability; disordered structure. In microcline Al has a preference for the B_1 sites, B_1 has a higher probability with respect to the presence of Al; ordered structure. See Fig.2 for the place of the B_1 site in the four-membered ring.

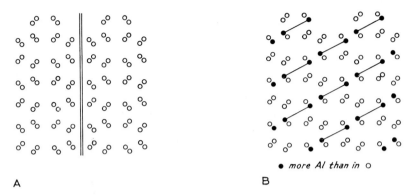

• *more Al than in* o

A   B

Fig.5. Schematic representation of the Si/Al distribution in ordered (triclinic) and disordered (monoclinic) feldspars. The way of illustrating these properties of feldspars has been adopted from LAVES and GOLDSMITH (1961).
    A. Disordered feldspar. The presence of a symmetry plane brings about a monoclinic structure.
    B. Ordered feldspar. No symmetry plane present, triclinic structure.

fields of the various feldspar phases can be entirely explained by the "*order–disorder*" theory. FERGUSON (1960), for example, argues that the highly ordered phases are not the most stable ones for they are less well-balanced electrostatically. This view is based on a representation of feldspars as ionic structures. Although the compound $KAlSi_3O_8$ has no spare valencies, it can be imagined that the charges of one ion such as the Si ion, are not fully balanced by the charges of the immediately surrounding "O ions".

This conception of the charge balance began with an observation that seems at variance with the theory of order–disorder relations. According to this theory, the highly ordered phases are considered to be the most stable phases at low temperatures. In nature, however, it is said to be observed that a large number of alkali feldspars have structures that are only partly ordered. If the frequency of occurrence of these partly ordered phases reflects a rule that *the phases that occur more than any other phase are consequently the most stable phases,* then the views expressed by the above mentioned authors are in accordance with observational evidence. If, however, the rule is that *metastable phases may either prevail in other temperature and pressure ranges, or may even form in the stability field of other stable phases under certain circumstances,* then there is no need to stress this argument any further for the sake of matching the observational evidence. Moreover, the author doubts that these partly ordered phases are more frequent than highly ordered phases, particularly because a rough inventory of the quantity of one of these phases in the total amount of alkali feldspars in accessible parts of the earth's crust is not completely lacking. LEDENT et al. (1963) described the composition of alkali feldspar concentrates in the United States of America, showing the relative importance of microcline.

Finally, it may be observed that the alkali feldspars growing under extremely low-temperature conditions, namely authigenic alkali feldspars in sediments, are sometimes highly ordered and show a maximum triclinic geometry in a number of cases. Besides these arguments objections have been brought forward by crystallographers, as witnessed by a discussion[1] between advocates of the consequences of the order–disorder theory and advocates of the importance of electrostatic neutrality.

Although the present author is not qualified to contribute to this discussion, one striking point may be stressed. Both groups are largely made up of crystallographers. The Cambridge group studied a number of rather rare samples collected by Spencer in or before 1930 in India and Burma; part of these came from localities where feldspars were mined for the making of gem stones. The regions are situated in rock provinces not commonly found on the earth's crust, as far as one can judge from SPENCER's description (1930). Others, such as Laves and Goldsmith, studied material from Alpine and northern American regions. The discussion may well have begun from the fact that the material studied by one of the groups, or even by both groups, may not be considered representative collections of alkali feldspars.

We may conclude this discussion by adducing the experimental results of HAFNER and LAVES (1963) which settle a great deal of the above argument; these will be mentioned on p.29.

CLASSIFICATION OF FELDSPARS

A classification of feldspars on a chemical basis is still very useful for soil scientists. Chemically, feldspars form a group of mixed crystals between the three end members with pure potassium, sodium or calcium[2]. As the pure end members are rather rare, it seems practical to deal with the three possible binary systems first, and with the ternary system afterwards. It is known from a number of chemically analysed samples that virtually every feldspar in nature contains small amounts of a third and even a fourth cation (p.33,40). Chemically pure, binary feldspars do not exist in nature. The amount of these "impurities", however, is so small that in most cases they hardly influence the physical properties. For practical purposes one can therefore deal with "binary systems". An additional feature simplifies matters; it is generally assumed that a series of mixed crystals between pure potassium and pure calcium feldspars does not exist in nature (Fig.1).

---

[1] See the discussion between Ferguson, Traill and Taylor, versus Laves and Goldsmith (*Acta Cryst.*, 1958, 11: 331–348; *Cursillos Conf. Inst. "Lucas Mallada"*, 8: 71–80), and between the first three authors and MacKenzie and Smith (*Acta Cryst.*, 12: 73–74, 716–718) and Wones et al. (*J. Petrol.*, 1963, 4: 131–137).
[2] As feldspars with a significant amount of the Ba ion such as *celsian* are rather rare, they are not discussed.

Large numbers of feldspars are virtually lamellar aggregates of two minerals, $KAlSi_3O_8$ and $NaAlSi_3O_8$. These lamellar aggregates, first discovered by Gerhard in a locality near Perth in Canada at the end of the 19th century, have been called perthites. As will be argued later, these perthites are assumed to represent the result of separation of an initially homogeneous alkali feldspar (a mixed crystal of sodium and potassium feldspar) into two different phases. The properties of these perthites are discussed in detail in Chapter 3. A comparable phenomenon has been found quite recently in mixed crystals of sodium and calcium feldspar. Such aggregates are called peristerites, a term familiar in the gem industry. For a description of peristerites, see Chapter 3.

For further discussion feldspars can be classified as given below.

Alkali feldspars: in nature a *discontinuous* series of either perthitic intergrowths or mixed crystals between pure potassium feldspar and pure sodium feldspar. The chemical composition of the end members may be written as:

$KAlSi_3O_8$, abbreviated *Or* (from orthoclase), and
$NaAlSi_3O_8$, abbreviated *Ab* (from albite).

Plagioclase feldspars: in nature a *discontinuous* series of mixed crystals between pure sodium feldspar and pure calcium feldspar or peristerites (see Chapter 3). The chemical composition of the end members may be written as:

$NaAlSi_3O_8$, abbreviated *Ab*, and
$CaAl_2Si_2O_8$, abbreviated *An* (from anorthite).

Ternary feldspars: FRANCO and SCHAIRER (1951) synthesized a series of crystalline substances of feldspar structure with a chemical composition of mixtures of *Or*, *Ab*, and *An* at intervals of 10 weight percentages. Upon cooling, these crystalline substances did not separate at lower temperatures. As little is known about these substances it is assumed for the time being that these ternary feldspars play a rather subordinate role, at least in nature. For this reason they will not be mentioned separately. The interested reader may consult the paper by MUIR (1962) for additional information.

A few remarks must be made concerning the use of the abbreviations just introduced. The symbols *Or*, *Ab* and *An* were defined by BURRI and NIGGLI (1945). The symbol *Or*, for example, stands for the chemical compound $KAlSi_3O_8$ divided by the number of cations in the substance; thus: $Or = {}^1/_5 \cdot (KAlSi_3O_8)$.

It has been ascertained that the molecular weight of minerals divided by the number of cations in the formula is about the same for all minerals, namely 60. This reduced molecular weight is called the "equivalent weight". The unit thus obtained is called the "equivalent norm-mineral". Such units enable the petrographer easily calculating the theoretical mineralogical composition of a rock sample from the chemical analysis. A comparison of the actual mineral assemblage with this theoretical set of minerals may lead to important conclusions about the genesis of the rock in question. The symbols have also been more loosely applied to the minerals themselves, to the weight percentages, or to the molecular percentages of the chemical compounds assumed to be present in rocks or minerals. It should be clear that such an application of the symbols may well lead to inaccurate statements. An alkali feldspar composed of 20% *Ab* and 80% *Or* is certainly not a mineral containing 20% of the albite molecule and 80% of the potassium-feldspar molecule. Both albite and potassium feldspar have different structures; the mineral under consideration has the same structure as a potassium feldspar throughout. For this discussion it is irrelevant whether we are dealing with a high- or a low-temperature structure. Using the symbols in the way defined, they indicate molecular percentages of a substance with the composition of pure feldspar, but do not tell anything about the structure. To avoid these symbols would be impractical, although their use may well be criticized by chemists and mineralogists with a more thorough chemical background. The alternative would be the use of graphs listing the weight or cation percentages of K, Na and Ca. A recalculation of the analytical data, with respect to the complications met with such impurities as Fe, Mg and Ba, would be necessary. Moreover, the terms are so widely accepted that it is considered unwise to strive against their use, the more so because it is possible to use these symbols in the proper way without causing trouble. In order to stress the proper character of these terms they will be printed in *italics* throughout this text, indicating that they do not stand for minerals and that they do not indicate a structure, but that they function as an arithmetical unit giving information about a part of the chemical composition of a substance, whether a glass or a crystalline substance of a homogeneous or heterogeneous nature.

ALKALI FELDSPARS

Formerly the feldspars in this group were usually called orthoclase. If a distinction was made, the clear monoclinic alkali feldspars occurring in volcanic rocks were called *sanidine*. Feldspars that looked homogeneous, do not show cross-hatched twinning and have optical properties in accordance with the monocline symmetry, were called *orthoclase*. The alkali feldspars showing the typical cross-hatched twinning and with optical properties in accordance with triclinic symmetry were called *microcline*. The alkali feldspars encountered in crystal pockets and showing a specific morphology and optical properties in accordance with monocline symmetry were called *adularia* (Fig.6). *Anorthoclase*, a sodium-rich alkali feldspar, sometimes shows rather typical optical properties and a very fine cross-hatched

Fig.6. Adularia from the Dachberg region, Vals, Graubünden, Switzerland.

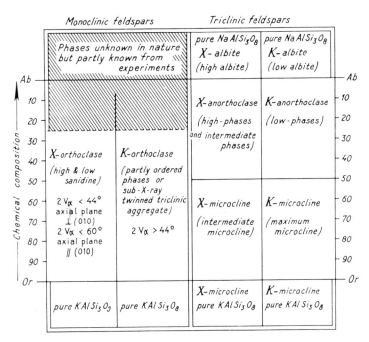

Monoclinic feldspars		Triclinic feldspars	
Phases unknown in nature but partly known from experiments		*pure NaAlSi₃O₈* X-*albite* (*high albite*)	*pure NaAlSi₃O₈* K-*albite* (*low albite*)
		X-*anorthoclase* (*high-phases and intermediate phases*)	K-*anorthoclase* (*low-phases*)
X-*orthoclase* (*high & low sanidine*) 2V$_\alpha$ < 44° axial plane ⊥ (010) 2V$_\alpha$ < 60° axial plane ∥ (010)	K-*orthoclase* (*partly ordered phases or sub-X-ray twinned triclinic aggregate*) 2V$_\alpha$ > 44°	X-*microcline* (*intermediate microcline*)	K-*microcline* (*maximum microcline*)
pure KAlSi₃O₃	*pure KAlSi₃O₈*	X-*microcline* *pure KAlSi₃O₈*	K-*microcline* *pure KAlSi₃O₈*

Ab — left axis: Ab, 10, 20, 30, 40, 50, 60, 70, 80, 90, Or
Chemical composition
right axis: Ab, 10, 20, 30, 40, 50, 60, 70, 80, 90, Or

Fig.7. Scheme of classification of alkali feldspars, based on their composition and degree of ordering of Si and Al in the crystal lattice. (After ANSILEWSKI, 1959.) The scheme has been slightly simplified and some alterations have been made in order to account for recent experimental results. The *X* phases indicate "chaos-phases" or disordered phases; the *K* phases indicate "kosmo-phases" or ordered phases. Both terms chaos-phases and kosmo-phases are introduced by the author of the scheme.

twinning. The morphology, mode of occurrence, and optical aspects of these alkali feldspars do vary in some respects. The most conspicuous characteristics of the members just enumerated are illustrated in several photographs in the text (Fig.6, 39–41).

After the work of Taylor, Goldsmith and Laves, Marfunin, and several others, it became apparent that the above classifications could give rise to confusion. On the other hand, the different proposals of the members of these groups may contribute to this confusion in some cases, for the distinction to be made on the basis of optical properties and genesis does not easily coincide with the distinctions based on structural phenomena. Recently, ANSILEWSKI (1959) wrote a paper summarizing the data to be found in this literature. He tried to build up a synthesis between the different classificatory possibilities (Fig.7). Taking into consideration the limitations of current petrographical routine methods, he proposes a system based on structural and chemical properties. He is quite aware of the fact that his classification is significant only as far as it comprises both the facts and the ideas known at that time (ANSILEWSKI, 1959, p.6). New viewpoints may r ecessitate essential modifications.[1]

Before suggesting a choice among the various systems of classification, a look at the present situation would be useful. SCHAIRER (1950) and BOWEN and TUTTLE (1950) showed that Or and Ab form a complete series of solid solutions at high temperatures, with a minimum in the melting curve at about 68 weight percentages Or. If these melts are rapidly cooled from temperatures well above 700 °C, a series of monoclinic crystalline substances between $Or_{100}Ab_0$ and $Or_{20}Ab_{80}$ results; the remainder of the series of crystalline substances on the Ab side shows triclinic symmetry. If rapid cooling is begun at well above 1,100 °C, the series of monoclinic crystalline substances range even from $Or_{100}Ab_0$ to Or_5Ab_{95}; the remainder is again triclinic. These monoclinic crystalline substances may be compared with the alkali feldspars found in volcanic rocks. From these experiments it can be concluded that natural sanidine may be expected to contain a rather high amount of sodium. Chemical analyses of a number of natural sanidines prove indeed that the amount of the Ab component in some cases is even higher than 50 weight percentages (Table I).

The low-temperature phases of natural alkali feldspar form a series of triclinic, maximally ordered mixed crystals, with a chemical composition that is generally between Or_{100} and approximately $Or_{75}Ab_{25}$. Other feldspars found in nature, "intermediates" between the monoclinic high-temperature phase and this

---

[1] A point against this classification is the use of the ill-defined term "orthoclase" for the high-temperature feldspar known as sanidine. In this way, both the high-temperature phase sanidine and the other phases occurring in igneous or metamorphic rocks are placed in one group (note the objections of LAVES, 1952a, GOLDSMITH and LAVES, 1954a, b, and KUELLMER, 1960, p.307). Moreover, after the remarks of LAVES (1952a), it does not seem appropriate to use the term anorthoclase. This criticism, however, is not meant to detract from the essential quality of Ansilewski's work.

TABLE I

SELECTED ANALYSES OF ALKALI FELDSPARS

	Number of analysis[1]										
	1	2	3	4	5	6	7	8	9	10	11
SiO_2	64.40	63.66	64.28	64.38	63.52	63.58	67.27	64.95	65.22	64.98	66.24
Al_2O_3	18.70	19.54	19.19	19.50	19.00	19.07	18.35	20.11	19.58	19.64	19.89
Fe_2O_3	0.62	0.10	0.09	0.11	0.11	0.18	0.92	traces	0.08	0.64	0.08
FeO	0.09	—	—	—	0.00	0.07	(0.92)	—	traces	—	0.07
MnO	—	—	—	—	—	—	0.00	—	—	—	—
MgO	traces	—	0.10	traces	0.00	0.65	—	traces	traces	traces	0.00
CaO	traces	0.50	0.11	0.28	0.18	0.69	0.15	0.45	0.84	0.84	0.25
Na_2O	0.46	0.80	0.92	1.48	2.60	2.77	6.45	2.55	5.88	6.00	8.93
K_2O	16.14	15.60	15.30	14.32	13.58	11.96	7.05	11.85	7.64	7.33	3.95
H_2O^+	—	—	0.36	0.28	0.60	0.57	0.08	0.12	0.56	0.40	0.44
H_2O^-	—	—			0.54	0.22	0.08				0.09
BaO	—	—	0.11	—	—	—	—	0.00	—	—	—
TiO_2	—	—	—	—	traces	0.00	—	—	—	—	—
Total	100.41	100.20	100.46	100.35	100.13	99.76	100.35	100.03	99.80	99.83	99.94
Or	95.5	90.5	90.5	85.2	76.8	68.1	41.5	73.9	44.2	42.7	22.3
Ab	4.1	7.1	8.3	13.4	22.3	24.0	57.7	24.0	51.8	53.2	76.5
An	0.4	2.4	1.2	1.4	0.9	7.9	0.8	2.1	4.0	4.1	1.2
S.G.	2.563	2.563	2.566	2.569	n.d.[2]	n.d.	n.d.	2.565	2.596	2.595	n.d.

[1]
(1) SPENCER (1937)   ferriferous orthoclase   Itrongay, Madagascar
(2) SPENCER (1930, 1937)   colourless orthoclase   Mogok, India, Specimen C
(3) SPENCER (1937)   adularia   St. Gotthard, Switzerland, Specimen B
(4) SPENCER (1937)   microperthite microcline   Kodarma, India, Specimen U
(5) TUTTLE (1952)   sanidine   Eifel, Germany
(6) KRACEK and NEUVONEN (1952)   sanidine   Kokomo, Colo., U.S.A.
(7) TUTTLE (1952)   sanidine   Mitchell Mesa, Texas, U.S.A.
(8) WILSON (1950)   microcline perthite   Musgrave Ranges, Australia
(9) SPENCER (1930, 1937)   microperthite   Burma, Specimen Q
(10) SPENCER (1937)   orthoclase microperthite   Fredriksvärn, Norway, Specimen R
(11) TUTTLE (1952)   anorthoclase   Victoria, Australia

[2] n.d. = not determined.

specific triclinic low-temperature phase, are supposed either to have grown as stable phases in a specific stability field or to have grown as metastable phases in the stability field of a more ordered phase. In experiments it has been found to be extremely difficult to synthesize microcline of a maximum triclinic geometry. It has, however, been possible to synthesize a substance with comparable properties and a comparable structure beginning with Fe^{3+} instead of Al^{3+} (WONES and

APPLEMAN, 1963). This $KFeSi_3O_8$ was named iron-microcline. Its structural properties are rather similar to those of microcline, as can be seen from the following angles of the triclinic unit cell:

$KAlSi_3O_8$: α 90°40' β 116° γ 87°47'
$KFeSi_3O_8$: α 90°45' β 116°3' γ 86°14'

Numbers of alkali feldspars are of monoclinic structure, but X-ray results prove them to have a different structure than sanidine or synthesized high-temperature alkali feldspars. HAFNER and LAVES (1963) studied monocline alkali feldspars that show monoclinic behaviour on both optical inspection and X-ray investigation. Still some of these crystals showed large axial angles, i.e., larger than 44°, a property generally pointing to a triclinic structure according to MARFUNIN (1961). With nuclear magnetic resonance techniques it could be proved that these imposterous phases are aggregates of very finely twinned triclinic alkali feldspars. The result of Hafner and Laves settles the dispute between the Cambridge group and Laves on the nature of orthoclase and the properties of the monoclinic "orthoclase", specimen Spencer C, so intensively studied by the English investigators. Orthoclase is either a sub-X-ray aggregate of triclinic alkali feldspar or a homogeneous monoclinic phase. The value of the axial angle is rather important and the axial angle of specimen Spencer C (see SPENCER, 1930) is 43.6°, which is 0.4° below the critical limit of 44° indicated by MARFUNIN (1961). Consequently, we will avoid the term "orthoclase" in this review because it is an ill-defined term for a group of things, among which are monoclinic alkali feldspars and twinned aggregates of triclinic alkali feldspars. As the distinction between true monoclinic phases and such dubious aggregates is rather easy (the axial angle may not be larger than about 44°), it is possible to make a distinction between true monoclinic phases and triclinic phases even in practice.

Other investigations prove that in the light of geological circumstances it is highly probable that alkali feldspars originally of monoclinic symmetry, may well become triclinic after "cooling". The presence of stress conditions, widespread within the earth's crust, is assumed to trigger these changes under the influences of elevated temperatures and rather high partial pressures of H_2O. Moreover, high-temperature experiments give a clue as to the origin and further development of the various alkali feldspars occurring in igneous and metamorphic rocks.

In relation to the phases just considered, the term "intermediate" is used to indicate a group of phases with a geometry intermediate between monoclinic symmetry and the triclinic symmetry listed above.

The term intermediate may cause confusion. The symmetry concept knows two alternatives, monoclinic or triclinic symmetry. Strictly speaking the term "intermediate" is a misnomer if it is applied to the symmetry of a phase. If it is applied to describe the measure of order or disorder the term seems correct. It

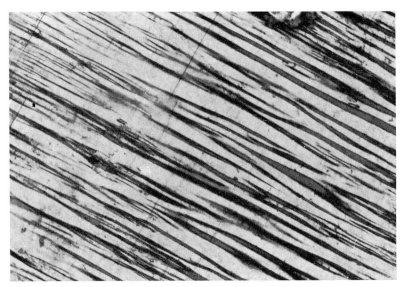

Fig.8. Micrograph of a perthitic alkali feldspar. The small dark lamellae of albite are seen in a lighter matrix of microcline. Crossed polarizers; × 150. The sample was collected at Bedford, N.Y., U.S.A.; sample no. WR 719A.

is, however, commonly used in connection with the structure of the phase and it is meant to describe a series of triclinic phases in which the obliquity increases from "nearly monoclinic" towards the geometry of a triclinic unit cell with angles: approximately α 90°40′, β 116°, γ 87°47′. If the angles α and/or γ are less than the values listed, the phase is described as "intermediate"[1].

In nature triclinic alkali feldspars are found intergrown with small lamellae of pure or approximately pure sodium feldspar (the so-called perthites, Fig.8). In syntheses this situation has, as far as we know, not yet been found. It is possible, however, to perform an experiment starting from the other side. If these natural intergrowths are heated long enough, at a temperature of about 750–900°C, the crystalline substance is homogenized (Fig.55).

A reformation of the two phases can be partially brought about (see SPENCER 1930, 1937). After prolonged heating of the same substance at temperatures of about 1,000°C, the material is homogenized irreversibly into a form which has the optical properties of sanidine. This effect was first observed by Des Cloizeaux in 1861 (see COLE et al., 1949). Consequently, the natural phases, grown at high temperatures and with relatively high sodium content, may separate under certain circumstances into an aggregate of a potassium-rich and a sodium-rich phase. Such an aggregate is known as a "perthitic" alkali feldspar.

---

[1] In the series of the plagioclase feldspars the term "intermediate" is used in three different ways: to designate a structural state between the high- and low-temperature structure, to indicate a specific structural type characteristic of the group of plagioclases between An_{25} and An_{70}, or to describe a part of this series with a chemical composition between approximately An_{20} and An_{60}.

These experiments are comprehensible in the light of the "order–disorder" theory. Heating at about 800 °C causes the diffusion of Na and K, but small domains in the crystal still preserve triclinic symmetry because the diffusion of Si and Al through the framework is known to be rather sluggish. Such small domains provide the pattern from which the diffusion and the rearrangement of the structure may start after slow cooling. If homogenization is virtually reached after prolonged heating and the structure is truly monoclinic, the process of rediffusion and structural change is impossible under laboratory conditions.

A number of alkali feldspars are assumed to have originated under low-temperature conditions, namely the adularia of some crystal pockets and the so-called authigenic feldspars. According to BERG (1952), BASKIN (1956), FÜCHT-BAUER (1956), HAY (1960) and HAY and MOIOLA (1962), authigenic alkali feldspars, generally having a high potassium content, may be either monoclinic or triclinic. The conclusions of MARFUNIN (1962a, b) are interesting in this respect. Minerals can form two continuous series between two end members, one series completely ordered, the other completely disordered. The ordered state is always the low-temperature state. Intermediate states between order and disorder belong to specific physical circumstances. A specific state of order may also be formed metastably in the stability field of a state of higher order, but not in the stability field of a state of lower order. This may explain why monoclinic alkali feldspars are found next to triclinic ones in veins containing adularia. It also may explain the presence of monoclinic alkali feldspars among authigenic minerals (see TEODOROVICH, 1958). Consequently, the symmetry of these feldspars must be influenced by the rate of growth: only if growth is too fast to permit a systematic rearrangement of the Al ions will the result show monoclinic symmetry. The presence of both monoclinic and triclinic domains in one crystal of adularia, as well as the presence of both monoclinic and triclinic adularia in one locality, has been reported by MALLARD (1876), CHAISSON (1950), BAMBAUER and LAVES (1960) and HUANG (1961), among others.

The above-mentioned considerations led LAVES (1952a, 1960) to state that there are only two stable modifications of alkali-feldspar composition, that is the monoclinic high-temperature phase sanidine and the low-temperature phase microcline with a maximum triclinic geometry. The conclusion of MARFUNIN (1962) is at variance with this statement, because according to his concept every member of the entire possible range of structures from maximum triclinic to monoclinic has its own specific stability field.

In summary, the present situation is as follows: The high-temperature phases of natural alkali feldspar, metastable at low temperatures, form a series of mono-clinic disordered mixed crystals with a chemical composition from Or_{100} to at least $Or_{45}Ab_{55}$. The low-temperature phases of natural alkali feldspar form a series of triclinic, maximum ordered mixed-crystals, with a chemical composition generally between Or_{100} and approximately $Or_{75}Ab_{25}$. Other feldspars found in nature, "intermediates" between the monoclinic high-temperature phase and this specific triclinic low-temperature phase, are supposed to have grown either as stable phases in a specific stability field or as metastable phases in the stability field of a more ordered phase.

This description, though too general to do justice to the alkali-feldspar complexity, seems sufficient for the purpose at hand. The interested reader may find a more precise and detailed treatment in the papers already mentioned in the text and in the work of DEER, HOWIE and ZUSSMANN (1963).

The identification of natural alkali feldspars is as complicated as the structural relationships considered earlier. The works of both ANSILEWSKI (1959) and MARFUNIN (1962a, b) illustrate that the optical properties of alkali feldspars do not reflect the structural geometry and the chemical composition in such a simple way. On the basis of these optical properties the composition and the structural state cannot be evaluated by simple methods. Petrologists dealing with igneous or metamorphic rocks will perhaps make objections. If so, they forget that their samples derive from rocks about which there is more information at hand solely from the fact that the genesis of the rock is more or less known. In samples from soils or sediments, however, the conclusions about the identity of a feldspar fragment must be reached from the properties to be measured on *one crystal fragment* and nothing more.

The argument reported in this section should make clear the discrepancy between the old classification of alkali feldspars, based mainly on chemical composition and optical properties, and the present situation where structural investigations have brought about a different relationship between the possible phases of feldspar composition. The two classifications under consideration are schematically given below:

   sanidine: optically monoclinic, small axial angle;
   orthoclase: optically monoclinic, larger axial angle;
   microcline: optically triclinic, large axial angle, typical twinning;
   adularia: optically triclinic or monoclinic, special crystal habit;

or:

   sanidine:
     optically and structurally monoclinic, disordered high-temperature phase;
   intermediate phases:
     structurally triclinic, or monoclinic caused by systematically stacked sub-X-ray domains of triclinic geometry, partly ordered phases;
   maximum microcline:
     specific triclinic structure, ordered low-temperature phase.

For use in sedimentology and pedology, only that classification will be useful which can meet the requirements of these two special branches of earth science. It must also furnish such mutual exclusive classes as can be distinguished by means of practical and applicable methods.

THE CHEMICAL COMPOSITION OF ALKALI FELDSPARS

In the foregoing sections alkali feldspars have been treated as if they more or less represented a group of substances of rather simple chemical composition. Natural alkali feldspars, however, contain a number of other elements that may be of relative importance, as well as the elements on which the name of this group of minerals is based. For the sake of completeness a few representative analyses of natural alkali feldspars are listed in Table I. A rather complete list of reliable analyses has recently been published by DEER, HOWIE and ZUSSMANN (1963). From these analyses it is clear that alkali feldspars may contain fair amounts of CaO and Fe_2O_3.

Although the minor element content of feldspars hardly influences the physical properties, it is necessary to mention that feldspars in general do contain a number of other elements in small proportions. Reports on this trace element content can be found in the papers of NOWOCHATSKI and KALININ (1947), HOWIE (1955), BARABANOW (1958), HEIER and TAYLOR (1959a, b), OFTEDAHL (1959), HEIER (1960), STEFFEN (1960), CARL (1962), and others.

The presence of these trace elements is important for earth scientists, for trace elements play among others a rather important role in soil fertility. The absence of certain trace elements may cause both nutritional and metabolic disorders in grazing animals (Na, Mg, Cu and Co deficiency), as well as diseases in certain crops (Cu, Mn, Zn and Mg deficiencies). The amounts of minor elements in alkali feldspars are difficult to generalize. A certain trend, however, can be observed. Ca, Fe, Mg and Ba may occur in quantities of more than 1 volume percentage of the oxides. Rather important elements are Sr, Rb, Pb, Y, Ga and Cu, which occur in quantities of more than 5 p.p.m.; Sr and Rb are generally found in quantities over 500 p.p.m. In the majority of the reported analyses both lead and copper are always present. Mitchell, in BEAR (1955), reviews the sources of trace elements in soils. In doing so he puts too much weight on the trace-element content of heavy minerals such as amphiboles, pyroxenes and tourmaline. Soils poor in heavy minerals, and such soils are no exception, are thrown on the resources of trace elements present in such minerals as feldspars. It is the author's opinion that soils rich in feldspar will never suffer from Mg or Cu deficiency. The trace-element content of feldspars has been reviewed by HEIER (1962).

Another important feature is mentioned by BARKER (1962). He succeeded in the synthesis of ammonium–potassium feldspars. In these crystalline phases

NH_4^+ replaces K^+. This fact has an important bearing on weathering processes, because the exchange of NH_4^+ and K^+ goes comparatively rapidly, as is shown by MARSHALL (1962). In numerous feldspar analyses an excess of SiO_2 and Al_2O_3 is found that cannot be ascribed to defects in the structure or errors in the analysis. In the course of a silicate analysis with the conventional methods the presence of ammonium is not detected!

ERD et al. (1964) described the first ammonium alumosilicate found in nature. The substance is monoclinic and of chemical composition $4 \cdot [NH_4AlSi_3O_8 \cdot {}^1\!/_2 H_2O]$. From 370 to 430 °C, this phase is the ammonium analogue of monoclinic potassium feldspar, below this temperature range it adsorbs zeolitic water. The phase occurs in a hot spring at the Sulphur Bank quicksilver mine, Lake Cy., Calif., U.S.A. It is called buddingtonite. Finally BARKER (1964) proved that ammonium in nature can substitute for potassium and sodium in alkali feldspars. Some "zeolitic" water apparently is necessary to stabilize the structure of ammonium-rich feldspars. It turned out that the ammonium content of a number of natural feldspars is not negligible.

PLAGIOCLASE FELDSPARS

Plagioclase feldspars have a chemical composition between pure *Ab* and pure *An*. The properties of these two end members may lead to a better understanding of the properties of the different phases in this group. For this reason the minerals albite and anorthite will be discussed first.

Albite

The mineral albite, a pure sodium feldspar of triclinic symmetry, has long been known to geologists. Because of its widespread occurrence it was studied in some detail at an early stage.

MERWIN (1911) noticed a difference in the optical properties of sodium feldspars before and after heating. Consequently, more than one crystalline phase of *Ab* composition must exist. The possible existence of a monoclinic albite from Seiland, though at present made of submicroscopically twinned triclinic units, was mentioned by BARTH (1929). In 1931, Barth reported permanent changes in the optical properties of albites exposed to heat. BARBER (1936) reviewed the previous reports on the pronounced scatter of certain optical properties of plagioclase feldspars and discussed the possible explanations given so far. In addition he carried out heating experiments on a number of plagioclases, among which the albite of Alp Rischuna (Bucarischuna, Vals, Graubünden, Switzerland), the same material as will be used to illustrate some properties of albite later in this work (Chapter 10). His results confirmed previous work. It is concluded that the scatter of optical properties in his experiments is due to heat treatment. He did not, however, put the clue to an explanation of the irregularities noticed in writing. LARSSON (1940) is the first to point out that plagioclases of intrusive rocks have optical charac- teristics that differ from those of plagioclases of volcanic rocks. His conclusion is confirmed by the observations of LUNDEGÅRDH (1941). KÖHLER (1942a) finally states plainly that two series of plagioclase feldspar must exist, one of high-tem- perature origin and the other belonging to a relatively low-temperature genesis.

TUTTLE and BOWEN (1950) showed that *two* distinct *triclinic* phases of albite composition exist, a high- and a low-temperature form. A *monoclinic* form of albite composition is now definitely known to exist since the work of MACKENZIE (1952). As early as 1908, Barbier and Proust reported the existence of a monoclinic form, later called barbierite, which according to BARTH (1931) was based on an erroneous chemical analysis and inadequate crystal measurements. But after the work of MACKENZIE (1952), which was confirmed by BROWN (1960a), the name barbierite is being used once again (SCHNEIDER and LAVES, 1957).

ROSENQVIST (1954) stated that the low-temperature albite, commonly called low albite or α albite (Rosenqvist), is stable up to 835 °C. According to Rosenqvist the high-temperature form, high albite, is metastable α albite. He also reports the existence of γ albite, originated above 900 °C from β albite, the monoclinic phase. Rosenqvist's ideas are reported here only because he uses the otherwise purely chemical notations for the different feldspar phases.

The order–disorder theory has also been successfully applied to these crystalline phases (LAVES, 1952a). SCOTT MACKENZIE (1957) synthesized a series of crystalline phases of albite composition and structures between those of high and low albite. The "intermediates" have also been found in nature. MacKenzie reports the same phenomenon, observed in adularia crystals and in the associated albite crystals found in the Alps. These albites have a special morphology and are known as "periclines" in the mineral business. "Periclines" show structurally inter- mediate forms, together with low-temperature phases in crystals from one outcrop. Authigenic albites of intermediate structure have been reported by BASKIN (1956). The observations on albites thus conform to those on alkali feldspars. Here too the existence of low- and high-temperature forms, of intermediates, and of "high- temperature" forms in associations of low-temperature genesis.

Anorthite

The anorthite found in nature is never a chemically pure calcium feldspar, but always shows some admixture of sodium. Pure anorthite is rather easily syn- thesized. The first definite synthesis of anorthite took place in the nineteenth century (see KLOCKMANN, 1900). Rather pure anorthite is found in volcanic rocks. Those of Vesuvius and of a specific Japanese locality, Miakejuma are present in a large number of mineral collections.

The structure of natural anorthites has been investigated by GAY and TAYLOR (1953), MEGAW (1959), CHANDRASEKHAR et al. (1961), KEMPSTER et al. (1962), MEGAW et al. (1962), and others. Pure anorthite is known to have a high- and a low-temperature form, both of *triclinic* symmetry. The order–disorder relation so important in other feldspars with a large amount of monovalent cations does not play a role in anorthite. GAY and TAYLOR (1953), as well as MEGAW et al. (1962), point to this fact. GAY (1954) proved that the order–disorder relation plays a role up to An_{90}. Crystalline substances of *An* composition have also been studied by DAVIS and TUTTLE (1952). They describe a *hexagonal* and an *orthorhombic* phase so far never encountered in rocks.

In nature only the triclinic low-temperature form seems to exist.

Intermediate plagioclase feldspars

As early as 1898, Fedorov suggested that the plagioclase feldspars do *not* form a continuous series of solid solutions. Contrary to this view, a large number of mineralogists and petrographers cherished the idea that a continuous series of solid solutions exist in nature between pure *Ab* to pure *An*. WENK (1960) illustrates how it can be seen, even from the optical properties of these feldspars, that the series is a discontinuous one. DOMAN (1961) reports the same and adds the observation that available values of optical properties of natural plagioclases show the breaks he found in his own investigations. Little attention was paid to this evidence until quite recently. It is now established that certain combinations of *Ab* and *An* occur only rarely in nature, whereas others are found frequently.

X-ray investigations as well as optical investigations have proved that both high- and low-temperature plagioclases exist in nature. The existence of inter-mediates has also been proved optically by KARL (1954), BASKIN (1956), PRIEM (1956), and others. For X-ray investigations see GAY (1954, 1956), J. V. SMITH (1956), J. V. SMITH and GAY (1958). As early as 1913, Bowen made it clear that pure sodium and pure calcium feldspars form a complete series of solid solutions at high temperatures with a continuous rise of the melting point from about 1,120 to 1,540 °C. These phases have "high-temperature" structure.

If the high-temperature series is a continuous one, and the low-temperature plagioclases form a discontinuous series, it can be expected that in certain plagio-clases unmixing phenomena may be observed under favourable conditions. A study of the so-called "peristerites", or "moonstones" as they are sometimes called in the gem industry, revealed the presence of exsolution lamellae of approximately An_0 and approximately An_{30} (LAVES, 1954). These crystalline substances, of an average composition between An_5 and An_{17}, show a beautiful light blue schiller after polishing. Upon heating the schiller vanishes and the result is a physically homogeneous high temperature plagioclase. RIBBE (1960) was the first to give a rather detailed description of the physical properties of these substances. He

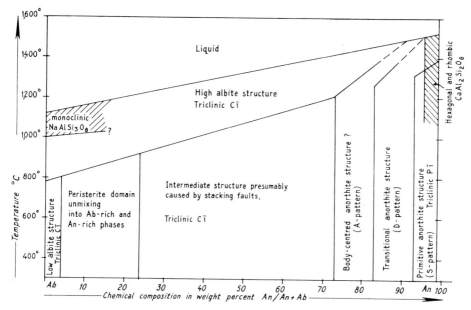

Fig.9. A scheme illustrating the chemical and structural relations in the domain of plagioclase feldspars. (Modified after GAY, 1956.)

reached the conclusion that exsolution is caused by internal stress due to an increase of the Al content with increasing Ca.

The complex situation of plagioclases is rather similar to the complexity encountered in the group of alkali feldspars. An additional complication, however, is due to the fact that the structure of low temperature plagioclases is not uniform

NOTATION I

POSSIBLE STRUCTURES OF PLAGIOCLASES

	Albite	*Plagioclase*	*Anorthite*
low temperature	triclinic C Ī low-albite structure	triclinic C Ī intermediate structures	triclinic P Ī primitive anorthite structure
high temperature	triclinic C Ī high-albite structure monoclinic albite structure	triclinic C Ī high-albite structure	triclinic P Ī primitive anorthite structure body centred anorthite structure rhombic and hexagonal structure

throughout (GAY, 1956). Three main groups with different structures have been shown to exist, namely a group with the albite structure, one with the anorthite structure and one with an intermediate structure. Again, the latter should not be confused with the "intermediate structures" between the high-temperature and low-temperature forms of the same chemical composition. The idea of these different structures was first expressed by CHAO and TAYLOR as early as 1940. In a more advanced stage of the study, Gay (1956) showed that the low-temperature plagioclases belong to six structural groups. This subdivision is schematically illustrated in Fig.9. Though it may be thought superfluous Notation I summarizes the possible structures of plagioclases for the sake of clarity.

In conclusion, it can be said that the plagioclase feldspars form a discontinuous series of mixed crystals or peristerites in the low-temperature region. The structure of low-temperature plagioclases is not the same throughout the series. The series is also a discontinuous one from a chemical point of view. In high-temperature plagioclases the high-albite structure persists up to large An contents. Order–disorder is unimportant in anorthite phases, but it plays a role in the other plagioclases. Apart from high- and low-forms, intermediate phases of the same chemical composition have been found with both optical and X-ray methods.

THE CHEMICAL COMPOSITION OF PLAGIOCLASES

The nomenclature of plagioclases is based on their chemical composition. Commonly the series is designated in terms of the mole fraction of the Ab component and the An component, as follows:

albite Ab_{100} $-Ab_{90}An_{10}$
oligoclase $Ab_{90}An_{10}-Ab_{70}An_{30}$
andesine $Ab_{70}An_{30}-Ab_{50}An_{50}$
labradorite $Ab_{50}An_{50}-Ab_{30}An_{70}$
bytownite $Ab_{30}An_{70}-Ab_{10}An_{90}$
anorthite $Ab_{10}An_{90}-An_{100}$

The chemical composition of natural plagioclases shows a great deal of variation. Apart from the most important cations Na and Ca, fair amounts of other elements may be encountered, namely K, Fe, Ti and Sr. The excess of SiO_2 and Al_2O_3 already mentioned on p.34 is also observed in plagioclases. Reports of ammonium plagioclases do not exist as far as I know. For the sake of completeness a selected number of analyses of plagioclases is listed in Table II. Representative analyses of plagioclases are reported in the *Geol. Soc. Am., Mem.*, 52, edited by EMMONS (1953). WEIBEL (1958) reported some analyses of albites from alpine regions. A rather complete list of reliable plagioclase analyses is again to be found in DEER, HOWIE and ZUSSMANN (1963).

TABLE II

SELECTED ANALYSES OF PLAGIOCLASES

	Number of analysis[1]											
	1	2	3	4	5	6	7	8	9	10	11	12
SiO_2	68.23	66.30	65.94	75.75	59.78	59.13	55.93	53.31	51.08	46.69	68.73	43.50
Al_2O_3	20.01	21.22	21.44	15.20	25.43	25.86	28.11	29.03	31.05	33.10	19.43	36.50
Fe_2O_3	0.01	0.04	0.08	0.10	0.06	0.05	0.08	0.57	0.43	0.17	—	—
FeO	—	0.03	0.04	0.10	0.07	0.05	0.08	0.26	0.12	0.19	—	—
MnO	traces	0.00	traces	0.01	traces	0.00	traces	0.01	0.01	0.02	—	—
MgO	0.00	0.02	0.02	0.01	0.05	0.05	0.11	0.19	0.22	1.03	—	—
CaO	0.03	2.21	3.03	2.53	7.01	7.44	10.10	11.69	13.85	15.78	—	20.00
Na_2O	11.38	9.85	8.99	5.80	7.17	6.89	5.43	4.24	3.38	1.90	11.84	—
K_2O	0.20	0.27	0.46	0.46	0.25	0.32	0.19	0.48	0.12	0.29	—	—
H_2O^+	0.09	0.03	0.00	0.10	0.07	0.06	0.09	0.28	0.05	0.80	—	—
H_2O^-	0.00	0.01	0.05	0.00	0.01	0.04	0.01	0.04	0.01	0.01	—	—
TiO_2	0.01	0.01	0.03	0.03	0.03	0.02	0.02	0.09	0.05	0.03	—	—
Ba	0.0001	0.007	0.007	0.038	0.033	0.025	0.013	0.035	0.01	0.019	—	—
Sr	0.0003	0.06	0.06	0.06	0.15	0.08	0.16	0.10	0.12	0.12	—	—
Li	0.001	0.0003	0.0004	0.002	0.0005	0.003	0.004	0.002	0.0006	0.009	—	—
Rb	0.0006	0.0003	0.0008	0.0005	n.d.[2]	0.0004	n.d.	0.0008	n.d.	0.0003	—	—
Total	99.86[3]	99.82[4]	100.15	100.19	100.11	100.02	100.33	100.33	100.50	100.16	100.00	100.00
Or	1.2	1.6	2.8	4.2	1.5	2.0	1.1	2.9	0.7	1.8	—	—
Ab	98.6	87.0	81.1	76.3	62.6	60.0	47.3	37.1	29.2	16.7	100	—
An	0.2	11.4	16.1	19.5	35.9	38.0	51.6	60.0	70.2	81.5	—	100
S.G.	2.615	2.631	2.639	2.640	2.665	2.664	2.683	2.694	2.715	2.721	2.617	2.759

[1] The analyses and further data of *1–10* are taken from EMMONS (1953); *11* and *12* are calculated from the ideal formulae. The analysis of a peristerite, *3*, is also discussed by RIBBE (1960). In the following the number of the analyses are listed together with the number in Emmons' work and the locality.

(1)	albite	Peerless mine, Keystone, S.D., U.S.A.	Emmons number 1
(2)	oligoclase	Peekskill, N.Y., U.S.A.	Emmons number 2
(3)	peristerite	Parishville, N.Y., U.S.A.	Emmons number 3
(4)	oligoclase	Tigerton, Wisc., U.S.A.	Emmons number 5
(5)	andesine	Spanish peak, Calif., U.S.A.	Emmons number 6
(6)	andesine	Crestmore, Calif., U.S.A.	Emmons number 8
(7)	labradorite	Shelby, N.C., U.S.A.	Emmons number 10
(8)	labradorite	East of Duluth, Minn., U.S.A.	Emmons number 15
(9)	bytownite	Lake Co., Oreg., U.S.A.	Emmons number 19
(10)	bytownite	Merrill, Wisc., U.S.A.	Emmons number 27
(11)	albite	theoretically	
(12)	anorthite	theoretically	

[2] n.d. = not determined.

[3] Total should be 99.96. The given total evidently incorporates the values for Ba, Sr, Li and Rb.

[4] Total should be 99.99 (without Ba, Sr, Li and Rb) or 100.06.

SEN (1959) argues that the potassium content of plagioclases increases along with an increasing temperature of genesis. In some cases the potassium content can be so high that on cooling the homogeneous phase is too unstable and separates into a potassium-rich phase and a sodium-rich phase, much the same as in perthites. Such unmixed aggregates are called antiperthites (see p.44).

In general, the trace-element content of plagioclases does not interfere with the physical properties to a measurable extent. For soil scientists it might be interesting to know that HOWIE (1955), BARABANOW (1958), YOUNG (1958), HEIER (1960, 1962), and STEFFEN (1960) reported the trace-element content of a number of plagioclases. Apart from rather large amounts of iron, magnesium and in some cases barium, the following trace elements are nearly always present in plagioclases: Sr, Li, Rb, Co, Cu and Pb. The amount of Sr is rather high and generally over 500 p.p.m. The amounts of Li, Rb, Cu and Pb are in most cases around 20 p.p.m. In connection with the trace elements of plagioclases one should again note the remarks on p.33. In a large number of cases it can be visualized that the trace elements stored in plagioclases present in soils may be of much more importance than the trace elements of heavy minerals. The amount of heavy minerals in numerous soils is so small that, in comparison with the trace elements present in a few weight percentages of feldspar, these amounts are negligible. It would therefore be advisable to begin an investigation into the trace-element content of feldspars, micas and clay fraction minerals.

Chapter 3

PERTHITES, MESOPERTHITES, ANTIPERTHITES AND PERISTERITES

INTRODUCTION

Chapter 2 has shown that the high-temperature series of mixed crystals between the pure end members *Or* and *Ab*, and *Ab* and *An* are rather continuous ones. Under low-temperature conditions, these phases are unstable. They not only show structural changes, but also tend to unmix. The result of this unmixing is a lamellar aggregate composed of lamellae whose composition is once again quite similar to that of the pure end members. The lamellar aggregate, composed of a large amount of alkali feldspar and a subordinate amount of albite, is called a perthite. It is the common experience of petrographers that a comparatively large number of alkali feldspars studied are "intergrown" with this kind of albite lamellae. Perthites may be recognized by the naked eye or with the help of a microscope (microperthites). They may, however, appear homogeneous upon optical inspection, but show both an albite and a microcline phase upon X-ray analysis (X-ray perthite or cryptoperthite).

A special type of perthites, the so-called mesoperthites, seem to be restricted to special rock types. The proportion of albite and microcline is about 1 : 1. This type seems to occur exclusively in the deep-seated, highly metamorphic rocks in such regions as southern Norway, Saxony, etc. The presence of such perthites in sedimentary rocks is an important indication in determining their provenance.

In addition to the two types of unmixed aggregates, another type of lamellar aggregate exists in nature, in which the amount of the potassium-rich phase is rather subordinate in importance to the amount of albite. These aggregates are called antiperthites. According to some authors, these antiperthites are the result of unmixing; others advocate a different genesis.

Recently, LAVES (1954) and RIBBE (1960) made it evident that a similar unmixing process occurs in plagioclases between approximately An_5 and An_{30}. Lamellar aggregates composed of lamellae with an albite composition occurring next to lamellae with a composition of An_{26} are called peristerites. Further investigations failed to bring about the same evidence in the group of labradorites. AGAFANOVA's observation (1953) still suggests that unmixing into two different phases may also occur in labradorites. She studied the schiller of labradorite and observed that this schiller sometimes vanishes after a heat treatment.

PERTHITES

A great many authors have emphasized the presence of perthites in different types of rocks. The earliest description of perthites appears to have been given by GERHARD in 1861. He proved that a feldspar from Bathurst and Township near Perth in Canada was a lamellar aggregate of albite and "orthoclase". Many authors later confirmed his result on other alkali feldspars (cf. ZIRKEL, 1873, pp.130–132). According to Zirkel, TSCHERMAK (1865) came to the conclusion that both K- and Na-containing feldspars are usually intergrowths of albite and "orthoclase". One of the most lucid papers on the significance and morphology of perthites is TUTTLE's (1952a) on the origin of the contrasting mineralogy of extrusive and plutonic salic rocks. In Tuttle's concept, the changed stability relations of the minerals of the igneous rocks, after cooling to their present temperatures, are responsible for the gradual recrystallization of the original homogeneous high-temperature alkali feldspars. This recrystallization, which leaves a K-rich and a Na-rich phase, may proceed from a sub-microscopic lamellar aggregate (an X-ray perthite) to a crystal aggregate in which the K-rich and Na-rich feldspars are found side by side as if originally formed as separate phases. The nongenetic classification of perthites put forward in TUTTLE's paper (1952a) will be chosen as the most adequate system for use in soil science and sedimentology, because the crystal relationship present in the original rock is lost as soon as crystal fragments of this rock land in sediments or soils. Following this system, perthites are classified according to the size of the unmixed domains:

(1) sub-X-ray perthites: probably less than 15 Å in the direction normal to ($\bar{2}$01);

(2) X-ray perthite: approximately 1 μ;

(3) cryptoperthite: 1–5 μ;

(4) microperthite: 5–100 μ;

(5) perthite: 100–1,000 μ.

Group *1* is recognized by X-ray methods, combined with chemical analysis. A case of the presence of such sub-X-ray perthites has been described by BOWEN and TUTTLE (1950, p.493). X-ray analysis and chemical analysis gave two different compositions in terms of *Or* and *Ab*. After heating, however, the X-ray results conformed to those of the chemical analysis. This proved that the phases present were homogenized upon heating, although the first X-ray analysis did not give evidence for the presence of an albite phase.

Group *2* is recognized only by the presence of albite diffraction lines, and lines of a K-rich phase in the X-ray analysis of a feldspar. They appear optically homogeneous under the highest magnification.

Groups *3* and *4* are recognized with the microscope, provided the thin section has the proper orientation. Perthites of group *5* are not so important for sedimentologists and soil scientists because the particle size of most sediments is of about the same value as the width of these perthite lamellae. Fig.8 shows a micrograph of a perthite.

Until now, perthites have been described in these general terms: potassium-rich phase, alkali-feldspar phase or sodium-rich phase. The reader who expects that perthites are always a combination of maximum microcline and low albite will be disappointed to learn that at least six different combinations of sometimes even more than two phases exist in nature. The combination microcline–albite is certainly one of the common combinations as can be seen, for instance, in KUELLMER's work (1960, 1961). Perthites showing a monoclinic alkali-feldspar phase are frequently found next to these microcline perthites.

Other possible combinations have been the subject of a large investigation on various perthites by MACKENZIE and SMITH (1962). They studied perthites from regions of particular petrographical interest. For convenience, these regions are named here: the Slieve Gullion ring dykes, northern Ireland; the Beinn and Dubhaich granite, Isle of Skye; the Arran and Mourne granite; the Dartmoor granite, southern England; the Kûngnât and Tugtutôg complexes, southwestern Greenland; the Finnemarka complex, Oslo region, southern Norway; the Tatoosh pluton, Mount Rainier National Park, U.S.A.; and other miscellaneous specimens. The interested reader can find details of the 150 samples studied in the paper just mentioned; only the conclusion will be repeated here.

Using single crystal X-ray methods for their study the authors discovered that the presence of a triclinic alkali-feldspar phase, otherwise detected by single crystal methods, may go undetected in powder patterns. Although this is theoretically true, the author ventures to doubt the practical correctness of this idea. His experience with the Nonius Guinier–De Wolff camera taught that the resolution of this instrument is rather superior to that of even the best calibrated and adjusted normal X-ray diffractometer. In the chapter on X-ray analysis more will be said of this aspect.

In the perthite samples studied by these authors not one of the alkali feldspars showed a maximum microcline structure. The potassium phases are nevertheless commonly associated with low albite. In some cases two alkali-feldspar phases co-exist; a triclinic and a monoclinic one. The sodium-rich phases show a much larger variation. In a number of cases the sodium-rich phase of perthites is a potassium-poor alkali feldspar. This type is found especially among sanidine–cryptoperthites. The sodium-rich member in other samples is present as two distinct phases, a potassium-poor alkali feldspar and a calcium-rich plagioclase. Another type consists of an alkali-feldspar phase next to two distinct plagioclase phases, which may or may not have any relation to peristerites. All these possible combinations are listed in Table III.

In the previous consideration perthites are treated as if they are always considered to represent an exsolution phenomenon of an initially homogeneous phase. This is not the case, although it is not important for a pedologist or a sedimentologist

TABLE III

THE COMPOSITION AND THE STRUCTURAL STATE OF THE MEMBERS OF PERTHITES[1]

The potassium-rich member	*The sodium-rich member*
(a) monoclinic	potassium-poor alkali feldspar (triclinic)[2]
(b) monoclinic	potassium-poor alkali feldspar + plagioclase
(c) monoclinic	two distinct plagioclases
(d) monoclinic	plagioclase
(e) monoclinic + triclinic	plagioclase
(f) triclinic	plagioclase

[1] The scheme of this table is adopted from MacKenzie and Smith (1962).
[2] These phases are also known as anorthoclase.

to know what a group of petrographers would have decided about the genesis of the feldspars or perthites now found in sediments or soils, had they been able to study them in their original setting. It is, however, only fair to point out the existence of differing opinions. In a paper by Robertson (1959), the mechanism of another origin of perthites is described. In short, such mechanisms generally consist of the following stages:

(1) plagioclase is changed into albite by a replacement of Ca by Na;

(2) the albite thus formed is partly replaced by K-feldspar;

(3) the organization in space of Na-rich and K-rich phases after such a process of replacement may show either the same or a similar pattern such as the one observed after an exsolution of a homogeneous alkali feldspar phase.

In this connection a remark by Brett (1963) on exsolution textures in ores should be quoted. On the basis of extensive experiments Brett came to the conclusion that: "Because exsolution may produce mutual boundary, veining, and replacement textures, the textures observed in mineral pairs in which solid solution occurs appear ambiguous as genetic criteria".

MESOPERTHITES AND ANTIPERTHITES

According to the A. G. I. Glossary, antiperthites are "an intergrowth of sodic and potassic feldspar generally thought to have formed during slow cooling by unmixing of sodium and potassium ions in an originally homogeneous alkalic feldspar. In the antiperthites the potassic member (usually orthoclase) forms thin films, lamellae, strings, or irregular veinlets within the sodic member (usually albite)". Accepting this definition, one means that the difference between perthites and antiperthites is a question of grades rather than of principle, a view also expressed by Sen (1959). Because of the intermediate situation of mesoperthites the same holds true for mesoperthites. The following scheme makes this clear:

perthites   : alkali-feldspar phase $\gg$ sodium phase;
mesoperthites: alkali-feldspar phase $\approx$ sodium phase;
antiperthites : alkali-feldspar phase $\ll$ sodium phase.

The term "mesoperthites" has been defined by P. MICHOT (1961) as a "close intertwining texture of alkali feldspar and plagioclase. The pattern is similar to that of microperthites. In mesoperthites it is impossible to see which of the two phases encloses the other, because both alkali feldspar and plagioclase are present in equal quantities." The "type locality" of mesoperthites is the Egersund region in southern Norway. Other localities where these crystalline aggregates are found are the Charnockite regions of India, the basement rocks of Antarctica and the Granulites of Saxony and Finland. Eskola described the same perthites from Finland granulites as "hairperthites". According to P. Michot the Egersund mesoperthites are characterized by a plagioclase phase with 17% An. In exceptional cases even 25% An was found. These perthites are assumed to be the result of exsolution of a homogeneous alkali feldspar at rather high temperatures (over 600°C). The interested reader may find some information on these perthites in the account of the "International Colloquium on the Metamorphic Facies Problem" reported in the *Neues Jahrb. Mineral., Abhandl.*, 1961, which gives a comparatively complete report on mesoperthites. Quantitative data are still needed for a better insight in the true importance of these special perthites.

According to KÖHLER (1948), antiperthites are principally different from perthites; they represent oriented intergrowths of two separate phases; the plagioclase member functions as an orientation pattern for the alkali feldspar; the presence of antiperthites is more or less restricted to metamorphic rocks, showing the influence of a later addition of K-ions. According to this idea of Köhler, the phenomenon described by ROBERTSON (1959) and mentioned in the foregoing paragraph could better be called antiperthite, if only because the plagioclase or albite phase is more important than the alkali-feldspar phase.

Despite Köhler's ideas it has been rather well established that antiperthites, originating by exsolution from rather Na-rich alkali feldspar phases, in which the K-rich member is of much less importance than the Na-rich phase, exist in nature.

PERISTERITES

Nothing is known until now about the presence of peristerites in soils and sediments. The fact that peristerites are rare, together with the rather recent discovery of the real nature of these typical plagioclases may well explain this. For this reason no more will be said of these aggregates, and the reader is referred to papers by LAVES (1954), RIBBE (1960, 1962), BROWN (1962), and RIBBE and VAN COTT (1962) for further information.

Chapter 4

IDENTIFICATION PROCEDURES BASED ON CHEMICAL METHODS

INTRODUCTION AND REVIEW

The study of the light fraction of soil samples or samples of sediments is met with numerous difficulties. In the preceding 100 years a number of identification methods for phases of feldspar composition have been devised. These methods, however, have been developed in order to determine the various feldspar phases present in igneous and metamorphic rocks. Such rocks have one rather important common characteristic; i.e., the mineral assemblage present is governed by the laws of thermodynamics as was shown by FYFE et al. (1958). Consequently, these rocks contain a limited number of crystalline phases. These phases, however, are present as a large number of crystals. In general, such rocks contain no more than two feldspar phases, present as numerous crystals of different sizes and shapes. On the contrary, clastic sediments may hold a relatively large number of crystalline phases present in only small numbers of crystals. Sedimentologists and soil scientists are familiar with this phenomenon from experience.

Imagine the large number of different minerals present in such a sample, for the total includes all the categories listed in the heavy mineral analysis, plus the number of various light minerals in the sand fraction, plus the number of different minerals observed in the fraction smaller than 2 μ. Consider, too, the number of minerals in one of these categories, such as the number of zircons or the number of garnets expressed in percentages of the total number of particles. Such a consideration also holds true for the feldspar content of detrital rocks because of the numerous possibilities that may result from the combination of different chemical compositions and various structures. Theoretically a sediment may have as many feldspar phases as an artichoke holds leaves.

In order to gain insight into the possible ways of identifying feldspar phases in soils and sediments, a survey of the different techniques seems rather useful. Methods of identifying a crystalline substance are based either on the possibility of obtaining information on its chemical composition, or on the measurements of various physical properties dependent on the chemical composition and/or the structure of such a substance.

Chemical-analysis methods are destructive. This is one of the important limitations of chemical analysis. It is often impossible to prepare a sample of such purity and/or quantity to make the analysis worthwhile. The chemical analysis of a glass of feldspar composition and the analysis of a crystalline phase of the same composition produce the same results. Moreover, modifications are not recognized. If the crystalline substance to be analysed is an aggregate composed of extremely small, mutually exclusive homogeneous domains such as microperthites, the chemical analysis gives only bulk composition as a result. Chemical analysis is useful only if one is interested in bulk composition, or if it has been established by other methods that the substance under analysis is a homogeneous crystalline material.

In some cases it is highly desirable to know the exact chemical composition of a definite phase if it has been established by other methods that only one phase is present, or that two or more phases are present in a known or estimated proportion. For these special cases some comments on the methods of chemical analysis must be made. Generally speaking, feldspars are analysed by current-analytical procedures.

In addition to these techniques, modern quantitative chemical analysis uses a large number of methods based on measurements of physical characteristics. Such methods are flame spectroscopy, X-ray fluorescence, infra-red spectrometry, colorimetry, activation analysis and others. Strictly speaking a discussion of these methods should be treated in the next chapter on identification techniques based on physical methods. In that case, however, these methods for the determination of the chemical composition of a substance not essentially crystalline will get mixed up with such methods that are essentially based on the physical properties of a feldspar. Moreover, the methods discussed here can be applied to any mixture of chemical compounds, whether a feldspar or a mixture of laboratory chemicals.

The introduction of flame photometry brought a notable increase in the accuracy of the values of Na_2O and K_2O. At present reliable methods are being developed for the colorimetric analysis of SiO_2 and Al_2O_3 (see SHAPIRO and BRANNOCK, 1956). Spectrographic methods are currently applied and not only for the purpose of analysing minor elements (PETERS, 1963; VAN DER VEEN, 1963).

Besides these analytical methods, a number of non-destructive techniques are available at present. BRADLEY and BRADLEY (1956) describe a first attempt to use the so-called activation analysis for the determination of K, Na and Ca in feldspars. The feldspars are stored in an atomic pile for some time and afterwards the radiation is measured by a discrimination method. The results were fair for Na and K, but measurements for Ca were difficult and not accurate.

EMERSON (1959) determined the K_2O content of powdered alkali feldspars with X-ray emission. The measurements were controlled with a flame photometer. His conclusion is that both methods are similarly accurate.

Two rather recent developments warrant high expectations regarding feldspar analysis. The first of these techniques is known as electron probe microanalysis. The best information on these tools at present has to be obtained from the manufacturers of appliances. The other method is based on recent developments in Laser technology. From a newspaper (June, 1964) clipping it can be inferred that even objects under a microscope can be analysed with a light beam of a ruby laser. The laser has been already used in mineral identification, as witnessed by the report of MAXWELL (1963). As it is premature to judge the performance of these instruments in our special field of mineralogy, it is left to the reader to follow the developments pertinent to our subject with the necessary interest.

It is noteworthy that numerous feldspar analyses show an excess of SiO_2 and Al_2O_3 (BELYANKINA, 1953). Although the accurate determination of the two mentioned oxydes is rather difficult, and more or less a privilege of experienced analysts, the trend observed is too striking to be ascribed to errors in the analyses, to lattice deficiencies or to chance. On p.34, some remarks have been made concerning these anomalies. The observation of MARSHALL (1962) on the influence of NH_4 ions in hydrolysing feldspars has been related with this remarkable excess, while it was observed that ammonium is not detected in normal analytical procedures.

In summary, the modern procedures for the chemical analysis of silicates are more reliable, less time-consuming and often easier to perform than the classical ones. The use of complexometric titration in particular leads to highly accurate results. Details of such procedures are treated carefully in numerous handbooks. A chemical technique, not yet mentioned, will be treated in detail in the following pages. It has to do with staining methods. The staining of feldspars leads to a proper insight of the amount of these minerals in samples; the distinction between alkali feldspars and plagioclases can be easily made. Moreover, stained samples enable the analyst to select by handpicking a small amount of feldspars for optical or X-ray investigation.

STAINING METHODS

GABRIEL and COX (1929) suggested a method for staining alkali feldspars in rock slabs and thin sections. The method is based on the fact that potassium cobaltinitrite has a strong yellow colour. Alkali feldspars are etched with HF, and the etch-residue is made wet with a solution of cobaltinitrite to form the yellow potassium cobaltinitrite. This looks like a very simple procedure, but the fact that so many authors found it necessary to comment on the details of the procedure proves that, in practice, there are some difficulties to overcome. Moreover, the staining of rock slabs is quite a different matter from the staining of sand fragments.

Methods for staining plagioclases have also been suggested (see BAILEY and STEVENS, 1960). They advocate staining with barium chloride and potassium rhodizonate after etching. Plagioclase feldspars show a brick red stain afterwards.

REEDER and MCALLISTER (1957) suggest a method for staining the Al ion in feldspars with hemateine after etching. The feldspars then reveal a lilac blue colour. A review of methods for staining feldspars can be found in the papers of CHAYES (1952a), REEDER and MCALLISTER (1957), HAYES and KLUGMAN (1959), and BAILEY and STEVENS (1960).

Favejee developed a method for staining sand particles having a minimum size of about 50 μ. This method, based on the formula of Gabriel and Cox for the cobaltinitrite staining, and on the formula of Reeder and McAllister for hemateine staining, is successfully used as a routine procedure in the Mineralogy laboratory of the Wageningen Soil Science and Geology Department, and in many other places where Wageningen alumni now operate. The need to modify Reeder's and McAllister's procedures came about as soon as small particles had to be stained. Such particles agglomerate and glue together, forming unsurveyable aggregates. Favejee could explain also why the formula of Gabriel and Cox is better from a theoretical point of view, the difference being the properties of the Al ion when etching is done at elevated temperatures. Therefore, the particles are etched in HF-vapour of 90 °C for exactly 1 min. Afterwards, the etch-residue is fixed on the surface of the particles by a 400 °C heat treatment in an electrical furnace for a period of 5 min. Then the particles are stained in much the same way as described in the papers of the above-mentioned authors. Staining one part of the sample with cobaltinitrite and the other part with hemateine, is preferred above the staining of the whole sample as suggested by Reeder and McAllister. For further comments on this procedure one may consult DOEGLAS et al. (1965).

METHODS FOR STAINING FELDSPARS

Staining samples of feldspar grains with cobaltinitrite

Reagents
A solution of 1 g of sodium cobaltinitrite in 4 ml of distilled water.

Procedure
The sample, just covering the bottom of a small Pt dish, is etched with HF vapour. In order to perform such a treatment one should use a container of HF-resistent material that can be kept at a temperature of about 90°C. The entrance into the container must be small to avoid the loss of too much vapour while inserting the sample. The experiment must be carried out in a well-ventilated hood! The sample to be etched must be free in the vapour and situated above the small inner-container that holds the liquid HF 35%. The container must be wide enough that the vapour can easily play around the sample. The set-up must be stable and easy to handle because HF liquid, as well as the vapour, is rather dangerous. Take care not to spill the liquid on the skin and by all means avoid touching HF vapour to the skin or eyes.[1]

---

[1] Prevent spilling HF by using gloves, as well as spectacles while etching. If, unfortunately, HF is spilt in large amounts a proper treatment is prescribed. Recently, HOOGENDAM and VAN DIJK (1963) described a method for the treatment of such accidents. In our laboratory both a reprint of their paper as well as the necessary drugs are part of the emergency chest, because it was experienced in a number of cases that the medical doctor was not familiar with the treatment of such accidents, and prompt treatment is very essential in this case. As the paper just mentioned is in Dutch, we repeat here the four steps from the English summary: (*1*) rinse immediately with water for 2–3 min, (*2*) infiltrate with a calcium preparation (the authors use calcium-gluconolacto bionate), (*3*) rinse again for 15 min, (*4*) apply a skin ointment containing a corticosteroid.
It goes without saying that this treatment must be administered by a qualified medical doctor.

After etching, the sample is treated in an electrical furnace at about 400°C for 5 min. The sample thus treated is brought into contact with the above solution of cobaltinitrite for 1 min. The sample is washed free of the solution with distilled water, removing the supernatant liquid with a small siphon. As a result the alkali feldspars show a yellow stain.

Staining samples of feldspar grains with hemateine

Reagents
A solution of 50 mg of hemateine in 100 ml of 95% ethanol (alcohol).
A buffer solution consisting of 20 g sodium acetate in 100 ml of distilled water, to which 6 ml of glacial acetic acid is added afterwards. This solution is diluted to 200 ml, buffered at pH 4.8, with an acidity of 0.5 N.

Procedure
After the etching and heat treatment (see above), about 10 drops of hemateine solution and 5 drops of the buffer solution are added to the sample covering the bottom of the Pt dish. The whole is mixed by swirling the dish for about 2–3 min. The grains are left in contact with the solution for about 5 min. The solution is then washed away with 95% ethanol, the supernatant liquid is siphoned off, and the sample is finally washed twice with acetone. As a result the feldspars show a purple bluish stain.

Staining simultaneously for the K ion and the Al ion is possible. In this case the cobaltinitrite staining method must precede the hemateine staining. If the staining of the fragments is not well performed under certain circumstances, the grains can be cleaned with diluted HCl and after rinsing with distilled water and drying with acetone the etching can be performed anew, followed by staining. In almost every case the second etching gives satisfactory results. It is perhaps necessary to draw attention to the fact that coatings on the grains have to be removed before etching and staining. Numerous methods are available for this, each having its own merits. Handbooks on methods for sedimentary petrologists give numerous variants with all details. Barium rhodizonate staining of the calcium ion is not mentioned here for unconsolidated or friable material, because the author has no experience with it.

Staining rock slabs or thin sections with cobaltinitrite

Reagents
A solution of 1 g of sodium cobaltinitrite in 4 ml of distilled water.

Procedure
The rock slab or thin section should be polished before staining for better results. Porous surfaces constitute a difficulty. Moreover, the surface has to be carefully cleaned of Canada balsem, resins or grease with ether, acetone or another organic solvent, an ultrasonic cleaner gives also excellent results. After cleaning the surface may not be touched anymore with the fingers.
The cleaned and polished specimen is laid on a lead plate. If it is a thin section, the other side, the glass surface, is carefully covered with a grease resistant to HF vapour in order to avoid frosting of the glass, for this makes the sample unsuitable for microscopical examination with a normal polarizing microscope. For etching, the sample is laid on a small flat lead plate and brought into the etching vessel. The surface is etched for 1 min in HF vapour at 90°C. A heat treatment for thin sections after etching is not possible and unnecessary. Now the sodium-cobaltinitrite solution described above is spilled on the surface and left there for about 2 min. Afterwards the sample is

washed with distilled water and left to dry. As a result the alkali feldspars on the surface show a beautiful yellow stain.

Staining rock slabs or thin sections with hemateine

Reagents
A solution of 50 mg of hemateine in 100 ml of 95% ethanol (alcohol).

A buffer solution consisting of 20 g sodium acetate in 100 ml of distilled water, to which 6 ml of glacial acetic acid is added afterwards. This solution is diluted to 200 ml, buffered at pH 4.8, with an acidity of 0.5 N.

Procedure
After etching, having taken care to avoid the difficulties just described, the sample is wetted with a solution of hemateine and the buffer solution mentioned earlier. The mixing of both solutions is done just before wetting in the proportion 2/1. The solution is left on the surface for 5 min and afterwards the surface is rinsed with ethanol 95% and with acetone. Feldspars show a bluish stain afterwards.

Staining rock slabs or thin sections with bariumrhodizonate (After BAILEY and STEVENS, 1960)

Reagents
A 5% barium chloride solution.

A solution of 0.05 g of rhodizonic acid potassium salt in 20 ml of distilled water. This solution is unstable and must be freshly made each time in a small dropper bottle.

Procedure
After etching the thin section or the rock slab, prepared as above (the authors etch in cold HF vapour for 3 min), dip the sample in distilled water and twice quickly in the barium-chloride solution. Rinse again, being careful not to use too much water, and cover the surface with the rhodizonate solution by dropping it on the surface until this is adequately covered. Let the brick red colour of barium rhodizonate develop until it can be satisfactorily seen. Rinse the sample under running tap water. Bailey and Stevens advise staining thin sections to only a light pink. The rhodizonate stain can also be developed on a sample previously stained with cobaltinitrite. The cobaltinitrite staining is performed first. The sample is then rinsed with water and afterwards treated as described above.

Chapter 5

IDENTIFICATION PROCEDURES BASED ON PHYSICAL METHODS, AN INTRODUCTION

INTRODUCTION

Before discussing those methods used to determine physical properties of crystalline phases, we call attention to the fact that a number of modern techniques of quantitative chemical analysis are based on the measurement of physical characteristics of the sample under investigation. Such methods have been treated briefly in Chapter 4.

Sedimentologists expect a sediment to contain an arbitrary number of crystal fragments belonging to an arbitrary number of different phases. In the foregoing chapter it has been stressed that the mineral assemblage of igneous or metamorphic rocks is governed by the laws of thermodynamics. Consequently, these rocks contain a limited number of minerals and only one or two specific feldspars. Moreover, because of this characteristic, thin sections or polished specimens of igneous or metamorphic rocks generally enable the investigator to select only those sections from the numerous possible ones with the proper orientation for a definite measurement through one of the mineral species present. Once a small number of such measurements are made, the investigator is able to generalize the results for all the crystals belonging to the same mineral species present in the sample[1]. The petrographer dealing exclusively with these types of rock is so accustomed to this fact that he does not give it a second thought.

The mineral assemblage of clastic rocks is not governed by the laws of thermodynamics, but by a complex of factors such as mineral assemblages of regions of provenance, means of transport, etc. This consideration does not take into account the presence of authigenic minerals or minerals due to alterations under atmospheric influences. It follows that a large number of identification techniques, useful for the study of minerals in igneous or metamorphic rocks, is useless for the pedologist or sedimentologist *unless* he is able to modify them. Moreover, he must find methods that concentrate the light fractions of his samples in such a way that these fractions contain a sufficient amount of feldspar fragments before identification techniques can be efficiently applied.

---

[1] For the sake of simplicity, the difficulties observed when the rocks are polymetamorphic and where zonal structures are seen in the plagioclases, are not taken into consideration. Differences in chemical composition between plagioclases of the matrix and the plagioclase phenocrysts of an extrusive rock are also disregarded.

Physical properties of crystals

Homogeneous crystalline substances have specific physical properties at certain temperatures and pressures. For instance, they show certain characteristic features during the passage of light. They also show a specific crystal structure and have a specific density and heat capacity.

A number of identification techniques are based on the measurement of the variation of these properties caused by a variation of the chemical composition or the structure; such techniques are commonly used in mineralogy.

If the amount of only one element is gradually changed in favour of only one other element in a system of mixed crystals with only one type of structure, the physical properties of the substance will show continuous variation in most cases. Feldspars, chemically two binary systems, satisfy these conditions in some respects. Therefore, these features look promising. The main drawback, however, is that a large number of structural differences are encountered, and also that separation may occur in a homogeneous crystalline phase under certain circumstances. Consequently, complications are to be expected in the continuous variation of the physical properties with varying chemical composition. In a number of cases, however, it has been proved possible to identify the structure of the phase as well as the chemical composition by a specific method or by a felicitous combination of methods. Moreover, some structural changes do interfere only slightly with the continuous variation, for example, of the index of refraction of plagioclases, thus enabling the investigator to identify the chemical composition of an unknown feldspar phase with a minimum amount of error, considering he does not know the structural state. Mutatis mutandis, the same will be true of the influence of a variation in chemical composition on some aspects of the structure.

In the following chapters a systematic review will be given of the possible methods, their limitations, and the use a pedologist or sedimentologist can make of these methods in certain cases.

Physical properties of feldspars can be used either for an identification or for a concentration of these minerals. The specific gravity of feldspars and the magnetic susceptibility of these crystals are successfully used for a concentration of feldspars. The optical properties and the structural characteristics are more suitable for identification methods.

Concentration methods

The specific gravity of feldspars is low compared to the densities of other silicates. The specific gravity of quartz is about the same as that of oligoclase. This property provides us with the possibility of separating feldspars and quartz from other silicates. Afterwards we can try a separation of alkali feldspars from plagioclases. The presence of quartz together with oligoclase is a nuisance, but it will be shown that possibilities exist for limiting its annoying influence. The methods will be treated in detail in Chapter 6.

Flotation as a method for concentrating a specific mineral from a mixture is essentially a physico-chemical process. This technique, widely used for the production of feldspars on an industrial scale, is based on the chemical composition of the surface of feldspar fragments. Feldspar sands or crushed feldspar-bearing rocks are brought in water together with a number of chemical compounds. The surface of the fragments receives a special treatment. This treatment brings out rather specific surface properties. Afterwards a large number of small bubbles is produced in the liquid. The pretreated feldspars attach themselves to these bubbles and start to float. The other minerals remain settled on the bottom of the container. For practical reasons the aspects of feldspar flotation are also treated in Chapter 6; thus the two most promising concentration methods are described in the same chapter.

Magnetic separation methods as well as electrostatical concentration methods, though not used for identification problems, make it possible to obtain concentrates of one or only a few minerals. Especially if the feldspar identification of sediments and soils is going to be used as a routine technique, it is useful to avoid any time consuming performance in the complex of pretreatment and analysis. Feldspars are diamagnetic. Running the sample through a magnetic separator at the highest possible field, will result in most cases in a non-magnetic fraction containing quartz, feldspars and zircon. According to a paper by STIELER (1955), the electrostatical separation of quartz and feldspar is successfully used on an industrial scale.

Identification methods

In the course of time a confusing amount of data has been gathered on the optical properties of feldspars. Some of these data are of high precision and pertain to accurately defined phases with a known chemical composition. Others of high precision were also measured on phases of unknown structure and unknown chemical composition. A number of determination charts and diagrams, especially of plagioclases, are based on such accurate measurements of phases of which neither the structural state, nor the chemical composition has been determined by other methods. A set of measurements is available on feldspar phases whose structure has been determined by X-ray techniques, and where the chemical composition has been analysed. These data, however, are for the larger part virtually hidden in feldspar literature. They are based mostly, for example, on well-known sets of measurements on optical properties of chemically analysed samples (SPENCER, 1937; EMMONS, 1953). The original samples described in these papers were later used by others to study their structural properties with X-ray methods. Gathering these data may furnish a set of measurements that meet the present requirements of accuracy and reliability. Objections can be made about the use of such data. The determinations of structure with X-ray methods have been made on that part of the sample not used for the determination of optical properties. Moreover, the original investigators did not consider an X-ray investigation of their material at the moment of sample preparation. Therefore the optical measurements should properly be repeated on the material subjected to X-ray analysis.

In the following chapters the domain of optical properties will be surveyed as systematically as possible. The review does not aim at completeness and some well-known methods will be looked for in vain. One of the reasons for these omissions is the fact that such techniques, though rather useful for petrographers, are considered rather useless for sedimentologists and pedologists. For example, one may note the use of refractive indices of plagioclase glasses (FOSTER, 1955; SCHAIRER et al., 1956; GRADWELL, 1958), and the method advocated by NIEUWEN-KAMP (1948) based on a combination of measuring extinction angles in twins and the ratio of the birefringences of the two individuals. The interested reader may find these determination techniques in such textbooks as WINCHELL and WINCHELL (1951); TRÖGER (1959); MARFUNIN (1962a, b); and DEER, HOWIE and ZUSSMAN (1963).

Twinning of feldspars is a property that cannot be used for feldspar identification. Still, feldspar twins carry much additional information that can be used to the advantage of any sedimentological investigation. Twinning of feldspars is governed by the physical circumstances during the genesis of igneous or metamorphic rocks. Such twins in sediments may cast some light on questions of provenance.

The X-ray analysis of powdered feldspar samples reveals information about the chemical composition, the structural state and the presence of perthites. The powder patterns of selected fractions of feldspars from sediments give ample information on the composition of these fractions. X-ray powder patterns of clay fractions of sediments inform the investigator not only on the feldspar content of this fraction, but also on the nature of these feldspars. Information on the feldspars in the silt fraction and in the clay fraction cannot be obtained by other methods, with the exception perhaps of the use of phase-contrast microscopy.

SUMMARY

In summary, the analytical procedures using the physical properties of crystalline-feldspar phases may be divided into a number of categories. Such a division is more or less arbitrary, but it is needed in order to organize the presentation of the material to be reported. The division used in this text is as follows: (1) specific gravity of feldspars; (2) optical properties of feldspars; (3) twinning of feldspars; (4) X-ray powder data of feldspars.

Objections may well be made against this subdivision. Twins, for example, are frequently used to determine the orientation of the indicatrix of plagioclases. Therefore, twins could be treated together with the optical properties. It has proved practical, however, to use this division of subjects, for a surveyable description.

Chapter 6

CONCENTRATION OF FELDSPARS BASED ON SPECIFIC GRAVITY AND ON FLOTATION

In Chapter 11, it will be shown that efficient concentration techniques are a *conditio sine qua non* for a quantitative analysis of the feldspar content of a large number of sediments. Consequently, any promising concentration method needs our special attention. Sediments with a feldspar content of more than 40% are exceptional; and such sediments do not make a feldspar investigation difficult. It is the other sedimentary rocks, with a lower feldspar content, that are difficult to study. Unlike the study of feldspars of igneous and metamorphic rocks, an investigation of feldspars from soils or sediments has to be based on a large number of measured fragments. Consequently, the efficiency of such a study is highly increased as soon as the thin section, the grain mount, or any other sample is mainly a collection of feldspars.

Feldspars can be separated from a sediment or a soil by different methods. One may, for instance, collect the feldspars from a sand by handpicking stained-fragments under a binocular microscope. Though time consuming, this method is still used by many investigators. Handpicking is relatively efficient, as long as the average grain size of the sample is moderate to large.

Other methods for separating feldspars from a sample are based on the chemical or physical properties of these minerals. Two useful properties in this respect are the density of feldspars and the specific chemical composition of the feldspar surface. The concentration of feldspars with heavy liquids—a technique essentially similar to the separation of heavy minerals from a sample—is treated in detail in the first part of this chapter. The aspects of flotation, a method based on the composition of a feldspar surface, are treated in the second part.

Although flotation methods have no relation to specific-gravity separation, they are both treated in this chapter. This is done for practical reasons; the two promising concentration methods are handled in one chapter. Moreover, the methods have a superficial resemblance; both techniques float the feldspars and leave the other minerals settled in the liquid.

THE SPECIFIC GRAVITY OF FELDSPARS

The specific gravity of feldspars ranges from about 2.55 to about 2.76. The lowest values are found in rather pure potassium feldspars; the highest values pertain to anorthite. Pure albite has a specific gravity of about 2.62. Methods for concentrating feldspar fragments from sediments and soils depend largely on the specific gravities of these minerals. Using heavy liquids, the samples can be divided into several fractions between limiting specific gravities. The limitations of such methods are set by the properties of the liquids, as well as by the particle sizes of the feldspars. If ordinary separation funnels are used, particles smaller than about 200 μ cannot be separated efficiently, for the settling time of such particles is too long and the viscosity of the liquid does not permit reliable separation.

Well aware of these difficulties, Favejee developed a method that meets the above objections to a large extent (DOEGLAS et al., 1965). The liquid used must have two main characteristics: firstly, it must have good wetting properties, and secondly, the viscosity must be relatively low to allow small particles to settle fairly quickly. Another desirable characteristic of such a "heavy" liquid is a good tenability. In order to meet these requirements, Favejee suggests the use of a mixture of bromoform and decaline, two liquids with more or less the same vapour pressure and good wettability. Our experiments showed that the specific gravity of this liquid remains constant for a long time. He developed different types of apparatus for a specific-gravity separation of various feldspars, but a specially designed funnel with steep walls proved to be most efficient. The design of this funnel is given in Fig.10.

Fig.10. The Favejee funnel. A special funnel for the separation of light minerals with heavy liquids.

Centrifuge methods also have limitations. One of the main difficulties is extracting the two fractions from the tubes without remixing. For this reason a number of techniques have been suggested. Some investigators use plastic tubes which can be cut; others insert plastic bags in the tubes and tie them before taking the bags out of the tubes; others use specially designed tubes, Taylor tubes, Schröder tubes, Kunitz tubes, etc.; still others use special pipettes to collect the residue from the bottom of the tubes. These methods are described by KRUMBEIN and PETTIJOHN (1938) and by MARSHALL and JEFFRIES (1945).

Specific-gravity limits for concentration purposes

Specific-gravity limits for the separation of feldspar fractions have to be set at such values that the two important groups of feldspars are separated. As the specific gravity of alkali feldspars never reaches a value above 2.59, this seems to be the right value for separating alkali feldspars and plagioclases. Secondly, samples of sediments and soils contain a large amount of quartz. It is important that this mineral lands in a fraction between two specific-gravity limits as close to each other as possible in order to provide for other feldspar fractions that are to a large extent clear of quartz. The apparent specific gravity of quartz particles ranges from about 2.63 to 2.67, providing two ranges for separation limits. The

TABLE IV

SPECIFIC GRAVITIES OF A NUMBER OF MINERALS TO BE
EXPECTED IN THE LIGHT FRACTION OF SOME SEDIMENTS
OR SOILS

Mineral	Specific gravity
Opal	1.95–2.10
Sodalite	2.2 –2.4
Gypsum	2.2 –2.4
Serpentinite	2.5 –2.65
Alkali feldspar	2.54–2.59
Plagioclase feldspar	2.59–2.76
Chalcedony	2.60–3.0
Chlorite	2.6 –3.0
Quartz[1]	2.63–2.67
Beryl	2.65–2.85
Stilpnomelane	2.70–3.0
Calcite	2.71–2.72
Muscovite	2.76–3.00
Biotite	2.8 –3.5
Prehnite	2.8 –2.95
Dolomite	2.87

[1] The apparent specific gravity of quartz particles may vary considerably because of small inclusions of gas, liquid and heavy minerals.

TABLE V

SPECIFIC GRAVITY OF ALKALI FELDSPARS

No.	Or	Ab	An	s.g.	2V
sanidines					
1	42.1	52.3	5.6	2.606	47.7
2	49.9	41.6	8.5	2.577	17
3	63.1	35.4	1.5	2.564	38
4[2]	77.8	22.2	—	2.5763	24
5	64.7	33.2	2.1	2.565	18
adularia, Fe-orthoclase, Ca-anorthoclase					
6	92.8	6.6	0.6	2.559	n.d.[3]
7	90.5	8.3	1.2	2.5661	68.4
8	80.6	18.2	1.2	2.572	n.d.
9[4]	95.5	4.1	0.4	2.5625	34.8
10	12.2	76.4	11.4	2.646	46–66
true monoclinic orthoclase, 2V < 44°					
11	90.5	7.1	2.4	2.5632	43.6
12	46.7	51.2	0.5	2.5773	39.1
orthoclase microperthites					
13	82.2	14.7	1.8	2.5691	58
14	68.1	30.2	1.7	2.5778	69
15	61.6	35.8	1.0	2.5819	72
16	45.2	49.7	4.2	2.5960	81.75
microcline perthites					
17	85.2	13.4	1.4	2.5692	76.2
18	82.9	14.5	1.1	2.5736	63.5
19	80.3	17.8	0.4	2.5757	82
20	73.9	24.0	2.1	2.565	81
21	59.2	37.1	3.7	2.569	80
synthetic alkali feldspars					
22	100	—	—	2.553	n.d.
23	80	20	—	2.545	n.d.
24	60	40	—	2.550	n.d.
25	40	60	—	2.566	n.d.
26	20	80	—	2.584	n.d.

[1] DHZ, 6(3) stands for DEER, HOWIE and ZUSSMANN (1963), table 6, no.3.
[2] This sample holds about 3.2% of the celsian molecule.
[3] n.d. = not determined.
[4] This sample holds about 2.1% of the Fe-orthoclase molecule.

Type of phase and source

theralite, Bo Plei, Siam. DHZ, 6(3)[1]
dacite, Zvečan, Yugoslavia. DHZ, 6(5)
quartz rhyolite, Végardo, Slovakia. DHZ, 6(10)
Eifel, Germany. SPENCER (1937)
tuffaceous liparite, Taiji Kii, Japan. DHZ, 6(11)

adularia, V., Cristallina, Switzerland. DHZ, 8(8)
adularia, Gotthard, Switzerland. SPENCER (1937)
adularia, Bourg d'Oiseaux, Dauphiné, France. DHZ, 8(1)
Fe-orthoclase, Madagascar. SPENCER (1930)
Ca-anorthoclase, trachyliparite, North Caucasus. DHZ, 7(1)

colourless orthoclase, Burma. SPENCER (1930, 1937)
colourless orthoclase, northeast Korea. SPENCER (1937)

garnetiferous granite gneiss, Kalahandi, India. SPENCER (1937)
moonstone, Ceylon. SPENCER (1937)
Kandy, India. SPENCER (1937)
Burma. SPENCER (1937)

micro-pegmatite, Kodarma, Bihar, India. SPENCER (1937)
micro-pegmatite, Kodarma, Bihar, India. SPENCER (1937)
graphite-bearing pegmatite, Patna Orissa, India. SPENCER (1937)
Musgrave ranges, Australia. WILSON (1950)
Musgrave ranges, Australia. WILSON (1950)

synthetic high-temperature feldspars
prepared by DONNAY and DONNAY (1952)

only feldspars found inbetween these two limits are from the group of oligoclase and part of the acid andesines. JEFFRIES (1937), KRUMBEIN and PETTIJOHN (1938), JEFFRIES and JACKSON (1949), and some others have suggested specific-gravity limits for a fractioning of the sample. None of these suggestions, however, meet all the above requirements. After a number of experiments in the Department of Soil Science and Geology at Wageningen, Favejee suggested the following ranges, which were later successfully applied by KHADR (1960), NOTA and BAKKER (1960), and described in DOEGLAS et al. (1965). These ranges are:

> < 2.59 alkali feldspars
> $2.59-2.63$ albite and quartz
> $2.63-2.67$ quartz and plagioclase
> $2.67-2.89$ basic plagioclases

It should be mentioned that in common practice these limits have proved efficient, but other minerals may be observed in these fractions (Table IV). A number of these minerals can easily be removed by special treatment, others cannot.

Alkali feldspars

The specific gravity of alkali feldspars ranges between the theoretical value for pure $KAlSi_3O_8$ and the value for pure albite. Specific-gravity values of alkali feldspars both from actual measurements and calculated from published unit-cell parameters, are listed in Table V. Another feature is the difference between the specific gravities of the high- and the low-temperature forms of the same chemical composition. This difference is so small that in practical work it does not cause difficulties. For practical purposes the specific gravity of alkali feldspars is taken to be less than 2.59.

The specific-gravity difference between the two pure end members albite and potassium feldspar, approximately 2.56 and 2.61, is too small to permit an efficient separation into a potassium-rich and a sodium-rich group of alkali feldspars. In our own routine work Favejee has experienced that differences between fractions have to be at least around 0.04. An additional difficulty may be the presence of arbitrary contents of Fe_2O_3, BaO or CaO in the framework of these minerals. The presence of small mica flakes, small flakes of iron oxide, and small cavities filled with a liquid or a gas constitute a further complication. The cavities in particular are rather common. A number of such feldspars are often termed "dusty", or "altered", or "filled with extremely small flakes of mica or even kaolinite (!)" in petrographic descriptions. On inspection with magnifications over $1,000 \times$ with oil-immersion objectives, they sometimes seem almost opaque because of the presence of thousands of extremely small cavities, giving the feldspar a "dusty brownish appearance" under normal microscopic observation.

Because of the similar framework of albite and alkali feldspar, the specific gravity of perthites is more or less equal to that of the homogeneous phase of the same chemical composition.

Plagioclase feldspars

The specific gravity of plagioclases ranges between the theoretical value of pure albite and the value of pure anorthite, 2.61 and 2.76 respectively. Specific gravity values of plagioclases are listed in Table VI. Here again the difference between the high- and the low-temperature form must be considered, but from this table and Fig.11, it follows that this difference is too small to permit a differentiation between the two phases with heavy liquids. The density of plagioclases permits a subdivision, by means of heavy liquids, into a few groups with a specific chemical composition.

Again the presence of varying contents of K_2O and Fe_2O_3 may cause some problems. In addition, plagioclases of igneous and metamorphic rocks may contain a rather large amount of enclosed minerals such as epidote, calcite, mica and quartz. In a number of cases these minerals are the result of metamorphic or hydrothermal alteration of the original feldspar substance. Apart from these minerals others may frequently be found enclosed in plagioclases. This is especially true of plagioclases from metamorphic rocks showing what has been called

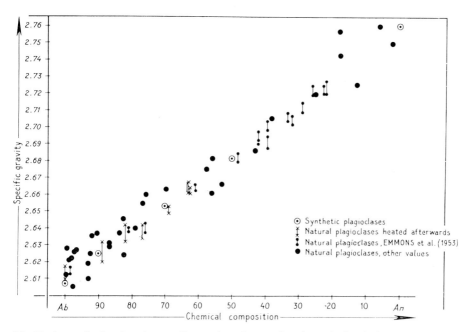

Fig.11. A graph showing the specific gravity of natural and synthetic plagioclases and their chemical composition. In addition to other values from the literature the values given in Table VI are listed without exception.

TABLE VI

SPECIFIC GRAVITY OF PLAGIOCLASES

No.	Or	Ab	An	s.g.	s.g. after heating
natural plagioclases					
1	1.2	98.6	0.15	2.613–2.617	
2	1.6	87.0	11.4	2.629–2.633	
3	2.8	81.1	16.1	2.638–2.640	
4	4.2	76.3	19.5	2.637–2.643	
5	1.5	62.6	35.9	2.663–2.668	
6	2.0	60.0	38.0	2.662–2.666	
7	1.1	47.3	51.6	2.678–2.688	
8	2.6	45.2	52.2	2.683–2.690	
9	2.5	41.3	56.2	2.691–2.697	
10	2.9	37.1	60.0	2.691–2.697	
11	2.8	32.7	64.5	2.703–2.708	
12	0.7	29.2	70.2	2.713–2.718	
13	1.0	25.2	73.8	2.719–2.724	
14	0.8	22.4	76.8	2.719–2.724	
15	1.8	16.7	81.5	2.718–2.724	
natural and heated plagioclases[1]					
16		100	—	2.617	2.608
17		88.8	11.2	2.632	2.620
18		82.1	17.9	2.642	2.632
19		77.1	22.9	2.642	2.634
20		69.0	31.0	2.653	2.649
21		63.6	36.4	2.667	2.661
22		62.7	37.3	2.664	2.660
synthetic plagioclases[1]					
23		100			2.607
24		90	10		2.625
25		70	30		2.653
26		50	50		2.681
27			100		2.759

[1] The specific-gravity data in these categories were calculated by the author from published unit-cell data.

poikiloblastic textures. The term describes metamorphic textures due to the development of a new mineral around numerous relics of the original minerals during recrystallization; the term poikiloblastic is a combination of the Greek ποικιλος, meaning spotted, and the Greek βλασταγειν, meaning to grow. In Fig.66 a photograph of such a poikiloblastic albite filled with garnets and hornblendes is shown. Such albites or plagioclases may enclose a large number of minerals such as amphiboles, garnets, chlorites, biotites and quartz. For these

Type of phase and source

pegmatite, Peerless Mine, Keystone, S.D. EMMONS (1953), no.1
two-mica granite, Peekskill, N.Y. EMMONS (1953), no.2
biotite granite, Parishville, N.Y. EMMONS (1953), no.3
granite, Tigerton, Wisc. EMMONS (1953), no.5
gneissoid granodiorite, Spanish Peak, Calif. EMMONS (1953), no.6
granodiorite, Crestmore, Calif. EMMONS (1953), no.8
hornblende gabbro, Shelby, N.C. EMMONS (1953), no.10
diorite, Fresno County, Calif. EMMONS (1953), no.11
anorthosite, Tigerton, Wisc. EMMONS (1953), no.13
anorthosite, east of Duluth, Minn. EMMONS (1953), no.15
anorthosite, Grand Marais, Minn. EMMONS (1953), no.17
basalt porphyry, Lake County, Oreg. EMMONS (1953), no.19
gabbro, Lincoln County, Wisc. EMMONS (1953), no.23
large phenocryst in anorthosite, Split Rock point, Minn. EMMONS (1953), no.24
troctolite, Merril, Wisc. EMMONS (1953), no.27

Amelia albite. J. V. SMITH (1956)
pegmatite, Kenya. J. V. SMITH (1956), BM 1940, 27
pegmatite, S.C. J. V. SMITH (1956), 81822
pegmatite, Hawk Mine, N.C. J. V. SMITH (1956), 103086
pegmatite, Little Rock Creek, Mitchel County, N.C. J. V. SMITH (1956), 97490
gneissoid granodiorite, Spanish Peak, Calif. J. V. SMITH (1956), 152. See no.5
dacite, San Luis Obispo County, Calif. EMMONS (1953), no.7, J. V. SMITH (1956), 64

J. V. SMITH (1956)
J. V. SMITH (1956)
J. V. SMITH (1956)
J. V. SMITH (1956)
COLE et al. (1951)

reasons the fractions obtained after a separation by means of heavy liquids need a thorough microscopical inspection afterwards to make certain that the plagioclase crystals are free from such enclosed minerals. If fractions of plagioclases obtained by specific-gravity separation contain a number of crystal fragments rich in such impurities, the fraction can be cleaned by magnetic-separation techniques. Further practical aspects of the separation method described here will be treated in Chapter 11.

Flotation is one of the most common ore-dressing techniques. Its application is not only attractive for the production of concentrates of sulfide ores, but is widely applied in other fields also. Especially for the production of high-grade concentrates of feldspar, glass sand and kyanite is flotation successfully used. Numerous textbooks, manuals and information sheets handed out by the chemical industry contain cut-and-dried formulas for feldspar flotation. Moreover, a survey of the available information up until 1955 has been prepared by KIRCHBERG (1955).

It is assumed that the readers of this book are not familiar with flotation methods. Therefore, its practical aspects will receive detailed treatment. The theory of flotation, especially of cationic flotation, is still a controversial subject. Consequently, some general remarks will be made on this theory only. In short, flotation is a separation procedure entirely dependant on the surface properties of minerals. The process involves a physico-chemical treatment of a large number of small fragments of various minerals in a watery surrounding. The treatment creates conditions favourable for the attachment of specific minerals to air bubbles. These air bubbles carry the specific minerals to the surface of the liquid just as a balloon carries its gondola.

The physico-chemical aspects of flotation

The chemical compounds that promote flotation of a specific group of minerals act in two ways. These reagents consist of molecules containing a polar and a non-polar group. The polar group of the molecule must have an affinity for a special property of the mineral surface. The non-polar group is extending outward. A layer of these non-polar groups surrounding the fragment makes the mineral particle wary of contact with water. In other words, this layer has formed a hydrophobic film on the surface of the mineral.

As soon as an air bubble comes into contact with such a pre-treated surface, the bubble is forced to produce a contact surface with the mineral in question. Here we enter upon one of the most fascinating and difficult aspects of flotation. For a proper treatment the reader should consult one of the handbooks (e.g., GAUDIN, 1957). The attachment of an air bubble to a mineral surface in a liquid depends on three interface tensions; the interface tension liquid–air, better known as the surface tension of the liquid; the interface tension liquid–mineral; and the interface tension air–mineral. If we assume an equilibrium state of the liquid–mineral interface, then it is possible to characterize the situation observed by a relation between the three tensions and the angle of the liquid–air interface on the mineral surface. This angle ϑ is shown in Fig.12. If the value of ϑ is close to 180°, the mineral cannot be wetted at all. If this value is near to 0°, the mineral is completely wetted and attachment of air bubbles to such surfaces is nearly impossible.

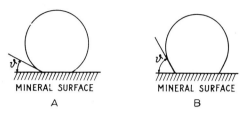

Fig.12. An illustration of the contact between an air bubble and the mineral surface (A) without and (B) with a collector. Without a collector compound the air bubble makes only negligible contact with the surface of the mineral. Consequently the angle ϑ is small. If the contact is favourable for flotation, this angle ϑ is much larger and the common surface of air bubble and mineral is rather large too.

For a successful flotation the contact angle must have a value of about 50°, but flotation is still possible with much lower angles. In order to illustrate the effect of pre-treatment of a mineral surface on the attachment of an air bubble, Fig.12 shows a comparison between a mineral surface that is pre-treated and a mineral surface that is not. The contact angle on the surface is seen to be much larger in case the molecules of the typical chemical compound have covered the surface of the mineral. Such chemical compounds enable the air bubbles to collect these minerals. Hence the name *collector* for such reagents.

The collector must have another specific property. It must have an affinity for the surface of a specific mineral or a group of specific minerals and a strong dislike for others. In other words, it must show a certain selectivity. In the case of feldspars we may note that they are characterized by a large number of cations and oxygen ions at their surface. The same, however, must be said of quartz! Therefore, it is not difficult to predict that both minerals will behave rather similarly towards certain collectors. The proper collector must therefore have a specific affinity for a feldspar surface and a dislike for quartz. As far as we know such collectors do not exist.

As soon as it was established that both quartz and feldspar could be floated with certain collectors, it became evident that one had to search for additional information. This information had to make clear the difference between the properties of both minerals in a flotation process in order to find some way to separate them. It turned out that an addition of hydrofluoric acid had the necessary properties. It controls the pH of the liquid and produces reaction products on the mineral surfaces having different properties.

BUCKENHAM and ROGERS (1954) describe the effect of a cationic collector for feldspar flotation. Moreover, they discuss the aspects of HF as a quartz depressant. The organic bases of composition RNH_2 (R is an aliphatic chain of 8–22 carbon atoms) and various modified derivates of this product promote cationic flotation. The substance with this composition is called an amine. Amines as such are rather insoluble in water. For this reason it is understandable that the much better soluble salts are used instead. Buckenham and Rogers used chemically pure dodecylaminehydrochloride. The products that are for sale consist mostly of amineacetates. If these acetates ionize in water they liberate the anion $(CH_3COO)^-$ and the cation $(RNH_3)^+$.

Such amine ions have an affinity for the surface of quartz and feldspar. It has already been mentioned that the affinity for quartz can be depressed by adding HF until the pH is well below 3. The depressant activity of HF is discussed by BUCKENHAM and ROGERS (1954). It seems to be based on the differing properties of aluminium and silicon fluorides. The authors state that the fluorides formed on the feldspar surface are rather insoluble, whereas those on quartz are soluble.

Pure dodecylaminehydrochloride or pure dodecylamineacetate are rather expensive chemicals. The less pure mixtures of amines are less expensive and may be used with the same good results. A number of firms produce such inexpensive amine salts. The present author has some experience with a product of the Armour Industrial Chemical Cy., Chicago. The product Armac T consists of:

    1 part tetradecylacetate
    28 parts hexadecylacetate
    25 parts saturated octadecylacetate
    46 parts mono-unsaturated octadecenylacetate

Currently we are testing other preparations from the same factory. A chemical produced by another industry is, for instance, the Aeromine 2026 promotor made by the American Cyanamid Cy. In general, the formulas that are used successfully differ from sample to sample and from analyst to analyst. They are also dependant on the type of flotation. If large samples are used, i.e., more than 500 g, the amount of chemicals is determined by the amount of dry material. For fine samples more chemicals are needed than for coarse samples. Still, we will venture to give more detailed indications about the procedures.

The procedure of flotation

The flotation technique can be described in five steps.

(*1*) Prepare the sample in such a way that the particles are neither too large nor too small. The size is determined by two factors: large, depending on the maximum load that can be carried by an air bubble, and small, depending on the preference of the chemicals to coat small particles first, and on the mechanical and less selective flotation of small particles. This constitutes a degradation of the concentrate. The proper grain size of a sample also depends on the size of the intergrowths of two different minerals. The product, especially if it is a sample obtained by grinding a solid rock, should consist of separate mineral fragments and not of aggregates of two or more minerals.

(*2*) The measured mineral sample is then pulped in water. The mining engineer uses this term to describe the wetting of the mineral sample in a surplus of liquid by one or another agitation. The result is called a pulp. To this pulp dilute solutions or emulsions of certain chemical compounds are added. These reagents must change the surface properties of the desired minerals in such a way that they prefer contact with air above contact with water. This implies also that the surface of the mineral betrays its own composition. Minerals that are, for instance, coated with hematite behave as hematite in a flotation process. Therefore, the minerals must be thoroughly freed from grease and coatings prior to the pre-treatment.

(3) After the sample has been in contact with these chemicals for some time, a continuous stream of small air bubbles must be produced in the liquid containing the pulp. This period of time prior to the production of air bubbles, during which the minerals are in contact with the chemicals, is called the conditioning time. The process is called conditioning.

(4) The mineral particles selectively brought to the surface by air bubbles, float on the surface of the pulp. To increase the storage capacity of floating minerals on the surface, the interface liquid–air has to be enlarged. This can be done by adding a small amount of a surface-tension lowering reagent. The effect is that air bubbles which reach the surface do not collapse but build up a layer of froth. Another way of separating floating minerals can be achieved by the special design of the container in which the experiment is carried out (Hallimond tube, see Fig.13)

(5) In case the froth-flotation method is used, the mineral-laden froth is continuously removed from the pulp. The minerals stored in this froth can be secured because the froth collapses due to drainage of the liquid.

The practical aspects of these five steps, as well as an additional theory, will be considered now. The reader must be content with a treatment dealing exclusively with feldspar flotation. It is necessary to mention that other minerals such as micas or heavy minerals can be floated as well and sometimes even rather easily. Further information about these aspects of flotation can be found, for instance, in Gaudin's book *Flotation*.

The pre-treatment

The pre-treatment of the sample determines the success of a flotation experiment. In discussing pre-treatment we will consider both the "sizing" of the sample and the treatment of the fragments prior to conditioning. KIRCHBERG (1955) shows that particles over 500 μ are rather large for flotation of feldspars. An *Armour Bulletin* of 1955 gives 20 mesh as the coarsest size for successful feldspar flotation. This is about 800 μ. Consequently, the largest particles must be removed. Authors on this subject leave no doubt as to the fact that the fine fraction must also be thoroughly removed. De-sliming of the sample is vital. As the smallest size limit we may choose about 50 μ. It is experienced that the best results are obtained with samples of about equal size. For this reason we advocate flotation of fractions within narrow size ranges.

The surface of sand fragments is usually covered with coatings, such as clay coatings, iron coatings or coatings of manganese. Such coatings must be removed, because coated minerals conform to the material of the coating in flotation cells. A paper by MESSNER (1955) illustrates how flotation of a feldspar-rich sand in a Del Monte Sand Plant nearly led to a total failure because of coatings. Scrubbing of the sand by abrasion prior to flotation cleaned the particles sufficiently. These cleaned particles did not give rise to further problems during the rest of the operation. If flotation is used as a concentration technique in a laboratory for the separation of quartz and feldspar from sand or other products, the fragments have to be thoroughly cleaned before further treatment. The feldspar-bearing aggregate may be boiled with HCl and HNO_3. It may also be cleaned of iron coatings by a sodium-dithionite method. Furthermore the product must be carefully freed of small particles.

Another critical aspect of successful flotation is cleanliness. The samples, the glass containers, the flotation apparatus and the bottles containing the reagents have to be *clean*, meticulously clean. In order to have clean samples, we may proceed in the same way as BUCKENHAM and ROGERS (1954). The sample, after removal of the fine fraction, the coatings and the heavy minerals is stored overnight in normal HCl. Afterwards, the sample is frequently rinsed with distilled water and stored in 0.1 N HCl. A few minutes prior to flotation the sample is rinsed again with water and then again with distilled water containing 2 drops of 40% HF solution per 100 cm³.

In order to clean the flotation cell, the beakers and other containers we use a strong 1 N solution of NaOH. Afterwards, the apparatus is rinsed frequently with distilled water, with alcohol and again with distilled water. In addition, the flotation cell is rinsed with a solution containing 2 drops of 40% HF solution per 100 cm³ just before the sample is brought into it.

Conditioning

If the sample is ready for flotation and the apparatus has been meticulously cleaned, the wet sample is brought into the flotation cell filled with the proper solution. This solution contains HF and amine acetate or aminehydrochloride at a pH of about 2.5. The pH can be controlled with a pH-paper. Measuring the pH with a glass electrode will damage this instrument in no time! If a hydrogen-electrode is present this may be used. The pH control with a paper is thought to be accurate enough. As a rule, it suffices to know that about three or four drops of a "40%" HF solution in 100 cm³ water contains about the right acidity. The number of drops depends on the freshness of the strong HF solution. The amount of amine salts depends on the composition of the mixture of amines, on the amount of feldspar in the sample, and on the ratio of liquid to sample. If the amount of liquid surpasses the amount of sample with a factor of about ten or more, the concentration of amine salts in the liquid is important and the amount of feldspars in the pulp subordinate. In such cases Buckenham and Rogers used a liquid containing 25 mg/l of dodecylaminechloride. In our experiments we used liquids containing 25 mg/l of Armac T, as well as liquids containing only 2.5 mg/l Armac T, with good results. The Armour Company cautions against overreagentizing with Armac, the effect of too much collector being a loss of selectivity.

BUCKENHAM and ROGERS (1954) spent rather a long time for the conditioning of the sample prior to flotation. We used times varying from 10 to about 30 min. It turned out that in both cases the conditioning time was long enough. It seems that for batch flotation with large quantities conditioning is not necessary at all. On the contrary, too long a conditioning results in a loss of selectivity.

Flotation

Turning to flotation itself, we may choose between a number of possible set-ups. The reader must be aware of the fact that metallurgists and mining engineers use laboratory flotation in order to obtain the necessary information about the various aspects of the combination of ore and chemicals. The sedimentologist using flotation has another objective. He wants to separate feldspars from his sample in such a way that the tailing is as clean as possible of feldspars, with a concentrate having the highest possible feldspar content. He does not want information about the process on an industrial scale. Therefore, it seems that the apparatus used by metallurgists and mining engineers can be better adapted to the specifications given above than they are now. Still, two extremely useful instruments exist at present. If the investigator prefers to treat only small amounts of sample, say about 0.5 g, he can make use of the so-called Hallimond tube. The design of this tube is shown in Fig.13.

The operation of the Hallimond tube is rather simple. The sample free from heavy minerals and mica, cleaned and de-slimed, is put on a porous disc at A in the tube. The reader who wants to put the instrument in practice himself will find that an old pipet is a useful instrument for trans-

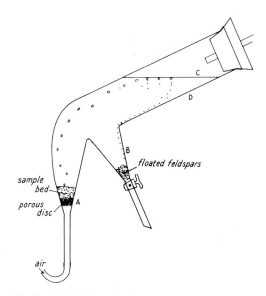

floated feldspars

sample bed

porous disc

air

Fig.13. The Hallimond tube. For an explanation of its use see p.70. The approximate measurements are width 2.5 cm, length of the straight part 20 cm, angle between the leg *A* and the straight part of the tube 120°.

ferring the wet sample from a beaker to the tube. The tube, filled with the liquid containing the reagents, is set in its proper position and the sample is left 10 min for conditioning. Subsequently, a stream of air is forced through the porous disc and a number of small bubbles is produced in the sample bed. It is advisable to control the pressure with a manometer, and the constant flow of air with a flow meter. The air bubbles forced through the sample bed collect the feldspars and carry them to the surface *C*. The special construction of the tube causes the surface of the liquid to be situated over the sloping wall *D*. As soon as the bubble with its mineral load reaches the surface it bursts. The mineral particle drops down on the slope *D* and is collected in the funnel *B*. By opening the funnel at *B*, the operator is enabled to collect the feldspars. A modified design that allows for magnetic stirring of the sample has been published by FUERSTENAU et al. (1957). This type uses about 3 g of sample.

If the investigator is interested in large samples of about 100 g or more, he must try the use of another flotation cell. A number of such cells have been designed and it seems that the Denver laboratory flotation cell is one of the most efficient. Such cells consist of a container and a stirring apparatus. The container may hold about 3 l of pulp. The stirrer is designed in such a way that it can agitate the liquid without disturbing its horizontal surface. Moreover, it can stir either with or without an injection of small air bubbles into the pulp. The pulp in these cells generally contains a 25% of dry material.

The cells are based on the principles of froth flotation. They are designed in such a way that the surface of the pulp is as high as the overflow. The froth can be skimmed and collected in a dish.

The operation is as follows. The sample and the liquid are put in the container. The pulp is stirred without an injection of air for some minutes in order to condition the pulp. Then the frother[1] is added. The air is injected and flotation begins. The mineral-laden froth formed on the surface of the pulp is skimmed off. The feldspars are afterwards secured from this froth.

[1] In laboratory experiments a watersoluble frother gives the best results. One may use, for instance, Aerofroth 65, an American Cyanamid Cy. product, or Dowfroth 250, a Dow Chemical Cy. product.

The efficiency of flotation

Contrary to heavy-liquid separation methods, flotation is not a quantitative method. The success of flotation depends on its ability to separate a sample into two fractions, one of which is much richer in a specific mineral than the other. Hence, its efficiency can be increased by a repetition of the operation. In flotation the investigator can start out from two different principles. He may want either a poor tailing or a rich concentrate. Both these approaches have their advantages and disadvantages. If the operator aims at a poor tailing, it means that he can manage with a not too rich concentrate. On the other hand, a rich concentrate still leaves a large amount of the desired minerals behind in the tailing. In flotation on an industrial scale such problems are solved by a specific arrangement of the flow sheet of the operation. This is not the place to discuss the advantages of certain flow sheets. Literature pertinent to this aspect of flotation will be mentioned in the next section.

For an evaluation of the efficiency of the flotation of a certain sample, it is necessary to study the feldspar content of the original sample, that of the concentrate and of the tailing. As flotation is not selective with regard to plagioclases and alkali feldspars, such a control can be easily made on a hemateine-stained preparation (see p.51). The stained preparations are counted with a stereomicroscope in incident light. For routine work, counts of about 100 grains suffice. Only if the sample is carefully sized within close limits, line-counting procedures may be used. If, however, a sample between 50 μ and 500 μ is used in a flotation cell, the results should be controlled either with ribbon-counting or with point-counting methods (see VAN DER PLAS, 1962b).

In order to get an impression of the results that can be reached with flotation in a Hallimond tube for the concentration of feldspars from natural sands, the following examples are given. With a Canadian beach sand having a feldspar content of about 54%, we reached a concentrate of 87%, leaving a tailing of 17% of feldspars. Flotation time was 2 min, the operation was performed only once. The grain size of this beach sand is, on the average, 350 μ. With a moulding sand (average grain size of about 250 μ) we reached a concentrate of 11% of feldspars in one operation. The concentrate was only 31.5 mg. The tailing of 450 mg is pure quartz! In both cases the reagent used was Armac T, 2.5 mg/l.

Practical aspects of flotation on an industrial scale

Only a few reports have been published on the industrial flotation of feldspars. Such reports and the additional flow sheets, though interesting from a technical point of view, do not offer much useful information for feldspar flotation on a laboratory level. Exact formulas are needed for this type of separation. The published flow sheets, in most cases, do avoid exact figures, except those on products and production.

The Kona Feldspar Plant in North Carolina, for instance, produces glass spar as well as pottery spar (LUTJEN, 1953). The ore is a leucogranite locally known as alaskite. Mica and glass sand are by-products. The difficulties encountered in a Feldspar Plant using dune sand have been considered earlier. Both these plants remove mica and heavy minerals with a flotation process prior to feldspar flotation. The minerals just mentioned are floated with a Cyanamid Aero promotor of the 800 series or a similar collector with sulphuric acid at pH of about 2.5. THOM and GISLER (1954) also advocate the flotation of mica. They used one of the amine acetates and H_2SO_4. Later, the iron-bearing minerals can be removed with a petroleum sulphonate and H_2SO_4. The present author has no experience with flotation of mica and heavy minerals. Up until now he prefers to remove mica and heavy minerals prior to flotation with a proper combination of magnetic separation, heavy liquids and a vibrating glass plate (mica). It may turn out that the flotation of these minerals is more efficient if such procedures are going to be used as a routine method for sedimentological investigations. This may be the case as soon as the samples are larger, and as soon as larger numbers of such samples have to be treated.

Final remarks

It is stressed that flotation procedures must be rather seriously regarded as the most promising and efficient concentration methods in the study of feldspars from sediments. Though beyond the scope of this paper, the petrographer of metamorphic or igneous rocks seems to have problems that may well be solved to a large extent by the use of flotation. Readers familiar with these problems may seriously question the adequacy of some currently used traditional concentration and separation methods. The more so because petrography is slowly but surely advancing towards that more mature state in which reliable quantitative data are a necessity for the acquirement of a deeper and better understanding. This trend receives a stimulus through the impact of new developments in chemistry, physics and mathematics on the "old intuitive art of geology". In the domain of isotope geology, the procedures for sampling and sample preparation already show a remarkable resemblance to industrial processes. The workers in the field of sedimentology are also obviously aware of the fact that only large numbers of samples, collected according to the pattern of an adequate sampling model, may be expected to give reliable information on the average properties and their variation in one sedimentary formation. The same can be said, without reserve, of soil scientists. With this in mind, it is certainly no exaggeration to state that flotation methods constitute a rather unexplored but promising group of experimental procedures for petrographers, sedimentologists and pedologists. It has been experienced, furthermore, that our colleagues in the mining departments are more than willing to give the necessary aid and advice.

Chapter 7

THE INDICES OF REFRACTION AND THE AXIAL ANGLE OF FELD-
SPARS

Introduction

The indices of refraction of a crystalline phase are determined by the arrangement of the chemical elements, as well as by the types and concentrations of atoms or ions in the framework. This conclusion was reached by physicists and mineralogists at the start of this century. Thus the indices of refraction of a set of mixed crystals may render information on the amount of a certain element replacing another element. In feldspars this relation is disturbed by the presence of different structural states, especially among the alkali feldspars. The presence of certain minor elements in the framework is another factor disturbing the usefulness of the measurements of refractive indices for determining the chemical composition of the crystal fragment.

In summary, the optical properties of feldspars may lead to an insight into the chemical composition in a number of cases. The presence of minor quantities of other elements may constitute a disturbing factor. The fact that a number of different structural states have been encountered in feldspars presents another difficulty for the optical determination of the chemical composition of feldspars. An additional difficulty, discussed earlier, is formed by the presence of submicroscopic twins or submicroscopic perthites. In Chapter 3 these subjects received a more detailed treatment.

Alkali feldspars

Accurate measurements of the indices of refraction of alkali feldspars have been published by SPENCER (1930, 1937) and TUTTLE (1952b), among others. These measurements were made on chemically analysed specimens. The structural state of these minerals, however, is not exactly known in a number of cases. Spencer's specimens, for example, include a number of moonstones from Ceylon and Burma, showing a characteristic schiller. Some of these samples are microperthites or even perthites. Spencer leaves no doubt as to the fact that at least a number of his specimens are not homogeneous. The available data point to the fact that the indices of refraction of these minerals tend to increase with an increasing amount of sodium.

TUTTLE (1952b) measured the indices of refraction of a number of alkali feldspars, both on natural high- and low-temperature phases. His data show that the values for heated natural specimens are somewhat lower than those for natural specimens, with the exception of the values found in sanidines. HEALD (1950) observed the same in his heating experiments. Moreover, Tuttle remarks that the values of microclines show a remarkable difference from the values of cryptoperthites, orthoclases and sanidines.

Measurements that were made with a full insight into the difficulties encountered in the presence of high-temperature, low-temperature, intermediate and unmixed phases have been published by ADAMSON (1944), WILSON (1950), SCHIAVINATO (1951), LEBEDSINSKIJ and TSCHU (1958), and MARFUNIN (1961, 1962a). Specimen C of SPENCER (1937) was used in a structural investigation by JONES and TAYLOR (1961). However, these authors describe only one or a few specimens. Consequently, data on refractive indices of chemically and structurally known alkali feldspar phases are scarce. On the other hand, the available data make it rather evident that the indices of refraction only allow a coarse determination of the chemical composition, provided the structural state is known. In Fig.14–16

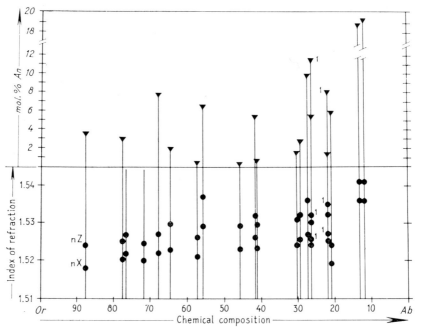

Fig.14. Refractive indices nX and nZ of natural sanidines and "anorthoclases". The corresponding An contents of these phases are shown in the top part of the graph. Data from various sources, in addition to data of Table VII, section a.

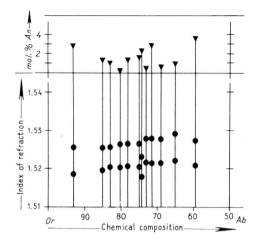

Fig.15. Refractive indices nX and nZ of natural microclines and microcline perthites. Data from Table VI, Marfunin (1962a) and Spencer (1937). The corresponding An contents of the phases listed are shown in the top part of the graph.

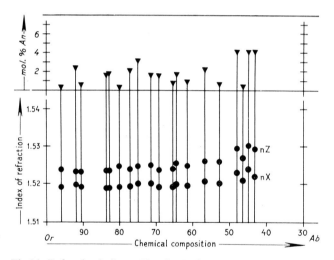

Fig.16. Refractive indices nX and nZ of natural alkali feldspars after prolonged heating. Data from Spencer (1937, tables I and II). The corresponding An contents of the phases listed are shown in the top part of the graph.

the trend of the refractive indices of alkali feldspars is shown. Contrary to other graphs the different phases are not pictured together, but separate graphs are given for sanidines and anorthoclases, for heated natural alkali feldspars, and for microclines. These graphs also list the amount of the calcium ion in the phases expressed in molecule percentage An. Although a number of exceptions can be noted, it may be stated that the indices of refraction of sanidines are influenced

TABLE VII

REFRACTIVE INDICES OF ALKALI FELDSPARS[1]

(a) natural true monoclinic sanidines and anorthoclases

No.	Or	Ab	An	X	Y	Z	2V	Source
1	77.8	22.2	—	1.5202	1.5247	1.5249	24.0	Eifel, Germany. SPENCER (1937)
2	76.7	23.3	—	1.5218	1.5267	1.5267	15	Gelkend, U.S.S.R. MARFUNIN (1962a), no.1
3	72.1	27.9	—	1.5198	1.5245	1.5245	18	Tyrny Ans I, U.S.S.R. MARFUNIN (1962a), no.3
4	68.1	24.0	7.9	1.522	1.527	1.527	27	Kokomo, Co., U.S.A. KRACEK and NEUVONEN (1952)
5	64.7	33.2	2.1	1.5229	1.5294	1.5296	18	Taiji Kii, Japan. KIMIZUKA (1932)
6	57.4	42.0	0.6	1.521	1.525	1.526	29	Grant Cy., N.M., U.S.A. KRACEK and NEUVONEN (1952)
7	45.9	53.6	0.5	1.5228	1.5284	1.5292	39.1	N.E. Korea. SPENCER (1937)
8	42.1	52.3	5.6	1.5264	1.5309	1.5317	47.7	Bo Plei, Siam. WEIGEL and KRÜGER (1934)
9	41.5	57.7	0.8	1.5232	1.5289	1.5296	33	Mitchell Mesa, Texas, U.S.A. TUTTLE (1952b)
10	26.5	67.9	5.6	1.524	n.d.[2]	1.530	42	S.E. Mongolia. VLODAVETZ and SHAVROVA (1953)

(b) natural true monoclinic alkali feldspars

No.	Or	Ab	An	X	Y	Z	2V	Source
1	95.4	4.1	0.4	1.5194	1.5237	1.5241	34.8	Fe-orthoclase, Madagascar. SPENCER (1930, 1937)
2	90.5	7.1	2.4	1.5188	1.5230	1.5236	43.6	Mogok, Burma. SPENCER (1930, 1937)[3]
3	83.8	14.5	1.7	1.5199	1.5240	1.5248	46.2	Mogok, Burma. SPENCER (1930, 1937). MP[4]
4	75.4	24.6	—	1.5238	1.5289	1.5300	49	Ortotokoy I, U.S.S.R. MARFUNIN (1962a), no.10
5	67.3	31.4	1.3	1.5205	1.5246	1.5257	38	Tyrny Ans III, U.S.S.R. MARFUNIN (1962a), no.8

(c) natural intermediate microclines and "orthoclases"

No.	Or	Ab	An	X	Y	Z	2V	Source
1	88.2	11.8	—	1.5192	1.5242	1.5256	56	Kukisvumchor I, U.S.S.R. MARFUNIN (1962a), no.12
2	82.7	17.1	0.1	1.5194	1.5242	1.5259	63	Kukisvumchor II, U.S.S.R. MARFUNIN (1962a), no.17
3	75.5	20.8	3.4	1.5212	1.5244	1.5260	67	Povosero, U.S.S.R. MARFUNIN (1962a), no.21
4	71.5	25.5	3.0	1.5215	1.5256	1.5278	70	Zezelev, U.S.S.R. MARFUNIN (1962a), no.24
5	58.8	40.4	0.8	1.522	1.526	1.529	74	Ceylon. KRACEK and NEUVONEN (1952). MP

(d) natural microclines and microcline-microperthites

No.	Or	Ab	An	X	Y	Z	2V	Source
1	93	4	3	1.5184	1.5251	1.5262	35–56	YUANG (1953)
2	85.2	13.4	1.4	1.5195	1.5232	1.5255	76.2	Kodarma, India. SPENCER (1937)
3	82.9	14.5	1.1	1.5203	1.5241	1.5256	63.5	Kodarma, India. SPENCER (1937)
4	80.3	17.8	0.4	1.5202	1.5237	1.5264	81.5	Patna, India. SPENCER (1937)
5	78.3	20.2	1.5	1.5206	1.5243	1.5266	76.0	Patna, India. SPENCER (1937)
6	75.1	23.2	1.7	1.5204	1.5240	1.5265	79.9	Ryagada, India. SPENCER (1937)
7	73.9	24.0	2.1	1.5178	1.5209	1.5232	81	Central Australia. WILSON (1950)
8	59.2	37.1	3.7	1.5210	1.5247	1.5273	80	Central Australia. WILSON (1950)

(e) adularia

No.	Or	Ab	An	X	Y	Z	2V	Source
1	90.6	7.4	2.0	1.5189	1.5235	1.5253	64.5	Mt. Forno, Italy. AZZINI (1933)
2	90.5	8.3	1.2	1.5192	1.5228	1.5245	68.4	Gotthard, Switzerland. SPENCER (1937)
3	87.8	8.5	3.7	1.5178	1.5205	1.5240	56.8	Kukutzu, Taiwan. HUANG (1953)

(f) natural and heat treated alkali feldspars[5]

No.	X	Y	Z	Xh	Yh	Zh	2V	2Vh	Source
1	1.5192	1.5228	1.5245	1.5190	1.5230	1.5233	68.4	22	SPENCER (1937), cf. e2
2	1.5195	1.5232	1.5255	1.5189	1.5232	1.5238	76.2	44.2 R[6]	SPENCER (1937), cf. d2
3	1.5188	1.5230	1.5236	1.5187	1.5227	1.5233	43.6	44.8 R	SPENCER (1937), cf. b2
4	1.5202	1.5247	1.5249	1.5199	1.5242	1.5247	24.0	29 R	SPENCER (1937), cf. a1

[1] The values of Or, Ab and An are given as molecule percentages in most cases. In a few cases this table lists weight percentages. As the differences are not thought important in the case of refractive indices such values were not recalculated.

[2] n.d. = not determined.

[3] This specimen is the well-known specimen C used by JONES and TAYLOR (1961a, b), among others.

[4] MP indicates that this specimen is considered a microperthite by the original author.

[5] The symbols Xh, Yh and Zh indicate the refractive index after prolonged heating.

[6] The symbol R behind the axial angles 2Vh of heat treated samples indicate that the axial plane has been reversed.

by the Ca-content of the minerals. This influence is less in heated natural alkali feldspars and not detectable in microclines.

The fact that a number of alkali feldspars, and especially those that are homogeneous, have rather important calcium contents may well obscure the increase of the indices of refraction with an increase of the albite content of the phases. That the influence of calcium is not detectable in microclines may be due to the fact that the calcium ion migrates preferentially into the albite phase.

For the purpose of sedimentologists and pedologists a coarse estimation of the chemical composition is sometimes sufficient. For these reasons a number of indices of refraction of alkali feldspars are gathered in Table VII. The data are arranged in five groups, viz.: group *a* natural true monoclinic sanidines and anorthoclases, group *b* natural true monoclinic alkali feldspars, group *c* natural intermediate microclines and so-called orthoclases, group *d* natural microclines and microcline-microperthites, group *e* adularia.

In addition, the change in refractive indices on heating is illustrated under *f* in this table. The data are selected from a much larger set of measurements published by SPENCER (1937). The numerical values of Table VII were also used to construct the graphs of Fig.14–16. We refrained from drawing trend lines in these graphs because the data show that such trend lines are misleading and suggest a more or less consistent behaviour of the optical properties with varying *Ab*-content. Collecting more measurements than are available at present may perhaps prove the existence of such a behaviour. For the time being, however, the influence of impurities such as Ca-ions or Fe-ions is unknown. Careful evaluation of a large number of measurements where structural state must also be considered may well give a better insight into the indices of refraction of alkali feldspars in the future.

Plagioclase feldspars

Accurate measurements of the indices of refraction of plagioclases have been made by several authors. A number of these measurements, however, are made on chemically analysed samples whose structural state was not determined. It has been established without any doubt that both high- and low-temperature phases of plagioclase composition exist in nature, whereas experimental results have shown that natural plagioclases of low-temperature origin show other physical properties after heating. Moreover, recent investigations by numerous workers have made it clear that in a large number of cases the plagioclases under investigation are in an intermediate state between the low- and high-temperature forms. To gain an insight into the frequency of this phenomenon as well as into its aspects, the papers of KARL (1954), BASKIN (1956) and PRIEM (1956) can be consulted for information on optically established intermediate phases. The papers of J. V. SMITH (1956), and of J.V. SMITH and GAY (1958), for example, make it quite clear that a large number of plagioclases prove to be of an intermediate structure on X-ray analysis.

The differences of the optical properties of the low- and high-temperature phases are rather important for calcium-poor members of this group of minerals. The experiments of J. R. SMITH (1958), as well as an earlier experiment of TUTTLE and BOWEN (1950) with Amelia albite, clearly indicate that sodium-rich members are more influenced by heating than calcium-rich members in respect to the indices of refraction.

CHAYES (1950, 1952b) published a collection of refractive indices gathered from published material. In discussing these data he stresses the fact that the greater number of reliable data on plagioclases with high-sodium content was obtained from samples of pegmatites; in other words, from low-temperature phases. The largest number of reliable measurements on phases with comparatively high amounts of calcium in the structure were made on phenocrysts from lavas; that is, high-temperature minerals. For that reason Chayes himself is a bit sceptical about the resulting curves. Still, the relation between the chemical composition and the indices of refraction is clearly established in these papers. KANO (1955) and SCHWARZMANN (1956) have shown that the curves of Chayes may lead to notable errors for high-temperature sodium-rich plagioclases, a fact that Chayes had more or less anticipated, see Fig.17 and 18.

Emmons and co-workers investigated a number of chemically analysed

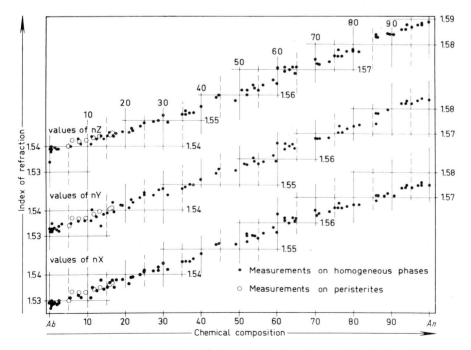

Fig.17. A graphical plot of a number of indices of refraction of natural plagioclases. Values are taken from CHAYES (1950, 1952b), EMMONS (1953), RIBBE (1960) and MARFUNIN (1962a).

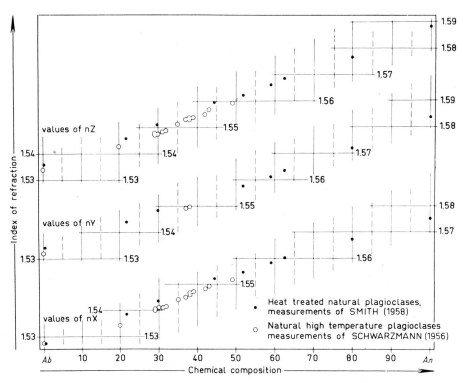

Fig.18. A graphical plot of a number of indices of refraction of natural high-temperature plagio-clases and heated natural plagioclases. Values are taken from SCHWARZMANN (1956) and J. R. SMITH (1958).

plagioclase specimens ranging from pure albite to practically pure anorthite. The refractive indices of these samples were carefully measured, and can be found in the well-known *Geol. Soc. Am., Mem.*, 52 (1953). The refractive indices reported in this paper are highly accurate, but the information on the structural state of these samples is rather poor and in some cases perhaps unreliable.

SCHWARZMANN (1956) studied the plagioclases of xenoliths of the tertiary basalts and basaltic tuffs from the surroundings of Göttingen and Kassel in Germany. He noticed that the plagioclases of these inclusions, gneisses, granites and pegmatitic rocks, in the basalts and tuffs show, in particular, remarkable optical properties. The *An*-content of the plagioclases studied varies from about 20% to about 50%, as can be seen from Fig.18, where the data of Schwarzmann are used. The refractive indices are lower than those given by CHAYES (1952). A comparison of these data with the available measurements of heated plagioclases, and of plagioclase from volcanic rocks, leads to the conclusion that the samples, providing the plagioclases under discussion, were taken from rocks that were heated within the melt of the basalt under relatively high temperatures and pressures before they were rapidly transported towards the earth's surface. Schwarzmann's data constitute a substantial contribution to our knowledge of natural high-temperature plagioclases, because the measurements were made in such a way as to provide a maximum amount of information. The chemical composition of a number of these samples was chemically evaluated. The Ca-content of three other samples was determined by a combination of at least 3 of the methods listed below; namely that of VAN DER KAADEN (1951), the method of SCHUSTER (1881) in combination with new graphs of A. Köhler (see TRÖGER, 1959), the method of RITTMANN (1929), and the *joined angle technique* developed by KÖHLER (1942a), see p.113. The information Schwarzmann lists about the axial angle leaves no doubt that the phases studied in this program are of high-temperature origin. They neatly coincide with the data reported by J. R. SMITH (1958) and with the measurements SLEMMONS (1962a) compiled in one of his graphs, although Schwarzmann's results seem to be unknown to Slemmons. It must be noticed that J. R. SMITH's (1958) measurements of the indices of refraction of heated natural plagioclases are even a bit higher than the indices observed by Schwarzmann. For these reasons the paper under consideration may be regarded as one of the most important sources of information on high-temperature plagioclases now available. Therefore they are listed without exception in Fig.18 together with those of Smith.

J. R. SMITH (1958) determined the indices of refraction of a selected number of plagioclases of known chemical composition. After this determination the plagioclases were heated both dry and under H_2O pressure. After heat treatment the indices of refraction were measured. Although it is not quite certain that all the phases studied completely reached the high-temperature structure, Smith's data clearly indicate the differences that may at least be expected.

MARFUNIN (1962a) lists 59 samples whose refractive indices are measured and mentions a number of data not published in the compilation of CHAYES (1952b). He also lists the mean index of refraction. It is shown graphically that this mean index of refraction exhibits a rather perfect linear relationship with the Ca-content.

RIBBE (1960) investigated a number of peristerite plagioclases. His work constitutes the first systematical analysis of no less than 8 samples. Both the optical properties and the structural state of these samples were measured. The author also went so far as to study the behaviour of these minerals after both short and prolonged heating. The indices of refraction given in the present text are averaged, see Table VIII and Fig.17. The plot of these data shows the conclusion of Ribbe to be in accordance with the observational evidence. The indices of refraction of peristerites are more or less the same as those of homogeneous phases of the same composition. Although it may well be expected that in most cases the presence of peristerites will go undetected in sediments and soils, the evaluation of the chemical composition of these aggregates with the aid of the indices of refraction will certainly not lead to serious errors.

After discussing the more prominent sources of data concerning refractive indices of plagioclases, it seems necessary to establish the value that can be attached

TABLE VIII

REFRACTIVE INDICES OF PLAGIOCLASE FELDSPARS

No.	Or	Ab	An	X	Y	Z	2V
(a) natural plagioclase feldspars							
1	1.2	98.6	0.15	1.5279	1.5311	1.5391	+ 76
2	1.6	87.0	11.4	1.5346	1.5382	1.5438	+ 81
3	1.5	62.6	35.9	1.5451	1.5488	1.5525	+ 87
4	2.0	60.0	38.0	1.5463	1.5500	1.5531	− 89
5	1.1	47.3	51.6	1.5528	1.5558	1.5598	+ 77
6	2.9	37.1	60.0	1.5637	1.5661	1.5706	+ 75
7	0.7	29.2	70.2	1.5633	1.5682	1.5724	+ 85
8	1.8	16.7	81.5	1.5675	1.5735	1.5772	− 85
9	1.7	12.5	85.8	1.5695	1.574	1.581	− 78
10	—	2.0	98.0	1.5754	1.5833	1.5885	− 77
(b) peristerites							
11	0.8	94.0	5.2	1.5298	1.5342	1.5400	
12	4.0	90.3	5.7	1.5334	1.5369	1.5425	
13	1.7	90.6	7.6	1.5331	1.5365	1.5422	
14	—	90.5	9.5	1.5327	1.5368	1.5426	
15	1.6	87.0	11.4	1.5347	1.5386	1.5435	+ 81
16	3.9	82.8	13.3	1.5350	1.5394	1.5443	
17	2.8	81.1	16.1	1.5362	1.5405	1.5452	+ 87
18	1.9	81.5	16.6	1.5448	1.5409	1.5368	
(c) natural high-temperature plagioclase feldspars[1]							
19	5.0	75.0	20.0	1.5344		1.5425	− 55
20	3.5	66.5	30.0	1.5410		1.5473	− 67
21	—	65.0	35.0	1.5440		1.5512	− 78
22	—	61.0	39.0	1.5472		1.5537	− 83
23	—	57.0	43.0	1.5493		1.5567	− 93
24	—	51.0	49.0	1.5518		1.5593	− 99
25	1.2	34.9	63.9	1.562	1.566	1.571	+ 83
26	—	—	100	1.5750	1.5834	1.5883	− 75
(d) heated natural plagioclase feldspars							
27	1.1	98.7	0.2	1.5273	1.5344	1.5357	− 47
28	1.4	98.2	0.4	1.5270	1.5342	1.5355	− 46
29	3.9	74.5	21.6	1.5386	1.5440	1.5459	− 62
30	0.5	69.7	29.8	1.5437	1.5483	1.5510	− 75
31	2.1	53.7	44.2	1.5522		1.5595	
32	1.9	46.3	51.8	1.5547	1.5576	1.5621	+ 77
33	2.2	38.6	59.2	1.5582	1.5611	1.5662	+ 74
34	0.7	36.8	62.5	1.5603	1.5634	1.5684	+ 76
35	0.5	19.5	80.0	1.5671	1.5716	1.5765	+ 88

[1] The chemical composition of numbers 21, 22, 23, 24 has been determined with optical methods.

Source

---

from pegmatite. Peerless mine, Keystone, S.D., U.S.A. EMMONS (1953) average of no.1
from two-mica granite. Peekskill, N.Y., U.S.A. EMMONS (1953) average of no.2
from gneissoid granodiorite. Spanish Peak, Calif., U.S.A. EMMONS (1953) average of no.6
from granodiorite. Crestmore, Calif., U.S.A. EMMONS (1953) average of no.8
from hornblende gabbro. Shelby, N.C., U.S.A. EMMONS (1953) average of no.10
from diorite. Fresno County, Calif., U.S.A. EMMONS (1953) average of no.11
from basalt porphyry. Lake County, Oreg., U.S.A. EMMONS (1953) average of no.19
from troctolite. Merril, Wisc., U.S.A. EMMONS (1953) average of no.27
from anorthosite. Bonskar, Stockholm, Sweden. LINDEGÅRDH (1941)
from anorthosite. Sittampundi complex, Salem district, India. SUBRAMANIAM (1956)

from pegmatite. Auburne, Me., U.S.A. RIBBE (1960) average of no.1
from pegmatite. Monteagle Tp., Ont., Canada. RIBBE (1960) average of no.2
from pegmatite. Villeneuve, Que., Canada. RIBBE (1960) average of no.3
from pegmatite. Haddam, Conn., U.S.A. RIBBE (1960) average of no.4
from two-mica granite. Peekskill, N.Y., U.S.A. (EMMONS, 1953, no.2) RIBBE (1960) average of no.5
from two-mica granite. Monteagle Valley, Ont., Canada. RIBBE (1960) average of no.6
from biotite granite. Parishville, N.Y., U.S.A. (EMMONS, 1953, no.3) RIBBE (1960) average of no.7
from granite. Llano County, Texas, U.S.A. (EMMONS, 1953, no.4) RIBBE (1960) average of no.8

from pegmatite xenolite in basaltic tuff. Druseltal, Germany. SCHWARZMANN (1956) no.24355
from pegmatite xenolite in basaltic tuff. Dornberg, Germany. SCHWARZMANN (1956) no. 15472
from granite xenolite in basaltic tuff. Taubenkante, Germany. SCHWARZMANN (1956) no.15471
from pyroxenegneiss in basaltic tuff. Druseltal, Germany. SCHWARZMANN (1956) no.25608
from anorthosite in basaltic tuff. Hirzstein, Germany. SCHWARZMANN (1956) no.24344
from pyroxene-scapolitegneiss in basaltic tuff. Druseltal, Germany. SCHWARZMANN (1956) no.24490
from volcanic rock. Clear Lake, Utah, U.S.A. KRACEK and NEUVONEN (1952)
synthetic. J. R. SMITH (1958)

from pegmatite. Ramona, Calif., U.S.A. J. R. SMITH (1958) average of no.D761-1
from pegmatite. Amelia, Va., U.S.A. J. R. SMITH (1958) average of no.D761-3
from pegmatite. Hawk Mine, Bakersville, N.C., U.S.A. J. R. SMITH (1958) average of no.80165
from pegmatite. Macon County, N.C., U.S.A. J. R. SMITH (1958) average of no.D638
from ferrogabbro. Skaergaard, E., Greenland. J. R. SMITH (1958) average of no.1963
from dolerite. Great Dyke, Rhodesia. J. R. SMITH (1958) average of no.GD29
from gabbro. Bushveld, South Africa. J. R. SMITH (1958) average of no.BV63
from gabbro. Stillwater, Mont., U.S.A. J. R. SMITH (1958) average of no.EB41
from norite. Stillwater, Mont., U.S.A. J. R. SMITH (1958) average of no.EB38

to the chemical composition of plagioclase feldspars determined by the immersion method. WENK (1945) compared the results obtained with the immersion method with those arrived at by the measurement of the orientation of the indicatrix with the universal stage. He concludes that both methods give comparable results, and that differences rarely exceed 5% *An*. If zonal crystals are measured, the immersion method only gives information about the rims of the fragments, whereas the measurements with the universal stage enable the investigator to first determine from the overall picture of the crystal under measurement the sites at which measurements must be made. Secondly, it is possible to carry out more than one measurement on one crystal with the universal stage. In non-zonal crystals the *An* values are practically identical. If we consider the values of Table VIII it is immediately clear that the index of refraction is a reliable indication of the chemical composition. The reliability of the method is greater if the structural state of the phases studied is known. If the structural state is unknown this will admittedly lead to data whose reliability is only such that the chemical composition is known within about 10% *An*. In a few cases a better result can be obtained in the region between 0% and 40% *An*. In this region the value of the axial angle is a good indication of the structural state. A negative axial angle that is also comparatively small is a clear indication for high-temperature forms.

Tsuboi's method

Finally, a rather important practical problem deserves some attention. If the crystals are observed with a microscope in a preparation of plagioclase fragments immersed in a liquid of known index of refraction, it is at once clear that only a small amount has the proper orientation for accurately measuring nX, nY or nZ. In general, we must be content with measurements of intermediate directions. For those who wish to do more precise work, the immersion method described by TSUBOI (1934) will be of some use. Tsuboi draws attention to the fact that plagioclases have two distinct cleavage directions, i.e., parallel to (010) and to (001), and that the direction of nX is such that the angle between (010) and nX is rather similar to the angle between (001) and nX. Measuring the value of nX' of cleavage flakes will give valuable information on the chemical composition, irrespective of the cleavage face present. In order to arrive at more precise measurements of the refractive index, Tsuboi developed a method based on the dispersion of the index liquid. The procedure is as follows:

(*1*) Orientate the fragment with X parallel to the vibration direction of the polarizer.

(*2*) Compare the index of refraction of mineral and liquid with a variable monochromatic light source by varying the wavelength.

(*3*) Enter the graph of Fig.19 with the value of the wavelength of the light at which both the index of refraction of nX' of the mineral and the liquid match.

The Ca-content of the mineral can be read from the right side of the graph. See Fig.19A, for detailed procedure.

A few remarks concerning this method may be made. At the time that the method was suggested (1934), a variable monochromatic light source was a rather expensive instrument. The dispersion of the index liquids had to be measured with an Abbe refractometer under controlled temperature circumstances by the investigator himself, again a difficult complication because a good Abbe refractometer was also considered an expensive instrument. At present, however, most laboratories are better equipped and a room where optical investigations can be performed under more or less constant temperature conditions is available to most investigators. A variable monochromatic light source is now a comparatively inexpensive instrument, since modern glass technology has made it possible to produce a filter with continuously varying absorption properties, constituting a reliable monochromator in combination with the normal light source of the microscope. Another aspect of modern conveniences is the availability of index of refraction liquids whose index is known exactly to three decimal places, and the dispersion at a certain temperature is printed on the label. A second advantage of such liquids is the fact that they are generally more stable and tenable than most home-made mixtures. The well-known Cargille set of index of refraction liquids provides the investigator with such reliable tools, with an index varying from 1.35 to 2.11. From these considerations it follows that at present the application of Tsuboi's method is possible for even small laboratories. This technique is rather promising, especially for the determination of plagioclases of consolidated sediments that have to be crushed in order to obtain small fragments. Tsuboi's graph is given as Fig.19, together with a key.

At the time Tsuboi's method was introduced the existence of high- and low-temperature plagioclases was not yet established. The method, therefore, does not make a distinction between these different phases of the same chemical composition. As it is known that the angles between X' and the two planes (010) and (001) differ only slightly in the two phases, the method still seems of high practical use. Nevertheless a calculation of the exact differences is needed.

The method under consideration can also be simplified. For instance, EMMONS and GATES (1948) published a variant that uses the specific properties of the Becke line phenomenon with day light. The method begins with the established fact that the dispersion of the frequently used immersion liquids is generally greater than that of the minerals under investigation, in our case, that of plagioclases or alkali feldspars. Consequently, the Becke line will show parallel, coloured zones. If the dispersion of the liquid and of the three indices of the mineral are drawn in a graph, the difference of the dispersion results in a different slope of both groups of lines. As a result the line of the immersion liquid will cross the lines of the indices of the mineral. The greater the difference in dispersion, the greater the differences of the slopes of these lines and the greater the spread of colours observed in the zones of the Becke line. The paper by Emmons and Gates illustrates this in a graph for the mineral microcline and a liquid with n being 1.520.

In order to bring this method into practice, the slopes of the immersion liquids should be known. N.B. the blue colours observed have approximately 500 mμ wavelength, that of the yellow colours approximately 600 mμ wavelength. By observing the behaviour of such a coloured zone in applying the Becke method it is possible to use the immersion liquids over a much larger range than that of their labelled index of refraction, i.e., the index observed with sodium light. The

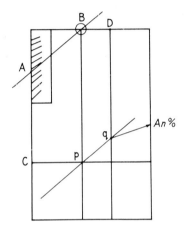

Fig.19A. A key to the use of Tsuboi's graph of Fig.19B. The four values for using this graph are indicated with capitals, denoting:

(A) The dispersion of the liquid $nF-nC$. This value must either be read from the label on the bottle or be measured with an Abbe refractometer.

(B) The value of 589,3 $\mu\mu$; on the graph this point is marked with a small circle.

(C) The value of the index of refraction of the liquid (nD). This value must be either measured or read from the label on the bottle.

(D) The wavelength of the monochromatic light at which both the index of refraction of the immersion liquid and nX' of the cleavage fragment of plagioclase match.

PROCEDURE

(*1*) Determine D (see above) with the microscope.
(*2*) Enter value A on the graph. Draw line AB.
(*3*) Determine the intersection of C and the vertical line through B, mark this point p.
(*4*) Draw a line through p, parallel with AB.
(*5*) Determine the intersection of the line through p, and a line starting from the point marking the value determined under *1*, the wavelength of the monochromatic light D at which both the index of refraction of the immersion liquid and nX' of the cleavage fragment match. Proceed from this point marking the intersection of the vertical line through D and the line through p, indicated as q, vertically downwards.
(*6*) Follow one of the parallel oblique lines of An percentages that goes through q.
(*7*) Read the chemical composition.

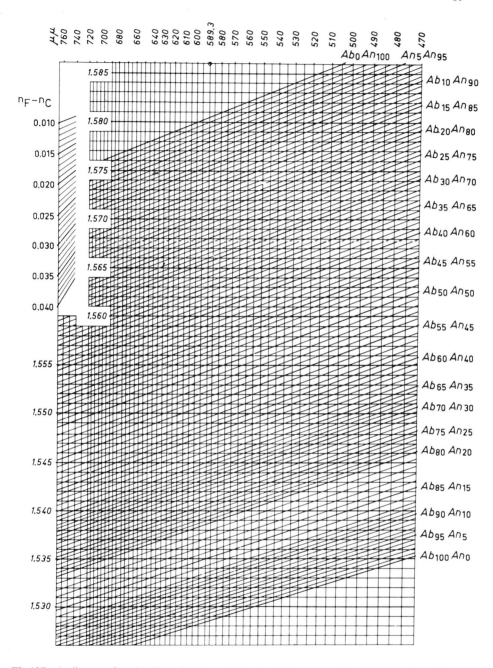

Fig.19B. A diagram for the determination of the chemical composition of plagioclases from the value of nX', as measured in cleavage fragments with the aid of monochromatic light and the dispersion of the index liquid. For the use of this diagram after TSUBOI (1934) see the instructions with Fig.19A and the text.

coloured zone that does not shift when raising or lowering the tube corresponds with the index of refraction of the mineral for that particular wavelength.

If the analyst is not accustomed to this method he is advised to draw a few graphs of the dispersion of the frequently used liquids. Such graphs listing the wavelength along the abscis and the index of refraction along the ordinate are of great help. Furthermore, the afore-mentioned paper gives a detailed treatment of a few examples along with the necessary illustrations. It is therefore thought super-fluous to repeat the details here.

If routine work is involved, soil scientists and sedimentologists, and perhaps even those investigators dealing exclusively with igneous or metamorphic rocks, have to measure a large number of plagioclase fragments in more than one index liquid. In most cases the feldspars have to be counted at the same time. This implies that one has to choose an efficient set of index liquids, depending on the plagioclases in the concentration, in such a way that a maximum amount of information is gathered with a minimum amount of work. It is worth while to make a qualitative inventory first; with the help of this inventory it can be decided later which procedure is the most efficient. In order to facilitate such a decision Table VIII lists a number of measurements on natural low- and high-temperature plagio-clases, on peristerites, and on heated natural plagioclases. In Fig.17 a greater number of data taken from CHAYES (1950, 1952b), EMMONS (1953), RIBBE (1960), and MARFUNIN (1962a) are plotted. We purposely refrained from drawing lines through the points, as it is not known how much bias occurs in these data because of undetected high-temperature phases. Moreover, it is felt that drawing lines obscures the information on scatter. In the author's opinion the measures of dispersion are as important as the overall consistency with a specific curve.

In summary, the determination of the chemical composition of plagioclases with immersion liquids is a reliable and efficient method. This is especially true for the workers for whom this review is intended. The inaccuracies that may result from not recognizing the presence of high-temperature phases are small, and do not constitute an annoying disturbance of the reliability of a set of measurements. Charts for the determination of plagioclases with the indices of refraction are also found in a number of handbooks, such as TRÖGER (1959, p.99) and DEER, HOWIE and ZUSSMANN (1963).

THE AXIAL ANGLE OF FELDSPARS

Introduction

Another rather important optical property is the value and the sign of the axial angle. The axial angle is shown as the angle between the normals to the two possible circular sections of the triaxial ellipsoid. From the geometry of this symmetrical body it follows that the axial angle is a function of the three axes. The axial angle $2V$ follows from the formula:

$$\text{tg } V = \frac{nZ}{nY} \cdot \sqrt{\frac{nY^2 - nX^2}{nZ^2 - nY^2}}$$

The optic sign follows from the expression:

$$1/nZ^2 + 1/nX^2 - 2/nY^2$$

It can be proved that the value of the axial angle depends mainly on the values $nZ - nY$ and $nY - nX$. The absolute values of nX, nY and nZ are not very important. This relation for the axial angle $2V$ and the position nY between nX and nZ is illustrated in Fig.20. In conclusion, it can be said that the axial angle is virtually independent of the absolute values of the indices of refraction (see WINCHELL, 1928, and MCANDREW, 1963).

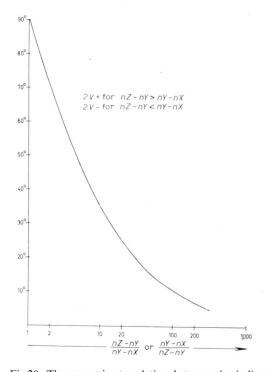

Fig.20. The approximate relation between the indices of refraction nX, nY and nZ and the axial angle $2V$.

Although the axial angle can be calculated from the indices of refraction, there are a number of reasons why mineralogists prefer to measure the axial angle, as well as the indices of refraction. First of all, with a universal stage the axial angle can be measured with a rather high degree of accuracy (see MUNRO, 1963). With the immersion method the indices of refraction can be measured with an accuracy of about 0.002, using sodium light and performing them in a room with a more or less constant temperature. There are other methods to measure the indices of refraction with higher precision, but these are laborious and require additional apparatus. From the data in Tables VII and VIII it is clear that such refractive indices lead to calculation results whose accuracy is inferior to the results of the measurements of the axial angle.

It has been shown recently for both alkali feldspars and plagioclases that the axial angle is an important indicator of the structural state of the phases concerned. For alkali feldspars MARFUNIN (1961, 1962a) has shown that those phases showing an axial angle less than 44° are generally virtually monoclinic[1], i.e., they have high-temperature structures. Phases with a larger axial angle are either submicroscopically twinned triclinic phases, cryptoperthites or true microclines[2]. The relation between the axial angle of plagioclases and the ordering of the plagioclase structure is already known from the papers of VAN DER KAADEN (1951) and SCHWARZMANN (1956). SLEMMONS (1962a), however, stresses this relation in a clear and unambiguous way. He also discusses the value that may be attached to information about the degree of ordering given by the value of the axial angle.

In the discussion about the nature of feldspars it turned out that information on the structural state is thought to be rather important at present. Considering the methods generally in use, it became apparent that information on the structural state was difficult to obtain in a number of cases. The possibilities now available mean a great simplification, for axial angles are not difficult to measure. This is even more true because a few well-known firms have developed universal stages together with the proper objectives which enable the analyst to study samples both orthoscopically and conoscopically. A rather rapid estimate of the value of the axial angle is now possible. Moreover, these instruments are equipped with a small cross-stage to facilitate the counting of thin sections or grain slides on the universal stage. In conclusion it may be stated that petrographers, sedimentologists and soil scientists now have a simple method at hand for the identification of high-temperature phases.

---

[1] Some notable exceptions exist, as witnessed by the paper of MICHAELIS DE SÁENZ (1963). The exceptions were observed in adularia from mineral lined tension joints. Therefore we provisionally stick to the general validity of Marfunin's rule for alkali feldspars from rock samples. Especially for sedimentological problems this rule is of great practical value, irrespective of Michaelis de Sáenz's pessimism.

[2] With 'true microcline' we want to describe homogeneous triclinic alkali feldspars.

Alkali feldspars

In this chapter (p.91), it is shown that the axial angle is a function of the indices of refraction, but that the accuracy with which these indices can be measured is less than the accuracy with which we are able to measure the axial angle. We may therefore expect the axial angle to reveal more detailed information.

The axial angle of alkali feldspars, with the exception of that of iso-microcline, is of a negative sign. Iso-microcline, however, seems to be rare. The general impression is that the axial angle of microclines is large, whereas the axial angle of sanidines is small. Axial angles of adularia were determined i.a., by CHAISSON (1950), BAMBAUER and LAVES (1960) and HUANG (1961). These authors measured axial angles between the extreme values of 22° and 64°. The results of these measurements can be found in Table IX. Axial angles of sanidine have been reported by various authors (see Table VII). A number of values of "orthoclase" are given by TUTTLE (1952b), which range from 35° to 90°. It follows from the considerations of Marfunin, which will be given in this section, that the specimens in Tuttle's list can certainly not be treated as one group. Table VII gives the values of a number of axial angles of microcline reported by SPENCER (1937), WILSON (1950), KRACEK and NEUVONEN (1952) and MARFUNIN (1962a, b).

Furthermore, MARFUNIN (1961, 1962a, b) found that a large axial angle is encountered only in those feldspars which are "unstable", in the sense used by HAFNER and LAVES (1957). Alkali feldspars, structurally intermediate between maximum microcline (ordered phase) and sanidine (disordered phase), may well be stable under specific temperature and pressure conditions. A number of partly ordered alkali feldspars seem to exist, however, which are always unstable, irrespective of the physical circumstances. The latter phases may be described as feldspars representing "short cuts" in the phase diagram. In these cases the transformation from a state of higher order to a state of lower order did not follow the equilibrium curves of the phase diagrams. For further information on this interesting subject the reader is referred to the paper of HAFNER and LAVES, loc. cit.

TABLE IX

AXIAL ANGLES OF ADULARIA

Locality	*2V*	*Source*
St. Gotthard, Switzerland	22 –64°	CHAISSON (1950)
Tavetschtal, Switzerland	28 –62°	CHAISSON (1950)
Mt. Vesuvius, Italy	22 –35°	CHAISSON (1950)
Guanajuato, Mexico	45 –56°	CHAISSON (1950)
Val Casatscha, Switzerland	23.5–54°	BAMBAUER and LAVES (1960)
Kukutzu, Taiwan	30 –53°	HUANG (1961)
Vals, Graubünden, Switzerland	17 –35°	This text, Fig.1

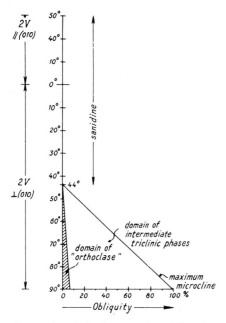

Fig.21. The relation between the axial angle and the structural state of alkali feldspars, simplified after MARFUNIN (1962a, b).

This, together with other available information, implies that phases with an axial angle larger than 44° are either:

(*1*) triclinic phases, identifiable as such on microscopical inspection by other optical properties or by the presence of typical cross-hatched twinning;

(*2*) triclinic phases, whose unit cell parameters show a slight deviation from the monoclinic cell only;

(*3*) submicroscopically unmixed aggregates of an albite phase and an alkali feldspar phase, the so-called cryptoperthites, or;

(*4*) submicroscopically and sub-X-ray twinned triclinic phases, and the eventually remaining possible phases that belong to the "unstable" group of feldspars just discussed.

If the axial angle is smaller than about 44° the phases present are monoclinic. In a number of tables in this book such phases are called "true" monoclinic phases. A diagram showing the ideas of Marfunin is given as Fig.21. Moreover, on this evidence it is concluded that the value of the axial angle of alkali feldspars is hardly influenced by the chemical composition. Consequently, it cannot be used for an evaluation of the chemical composition.

From Fig.20 it follows that a large axial angle, such as found in microcline, is a property of crystals in which the value of nY is more or less halfway between nX and nZ, or in other words, if $nY - nX$ is about the same as $nZ - nY$. Negative signs are found if nY is closer to nZ than to nX. The absolute value of the indices of refraction has been shown to have no practical influence on the axial angle.

In summary, the axial angle of alkali feldspars is virtually an independent characteristic which gives information about the structural state of the phase under investigation, and is hardly influenced by the chemical composition. Large axial angles, i.e., larger than 44°, indicate the probability of the presence of microcline and complicated structures such as submicroscopical perthites or the presence of submicroscopically twinned aggregates. Small axial angles, smaller than 44°, point to the probability of the presence of true monoclinic phases.

Plagioclase feldspars

Recent determinations of the axial angle of plagioclase feldspars made by EMMONS (1953) and J. R. SMITH (1958), showed the limitations of a determination of the chemical composition based on the value of the axial angle. Firstly, it became evident that large fluctuations of the axial angle may occur within crystal fragments belonging to one or more plagioclase crystals from one hand specimen. The fact that large fluctuations of the chemical composition may occur from site to site, cf. DOMAN (1961), may partially explain this. Secondly, the influence of structural characteristics on the value of the axial angle is not to be disregarded, the more so since Marfunin showed the important influence of the structure of the

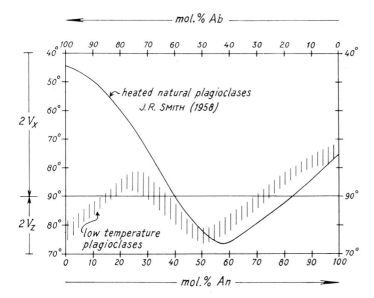

Fig.22. The relation between the chemical composition and the value of the axial angle in high- and low-temperature plagioclases. The area between the curve of heated plagioclases and the zone of low-temperature plagioclases contains all the possible values of plagioclases with an intermediate structure. In SLEMMONS' (1962b) conception the heated plagioclases have an "obliquity index" of 0, the low-temperature plagioclases have an "obliquity index" of 100.

phase of an alkali feldspar on the value of the axial angle. VAN DER KAADEN (1951), J. R. SMITH (1958), and SLEMMONS (1962b) clearly show the different behaviour of the value of the axial angle in the high- and low-temperature series of plagioclases. Fig.22 gives the curve for the value of the axial angle of plagioclases, with variations in both chemical composition and structural state, using the data of the afore-mentioned authors. From this curve it can be seen that in the low-temperature state albites, andesines, and labradorites are positive, while the remainder is of a negative optical sign. Authigenic albites with large axial angles are reported by FÜCHTBAUER (1956).

In the high-temperature series the only positive axial angles to be found are in calcium-rich andesine, labradorites and bytownites. Naturally, intermediate structural states may show all possible transitions, leaving a rather confusing amount of possible axial angles to be expected in phases of one and the same chemical composition. This is especially true for the more sodium-rich plagioclases.

Plagioclases are known to exhibit various degrees of order. The order–disorder relations observed in the structure influence the optical properties. The axial angle is one of the optical characteristics strongly influenced by the structural state. For this reason the axial angle should not be used for the determination of the chemical composition, as this may lead to rather large errors, especially with acid plagioclases. If one is interested in the structural state of plagioclases the axial angle may be helpful.

SLEMMONS (1962b) thoroughly treats the relation between the value of the axial angle and the degree of order. He shows that the axial angle can give accurate information about the structural state for plagioclases up to 40% *An*, provided the chemical composition of the plagioclase under investigation is known. In his paper a numerical expression of the degree of order observed in the plagioclases is also discussed. Because this is the first time that this aspect is treated he suggests two terms that may be used for the description of the structural state as measured by the axial angle, although he prefers the term "intermediacy index". The most ordered form is assigned an index of 100, and the most disordered an index of 0. Intermediate types of order receive an index inbetween these two values which depends on the relative position of the plotted measurements between the two extreme values.

In my opinion some objections must be made to the use of the term "intermediacy index". First of all, the degree of order found in alkali feldspars and plagioclases is not described by the same term, although the nature of the measured value is much the same in both cases. Secondly, the term "intermediate plagioclases" is already used for plagioclases with a moderate *An*-content, while "the intermediate plagioclase structure" describes a typical structural type. This leaves us with a confusing number of terms using "intermediate" for the description of a confusing number of properties of a confusing number of possible plagioclases. In considering the term "triclinicity", as applied to a similar phenomenon of alkali feldspars, another problem arises. This term, describing the degree of ordering in microclines, suggests that one structure can be more triclinic than another. This is at variance with the fundamental concepts of symmetry. It is suggested that the term "triclinicity", though of widespread usage, be dropped only because it is a misnomer.

The history of the numerous proposals for solving a chaotic system of terminology in geology and related sciences constitutes a substantial discouragement for making such attempts. Still, one must always try to use simple and comprehensible names. For this reason "obliquity index", a term used by DIETRICH (1962) and SMITHSON (1962) for alkali feldspars, is suggested instead.

In summary, the axial angle of a plagioclase may show a great deal of variation because of structural changes as well as chemical composition. Low-temperature plagioclases show positive axial angles for albite, andesine and labradorite composition. High-temperature plagioclases are only positive in the region of high calcium contents. For an evaluation of the chemical composition the axial angle is quite useless. For a determination of the structural state the axial angle gives adequate information in the region between An_0 and An_{40}, provided the chemical composition of the phases concerned is known.

Chapter 8

THE ORIENTATION OF THE INDICATRIX OF FELDSPARS

INTRODUCTION

The optical properties of a crystalline phase are determined by the arrangement of the highly polarisable ions or atoms in the framework. These properties are therefore symmetrically arranged. The arrangement, as well as the values of the optical properties, can be described by a geometrical figure, the indicatrix. The indicatrix of monoclinic and triclinic crystalline substances is a triaxial ellipsoid; the length of the three axes is determined by the values of the three principal indices of refraction. A triaxial ellipsoid has orthorhombic symmetry. In order to meet the requirements of the symmetry of the structure of a phase, the orientation of the indicatrix with reference to the symmetry elements of the crystal structure consequently has some degrees of freedom. In monoclinic crystals the orientation of this triaxial ellipsoid is such that one of the axes of the indicatrix is parallel with the crystallographical *b* axis. In addition, the indicatrix is free to rotate around this fixed axis. The amount of rotation provides information on the structural state and/or on the chemical composition. In triclinic crystals, lacking symmetry elements in the structure with the exception of a centre of symmetry, the indicatrix is not fixed and is free to rotate in such a way that its position is either determined by the structural state, by the chemical composition, or by both.

In the literature dealing with the identification of feldspars, the orientation of the indicatrix plays a significant role. In monoclinic and triclinic feldspars the indicatrix is rather free to rotate provided the obligatory symmetry requirements are observed. The only condition of a monoclinic structure is the presence of a symmetry plane. Triclinic structures are even more modest in their demands. Consequently, a feldspar phase that does not show the parallelism of a crystallographic element, for example the pole on a cleavage plane, and the optical *Y* axis does not have monoclinic symmetry.

The structure of feldspars is influenced by the presence of varying amounts of potassium, sodium and calcium. As the indicatrix is rather free to rotate, the influence of these elements may well be expressed by the orientation of the optical properties. Hence it is to be expected that the extinction angles inform us of the presence of a specific amount of the cations just mentioned. It is unfortunate that the structural state of feldspars also influences the extinction angles. We must therefore expect a number of complications in the comparatively simple relationships between chemical composition and orientation of the indicatrix.

It has been established that specific chemical composition ranges do represent unstable structures, at least in the low-temperature series of feldspars. These phases tend to separate, develop a pattern of transformation twins, or show a rather complex system of superstructures composed of a large number of unit cells. Such phases present difficulties that may lead to an additional variation in the orientation of the indicatrix. In alkali feldspars we know of transformation troubles of high-temperature phases towards low-temperature states. The presence of sub-X-ray perthites, submicroscopical perthites and submicroscopically twinned triclinic phases has been established. In plagioclases the transformation of a triclinic high-temperature form into a triclinic low-temperature form is not very difficult, but some phases are so unstable that separation occurs. Upon optical inspection the resultant crystalline aggregate may appear to be homogeneous throughout. In this respect some considerations reviewed by MARFUNIN (1962b), are of importance. He points out that the minimum resultant optical symmetry of submicroscopically twinned crystals is monoclinic! The monoclinic optics of a number of so-called orthoclases that are triclinic upon X-ray investigation are explained by these remarks. The details of the various relations between the chemical composition, the structural state and the orientation of the indicatrix will be treated in the following paragraphs.

THE USE OF EULER ANGLES

At present a number of workers are trying to unravel the remaining problems of indicatrix orientation by a critical examination of a large number of highly reliable sets of exhaustive measurements on feldspars. The quantification trend observed in the geosciences also influences feldspar investigations. The use of data processing and information-seeking machines requires data with a specific mathematical structure. If the numerical shape of our analytical results for feldspars is not of the type that can be fed into this modern equipment, we are faced with the problem of finding useful transformations.

The numerical properties of the indicatrix of any crystal can be described adequately within a three-dimensional system of Cartesian coordinates. The various properties of the structure of a crystal are traditionally described by one of the six three-dimensional frames of reference better known as the cubic, hexagonal, tetragonal, orthorhombic, monoclinic and triclinic systems. As soon as the orientation of the indicatrix, the properties of the indicatrix and the elements of the crystal structure have to be compared, the problem arises as to how to do this in a clear, unambiguous and efficient way. In particular, the non-orthogonal monoclinic and triclinic systems offer difficulties. These difficulties can be avoided

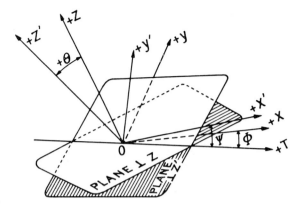

Fig.23. The three Euler angles Θ, Φ and Ψ, for two orthogonal systems of coordinates $X\,Y\,Z$ and $X'\,Y'\,Z'$, with the same origin O. (After BURRI, 1956.)

if the structure of triclinic and monoclinic minerals is also described by a system of Cartesian coordinates. In this case, however, we must take care that the axes of a Cartesian system are brought into the crystal structure in such a way that an efficient transformation procedure results.

If the optical properties and the crystal structure are described by separate orthogonal systems, the relations between the two systems can be easily and unambiguously described by "Euler angles". These three parameters that are sufficient for the characterization of the indicatrix orientation, can also be used for calculations with modern equipment. Various aspects are discussed below.

BURRI (1956) deserves credit not only for having recognized the problem just mentioned, but also for finding an elegant and efficient solution in a work of Leonhard Euler from 1748. Although the papers (BURRI, 1956; BURRI et al., 1962) speak for themselves, we will give some details as one is written in German, which may be inconvenient for some readers. Two problems must be solved. The first one is related to the question of how to transform data of one orthogonal three-dimensional system of coordinates into another such system. The second problem may be worded as follows: plagioclases and alkali feldspars are triclinic and monoclinic crystalline substances; in which way do we have to choose the three directions of a Cartesian coordinate system in the monoclinic or triclinic frames of reference? Both questions are thoroughly answered in Burri's papers.

It has been shown that the orientation of one system of references, with respect to another system of coordinates, can be precisely described by nine direction cosines (cf. MELLOR, 1955); the relations are found in Table X. Euler showed that as few as three angles are enough to characterize the mutual orientation of two orthogonal three-dimensional systems of coordinates.

If the systems are given as X, Y, Z and X', Y', Z', then the three angles just mentioned are as follows:

TABLE X

THE RELATIONS BETWEEN THE EULER ANGLES, THE DIRECTION COSINES AND THE ANGLES BETWEEN
THE AXES OF THE TWO ORTHOGONAL SYSTEMS OF COORDINATES

	X	Y	Z
X'	$\cos(XX') = \lambda_1$	$\cos(YX') = \lambda_2$	$\cos(ZX') = \lambda_3$
Y'	$\cos(XY') = \mu_1$	$\cos(YY') = \mu_2$	$\cos(ZY') = \mu_3$
Z'	$\cos(XZ') = \nu_1$	$\cos(YZ') = \nu_2$	$\cos(ZZ') = \nu_3$

$$\lambda_1^2 + \lambda_2^2 + \lambda_3^2 = 1 \qquad\qquad \lambda_1^2 + \mu_1^2 + \nu_1^2 = 1$$
$$\mu_1^2 + \mu_2^2 + \mu_3^2 = 1 \qquad\qquad \lambda_2^2 + \mu_2^2 + \nu_2^2 = 1$$
$$\nu_1^2 + \nu_2^2 + \nu_3^2 = 1 \qquad\qquad \lambda_3^2 + \mu_3^2 + \nu_3^2 = 1$$

$$\lambda_1\mu_1 + \lambda_2\mu_2 + \lambda_3\mu_3 = 0 \qquad\qquad \lambda_1\lambda_2 + \mu_1\mu_2 + \nu_1\nu_2 = 0$$
$$\nu_1\mu_1 + \nu_2\mu_2 + \nu_3\mu_3 = 0 \qquad\qquad \lambda_2\lambda_3 + \mu_2\mu_3 + \nu_2\nu_3 = 0$$
$$\nu_1\lambda_1 + \nu_2\lambda_2 + \nu_3\lambda_3 = 0 \qquad\qquad \lambda_3\lambda_1 + \mu_3\mu_1 + \nu_3\nu_1 = 0$$

	X	Y
X'	$\lambda_1 = \cos\Phi\cos\Psi + \sin\Phi\sin\Psi\cos\Theta$	$\lambda_2 = -\sin\Phi\cos\Psi + \cos\Phi\sin\Psi\cos\Theta$
Y'	$\mu_1 = -\cos\Phi\sin\Psi + \sin\Phi\cos\Psi\cos\Theta$	$\mu_2 = \sin\Phi\sin\Psi + \cos\Phi\cos\Psi\cos\Theta$
Z'	$\nu_1 = -\sin\Phi\sin\Theta$	$\nu_2 = -\cos\Phi\sin\Theta$

	Z
X'	$\lambda_3 = \sin\Psi\sin\Theta$
Y'	$\mu_3 = \cos\Psi\sin\Theta$
Z'	$\nu_3 = \cos\Theta$

Θ: the angle between Z and Z' (cf. Fig.23). The intersection line of the planes normal to Z and Z' is called the T axis. An arbitrary positive direction is assigned to the T axis. The angle Θ can be both positive and negative. Θ is positive when the transformation of Z into Z' is clockwise with reference to the positive direction assigned to the T axis.

Φ: the angle between the positive end of the T axis and the positive part of the X axis. Φ is positive if the transformation of $+T$ into $+X$ is clockwise with reference to the positive direction of the Z axis. The T and X axes are both in the plane normal to Z.

Ψ: the angle between the positive end of the T axis and the positive part of the X' axis. The angle Ψ is positive when the transformation of $+T$ into $+X'$ is clockwise with reference to the positive direction of the Z' axis. The T and X' axes are both in the plane normal to Z'.

Burri suggests the following names for the angles:

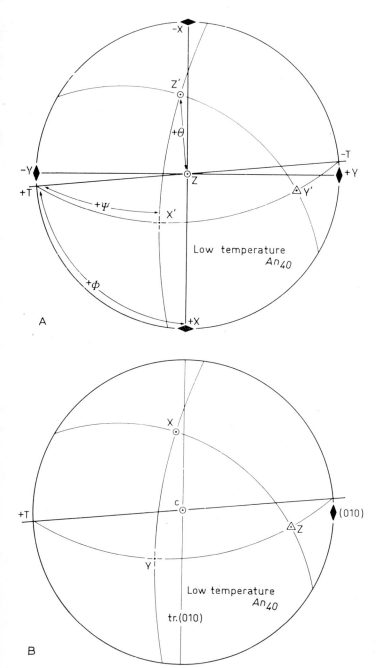

Fig.24.A. The optical orientation of a disordered plagioclase (An_{40}) expressed in Euler angles. This figure shows the two orthogonal systems of coordinates X Y Z and X' Y' Z'.

B. This stereogram attempts to explain the use of the unconventional symbols with the use of conventional ones. (After BURRI, 1956.)

Θ: "nutation", derived from the Latin word "nutare". For English nomenclature the term "inclination", which has about the same meaning, is suggested instead; Φ: "precession"; Ψ: "rotation". The illustration in Fig.23 may clarify things.

After this introduction we may begin describing the two systems as applied to the indicatrix and the crystallographic framework of plagioclases. For the structure of these feldspars Burri suggests the following reference directions:

X: the direction normal to the c axis in (010), symbolized as $\dfrac{\perp [001]}{(010)}$ according to Fedorov's system.

Y: the pole on (010), being also the twinning axis of the albite law, symbolized as $\perp$ (010).

Z: the crystallographic c axis, also being the twinning axis of the Carlsbad law, symbolized as $\perp$ [001].

It is certainly no coincidence that these structural directions have been chosen. Numerous older works on plagioclases demonstrate the important role of these directions.

The indicatrix is assigned the system $X'Y'Z'$. Burri considers the three possible ways in which this may be done. The convention he advocates is by no means the most obvious one. This convention may even be rather difficult for users of the English convention, which assigns the symbols X, Y and Z to the three axes of the indicatrix. The obvious convention, at least for these readers, will be $Nx = X'$, $Ny = Y'$ etc. Investigators accustomed to the French notation Np, Nm, and Ng, will have no objections against any of the three possible combinations. The same may hold true for those who use the notation $N\alpha$, $N\beta$, and $N\gamma$. Burri makes clear that the following scheme is the most efficient one:

$$X' = N\beta = Nm = Y$$
$$Y' = N\gamma = Ng = Z$$
$$Z' = N\alpha = Np = X$$

This convention has two advantages:

(1) Θ is always smaller than $90°$.

(2) Z' is always found to be on only one side of the plane determined by X and Y, as can be seen from the stereographic projections of plagioclase orientations in Fig.26, 28 and 29.

Usage of the Euler angles enables the investigator to describe the indicatrix orientation by just stating the three angles that have to be used in order to bring the indicatrix X', Y', Z' in the same orientation as the crystallographic frame described as X, Y, Z. Experienced users of both the universal stage and the stereographic projection will realize the practical possibilities of this system of three parameters immediately. For those who are accustomed to neither the universal stage nor the usage of Wulff's net, the following will provide further necessary information. In Fig.24A, the two systems of coordinates are given together with the three Euler angles. In Fig.24B the stereographic projection of a specific plagioclase is given together with the method for the graphical construction of the three Euler angles. For a concise description of the principles of the stereographic projection the reader is advised to consult either WAHLSTROM (1960) or DE JONG (1959).

BURRI (1956) also treats the calculation of Euler angles from published data and the calculation of the normal parameters from published Euler angles. For those who wish to do some calculating themselves, Table X lists the relations between the nine direction cosines of the two three-dimensional orthogonal systems of coordinates and the three Euler angles. The relations are given without any discussion. For further information the interested reader is requested either to consult Burri or a mathematical text treating the aspects of coordinate geometry, such as MELLOR (1955).

It is assumed that the use of Euler angles will become important in the near future, at least for plagioclases. At present about twenty papers exist which describe the properties of plagioclases by this new system of parameters. MARFUNIN (1962a), for example, treats the system in some detail and incorporates the Euler angles in tables giving optical data of plagioclases. GOTTARDI (1961) gives a diagram showing Euler angles versus chemical composition for the identification of plagioclases from a chemical and structural point of view. BURRI (1956) considers in detail the possibilities for the determination of the structural state of plagioclases.

No treatise exists at present on the usage of Euler angles for the characterization of alkali-feldspar properties. However, it can easily be seen that here too the Euler angles may well be an advantage, and that they may speed up the evaluation of structural properties in relation to optical orientation if data processing machines are to be used. It remains to be seen if the same conventions for the assignment of the symbols X, Y, Z and X', Y', Z' can be retained. The fact that some phases are monoclinic while others are triclinic must be incorporated in the convention, and the switching of the axial plane in high-sanidines needs consideration.

ALKALI FELDSPARS

As long as the true nature of the different alkali-feldspar phases was not known exactly, it was clear that the measuring of the orientation of the indicatrix did not lead to very satisfying results. The extinction angles on (001) or (010) in the group of microclines did not provide a method for evaluating the chemical composition. SPENCER (1930, 1937) showed qualitatively that in the alkali feldspars known as "orthoclase" (his group of orthoclase can no longer be regarded as a group of homogeneous true monoclinic crystalline phases), the angle between X and the *a* axis increases with the amount of Na in "solid solution". In high-temperature alkali feldspars, the so-called sanidines, the available data also point to an increase in the angle between X and *a* with an increasing amount of sodium. According to NIKITIN (1942), it is possible to distinguish anorthoclase, a sodium-rich alkali feldspar, from other alkali feldspars solely on the orientation of the indicatrix. DOLAR MANTUANI (1952), however, was not able to obtain impressively conclusive results with this method in his own special case. The work of Dolar Mantuani is illustrative of the difficulty one meets in trying to come to an unambiguous determination of the chemical composition of alkali feldspars by optical methods alone.

The data reported by TUTTLE (1952b) do not give better results. Among the alkali feldspars optically monoclinic but structurally triclinic phases are found, as well as true monoclinic and true triclinic phases. This makes it rather difficult to construct useful curves for the determination of the chemical composition starting from the orientation of elements of the indicatrix.

Recently, MARFUNIN (1961) found a relationship for cryptoperthites based on a combination of the value of the axial angle and the extinction angle on (010). A tentative diagram for the determination of the chemical composition of cryptoperthites is given in his paper. His methods at present, however, seem rather time consuming for pedologists and sedimentologists.

If alkali feldspars present in a sample are brought to a homogeneous high-temperature state by heat treatment (heating for one month may be required), the measurements of the extinction angles may lead to better results, provided enough reference data are gathered about chemically analysed high-temperature phases of varying composition. The amount of work necessary for such a treatment of the feldspar fraction of a rock sample only seems justified if rather special information is wanted. As a routine method this type of analysis does not seem promising at all.

PLAGIOCLASE FELDSPARS

An enormous amount of information is available about the relation between the chemical composition of plagioclase feldspars and the orientation of the indicatrix. Petrographers of metamorphic and igneous rocks use one of the numerous variants of this relation almost exclusively. As this treatise is not meant to give a historical review of the development of identification methods of feldspars, only those methods that will be of some use to the group addressed by this book will be treated. In addition, an ample number of references are given to enable the interested reader to study the various possible methods in further detail.

The crystallographic elements of the plagioclase crystal, frequently used for measuring the orientation of the indicatrix, are the traces of the cleavage planes (010) and (001). These planes are nearly always visible, provided the crystal fragment has the proper orientation. Plagioclase feldspars are often, but not always, twinned with (010) and (001) as composition planes. This facilitates the recognition of the traces of these planes. The presence of twins, however, is by no means necessary for a determination of the orientation of the indicatrix.

Until quite recently information on the orientation of the indicatrix of chemically analysed samples before and after heating, or of natural low-temperature and high-temperature phases, whose structure was established by independent techniques such as X-ray diffraction methods, was both scarce and scattered in literature. Even such useful and reliable data as those of VAN DER KAADEN (1951) were not all obtained from chemically and structurally analysed specimens. The memoir on plagioclases by EMMONS et al. (1953), which reports the indices of refraction, axial angle, orientation of the indicatrix, specific gravity and chemical composition, disregards the existence of low- and high-temperature phases to a certain extent. At present, however, we may consult the work of SLEMMONS (1962a) for a reliable set of data. His low-temperature curves are based on 27 chemically analysed specimens, 17 of which he analysed himself. The high-temperature curves are based on a smaller number of chemically analysed specimens, namely 5. In addition, the traces of the curves were determined by making use of data from specimens whose chemical composition is unknown. These data were taken from literature dealing with such measurements. Slemmons selected only those values found reliable according to present standards. In a later paper SLEMMONS (1962b) reports a number of measurements on a large amount of plagioclases about which information has been published previously. The structural state of these plagioclases is determined by X-ray powder methods. The axial angle of a number of these samples has been measured. In table 5 of his paper 24 samples are listed, of which the orientation of the indicatrix in relation to the pole on (010) is given, including 11 new samples. In addition to these measurements the papers of Slemmons and co-workers, such as DAVIS and SLEMMONS (1962), EISINGER et al. (1962) and LEAVITT and SLEMMONS (1962) contain a wealth of information.

After the general remarks on the orientation of the indicatrix we must treat the methods for the determination of the chemical composition of plagioclases that have been developed on the basis of this property. These methods may be divided into two groups. For the first group a universal stage is needed; the second group tries to make the best of the information that can be drawn from inspecting a thin section with a normal petrographic microscope. This seemingly reversed order has been chosen because it is necessary to have a clear understanding of the possible behaviour of sections of plagioclase fragments in order to make the proper guesses, simply by looking at a thin section with an ordinary microscope. It must be admitted that the study of plagioclases in thin sections of sediments without a universal stage, engaging as it may be, is a rather difficult job.

Universal stage methods

In 1943, EMMONS wrote the following sentence as a preface to his famous memoir on the five-axes universal stage: "The universal stage is beginning to receive in America the attention which is due so powerful an instrument". At that time the most important contributions towards the identification of plagioclases with this instrument had already been written. FEDOROV published his important papers on this subject before the end of the last century. NIKITIN's work was made available to West European geologists as early as 1914. The work of REINHARD dates back to the years 1924, 1928 and 1931. Berek wrote a lucid manual on these methods in 1924 and RITTMANN published his work on the "zone" technique in 1929. NIKITIN's comprehensive German treatise on the Fedorov method was published in 1936. Finally, KÖHLER published (1942a,b) data on the "joined angle" method, a technique that makes use of the angles between equivalent optical directions in related twin lamellae. Since the work of EMMONS (1943), American contributions have been increasing, and the contribution of SLEMMONS (1962a) may well be called the most important one.

Work on the reliability of measurements with the universal stage has been done by numerous authors, but the investigations of MUNRO (1963) are of out-standing quality and constitute a real experimental contribution towards the understanding of the precision of universal stage performance. The differences between orthoscopic and conoscopic observation techniques are treated in par-ticular detail. His results show the universal stage to be a very reliable apparatus. The measurements are generally accurate to 1°. The present author was able to make use of Munro's standard samples for measurements with a Zeiss universal stage on a Zeiss microscope (Munro worked with a Leitz outfit) because Mr. M. Munro kindly put sections of his samples at the disposal of my colleague, Dr. A. C. Tobi. The results were more or less the same as those found for the Leitz apparatus except for some minor details that will perhaps be reported elsewhere.

It seems that the use of the various types of universal stages is geographically determined. However, it may be concluded from recent papers that the stage with four axes is also becoming a routine tool in those regions where stages with five axes have been more generally in use. The three-axes stage (Cooke and Throughton) is going out of fashion judging from recent papers.

Finally, some remarks must be made concerning the use of the universal stage for routine measurements. In studies of igneous or metamorphic rocks this instrument has become a standard tool, for both mineralogical and petrofabric studies. A certain reluctance to use this powerful and practical accessory to the petrographic microscope is noticed among sedimentologists.

The following considerations may help to remove the unwarranted awe for this accessory to the microscope which is nothing more than an improved Car-danian suspension system. An understanding of spatial relationships comes naturally to most geologists and this is exactly what is needed for a proper use of the universal stage. If the investigator imagines the crystal under observation as a matchbox pierced by a number of knitting-needles, and visualizes the orientation of this matchbox from the position of the rings and bearings of the Cardanian system, the instrument will not surprise him with insuperable difficulties. As a matter of fact, the principles behind the technique are simple and the rules are few.

A plotting of the measurements is necessary, but here again some insight into solid geometry suffices. A projection method is needed to transform the data pertaining to a system with three dimensions into a system with only two dimensions, namely a sheet of paper. From a purely theoretical point of view it is irrelevant which type of projection method is used. In our opinion the stereographic projection method (Wulff net) has advantages over an equal area projection (Schmidt net) because the stereographic projection is "angle-true". From the projection on the Wulff net even beginners can get a clear picture of the orientation of the various directions of the crystal fragment. A large number of books have been written on the properties of the stereographic projection as well as on the technique of plotting observations. The work of FAIRBAIRN (1949), which deals with these procedures in relation to structural petrography, enjoys a certain reputation. The author relies entirely on the Compendium of DE JONG (1959). WAHLSTROM (1960) also dedicates much space to the stereographic projection, the universal stage, the measurement and plotting of crystal planes and the rotation of projections in the net itself. As the latter text is simple, comprehensive and illustrated with clear pictures, beginners are advised to start with this text.

Those who have not attempted the use of the stereographic or any other projection may believe it to be complex and cumbersome. However, if they are willing to devote some time to exercises using a geological compass, measuring various directions drawn on a piece of cardboard placed obliquely on their desks, they will generally become experienced plotters in a rather short time. It is the author's conviction that apart from plagioclase identification the universal stage also may well play an important role in the evaluation of numerous interesting problems of sedimentary structures. If one still feels uncertain about this instrument and is not yet willing to give it a try, he should read the final section of Emmon's introduction to the memoir mentioned earlier, or even the whole introduction.

As has already been said, a universal stage is nothing more than a Cardanian system of suspension, enabling a random orientation of a thin section in respect to the tube axis of the microscope. The number of extra rings is basically irrelevant. In order to rotate the thin section suspended in the inner ring, a small revolving stage is fixed within this ring. A number of manufacturers also produce a mechanical stage that can be mounted on this revolving stage to allow for counting procedures.

If the light is not perpendicularly transmitted through the thin section, a number of inconvenient effects make it impossible to have a good look at the

TABLE XI

PUBLICATIONS ON THE FEDOROV-NIKITIN-REINHARD TECHNIQUE

English

EMMONS, R. C., 1943. The universal stage. *Geol. Soc. Am., Mem.,* 8 : 205 pp.
TURNER, F. J., 1947. Determination of plagioclase with the four-axis universal stage. *Am. Mineralogist,* 36 : 389–410.
VAN DER KAADEN, G., 1951. *Optical Studies on Natural Plagioclase Feldspar with High-Temperature and Low-Temperature Optics.* Thesis, State Univ., Utrecht, The Netherlands, 150 pp.
SLEMMONS, D. B., 1962. Determination of volcanic and plutonic plagioclases using a three- or four-axis universal stage. *Geol. Soc. Am., Spec. Papers,* 69 : 64 pp.

French

NIKITIN, W., 1914. La méthode universelle de Fedorov.
DUPARC, L. et REINHARD, M., 1923. Les méthodes de Fedorov et leur application à la détermination des plagioclases. *Schweiz. Mineral. Petrog. Mitt.,* 3 (1–2) : 1–74.
REINHARD, M., 1924. Donnée complementaire pour la détermination des plagioclases par la méthode théodolite. *Schweiz. Mineral. Petrog. Mitt.,* 4 : 1–14.
REINHARD, M., 1928. À propos de la détermination des plagioclases par la méthode de Fedorov. *Compt. Rend. Soc. Phys. Hist. Nat. Genève,* 40 : 1–7.

German

BEREK, M., 1924. *Mikroskopische Mineralbestimmung mit Hilfe der Universaldrehtischmethoden.* Borntraeger, Berlin, 168 pp.
NIKITIN, W., 1924. *Mikroskopische Mineralbestimmung mit Hilfe der Universaldrehtischmethoden.* Borntraeger, Berlin.
REINHARD, M., 1931. *Universaldrehtischmethoden.* Wepf, Basel, 119 pp.
NIKITIN, W., 1936. *Die Fedorov Methode.* Borntraeger, Berlin, 109 pp.

Russian

Apart from Fedorov's original work and the compilation issued by the Publishing House of the Academy of Sciences of the U.S.S.R. under the title *The Universal Stage of E.S. Fedorov* (836 pp.), a few works will be named separately.
NIKITIN, W., 1912–1923. *The Universal Method of Fedorov.* St. Petersburg (in Russian).
NIKITIN, W., 1926. A diagram of the most important geometrical elements with regard to the indicatrix axes of feldspars. *West Russian Mining Soc.,* 55 (1–2).
ARSHINOW, V. V., 1952. *The Application of Inclinable Stage-hemispheres for Work on a Polarizing Microscope by Fedorov's Method.* Gosgeoltekhizdat, Moscow, 59 pp. (In Russian.)

---

mount. For this reason the section is mounted between two hemispherical bodies of glass. The influences of the air films between hemispheres and preparation are removed by an immersion liquid of about the same refractive index as the glass parts of the instrument. In this way incident light is normal to the surface of the glass sphere for any inclination of the section. It must be stressed here that a number of departures from the theoretically ideal arrangement cause deviations that need correction. The correction procedures are treated in the manuals listed in Table XI; graphs for such corrections are given in most cases as well as by TRÖGER (1959). Munro's paper also treats some of these aspects.

Lately the construction of the two hemispheres, as well as of the U-objectives, has been changed in such a way that the crystal fragments under study can be observed conoscopically. A study of the optic-axis figures is thus made easy. MUNRO (1963) proves that conoscopical measurements are more accurate than orthoscopical measurements for the Leitz apparatus.

The proper use of the instrument can be made easier with the help of available compensators. The Berek compensator and the Ehringhaus compensator give the operator much better information on the nature of the extinction position of a crystal fragment than the ordinary gypsum- or mica-plate (the names gypsum-plate and mica-plate are retained, although at present at least the first-order-red comparators are usually made of quartz). In order to locate the exact position of the optical axes in the optic-axis figure it may be easier to measure the position of small dark circular spots marking the emerging points of these axes. These spots are seen if the section is viewed through a mica-plate, while a second mica comparator is inserted at right angles to the first plate, just above the polarizer but below the thin section.

In case the crystal under study shows a marked extinction dispersion or a large axial dispersion, it is advisable to measure the mineral with monochromatic light. An illuminating outfit that allows one to switch from monochromatic light to white light and back again, without readjusting the optical parts of the microscope, is a contrivance especially convenient for those who deal frequently with accurate determinations of optical properties. For a routine investigation of feldspars in thin sections such a light source is not necessary.

After our remarks on the universal stage, its usefulness and some hints on how to handle it, we return to the subject under consideration, i.e., the identification of plagioclases with the universal stage. In the following sections a number of the current methods will be discussed, one of which will be treated in more detail than others. The methods not treated in detail are described in a number of excellent monographs that are easily available. This book will not include a complete set of graphs and stereograms necessary for the determination of the chemical composition of plagioclases or for the identification of the twinning types present. There are two reasons for leaving the stereograms out of this text. Firstly, a number of easily available textbooks give these stereograms (e.g., TRÖGER, 1959). Secondly, BURRI et al. (1961) announced a Swiss project for making a new general catalogue of data for the determination of plagioclases by the universal stage method at the International Geological Congress in Copenhagen of August, 1960. At the June, 1962 Feldspar Symposium in Oslo, new information was given on this project (BURRI et al., 1962). The publication of this work will certainly outdate all present available data.

Plagioclases are generally tabular crystals with excellent (001) and (010) cleavage planes. Methods for the identification of the different members of this group of minerals use this feature without exception. The orientation of cleavage planes or of composition planes of twins can be measured with a universal stage, as well as the orientation of the optical axes X, Y, Z and A and B. Two possible approaches can be envisaged: (1) The identification begins with the orientation of the *optical axes*, or (2) the identification begins with the orientation of the *cleavage planes* (010) and (001).

Methods begun with the orientation of optical axes

When the identification is begun with measurements of three, or only two, of the optical axes, X, Y and Z, the method is known as the *Fedorov-Nikitin-Reinhard technique*. In general the Y axis is taken as the reference direction. This means that after plotting the measurements on a stereographic net, the projections are all rotated in such a way that Y becomes the centre of the stereogram. Aside from the axes X, Y and Z, the poles on (001) and (010) are measured. These poles are also rotated. Afterwards the entire plot is compared with one of the several stereograms available. It is advisable to use the more recent stereograms because they also list the measurements on high-temperature phases. Such stereograms have been published by VAN DER KAADEN (1951), among others. The determinative tables collected by TRÖGER (1959) give such stereograms as separate plates of normal size, i.e., with a diameter of 20 cm. Stereograms listing Slemmons' measurements have not yet been published. On the other hand, SLEMMONS (1962a) also prepared a number of graphs listing the previous reliable data. This presentation of data is different from that of the authors, who lent their names to the method, and from that of Van der Kaaden. The original idea of presenting the data in this different form is that of TURNER (1947), but he only made use of low-temperature data.

The poles of cleavage planes cannot be determined as accurately as the direction of one of the axes X, Y or Z, or one of the optical axes, A or B. Fedorov pointed this out and suggested using the twinning laws of plagioclases, whose nature was known at that time. REINHARD (1924) also points out this possibility, while SLEMMONS (1962a) states that he prefers not to measure the composition face directly. It later became clear that the composition planes of twins, as well as cleavage planes, quite often show vicinal forms and are only more or less parallel to the ideal face (see the memoir of EMMONS, 1953; and others). A paper by TOBI (1965, in preparation) stresses these deviations from the ideal planes. For the reasons just mentioned only those face poles should be used with the Fedorov-Nikitin-Reinhard method that are constructed from measurements of two twinned individuals. The construction of the face pole from the measurements on two twinned crystals is given in detail by WAHLSTROM (1960), among others, and can be deduced from the theory of the stereographic projection. The manuals pertinent to the Fedorov-Nikitin-Reinhard technique give all the details. References will be found in Table XI.

As the method under consideration quite often makes use of twins, which are frequently observed among plagioclases, it is necessary to be able to determine the twinning law of any set of twins. The properties of twins are treated in Chapter 9. On the other hand, it is quite useless to give a cut and dried set of rules here because, as has been pointed out above, excellent monographs already exist. An enumeration of a number of such monographs, ranked according to the language in which they are written, follows in Table XI. It must be admitted that a number of them are out of print or hard to get, but others are easily obtainable at a rather low price.

The Fedorov-Nikitin-Reinhard technique makes use of stereograms in most cases. This, however, is not an essential part of the method. It is not important in which way the measuring results are interpreted. Instead of stereograms one may also use another graphical plot. Such a set of graphs was introduced by KÖHLER (1942b). They illustrate the variation of the optical properties with a varying composition by showing the relations between equivalent optical directions in related twin lamellae. When the measurements are plotted in these graphs the method is sometimes called the *joined angle* method.

As there is virtually no difference in the measuring procedure, there is no reason for treating the use of these graphs separately. Still, we may call attention to these graphs because they constitute a powerful tool for gaining a deeper understanding of the properties of twins. Moreover, these graphs compel the investigator to construct the composition planes of the twins from measurements of two adjacent twin lamellae. In this way the use of the sometimes unreliable face poles obtained from oriented cleavage traces is avoided.

The strength of Fedorov's method in combination with these graphs is illustrated by the work of NICKEL (1949). He was able to make it clear that in certain plagioclases the various twin lamellae may have a differing chemical composition. At the same time, he proved that a set of conflicting measurements does not alter the reliability of the Fedorov-Nikitin-Reinhard technique.

If one should wish to use these graphs it is advisable not to use the ones published by Köhler or Nickel, for TRÖGER (1959) has a newly drawn set of curves that also take the measurements of VAN DER KAADEN (1951) into consideration.

As the joined angle curves will not be often used by the readers of this book, the curves are not reproduced here. Moreover, the excellent work of Tröger is easily available to every geologist, this book being present in even the very smallest geological libraries.

In summary it may be said that the Fedorov-Nikitin-Reinhard method is reliable but time consuming. When one is accustomed to the technique, it is often found that in many cases a number of short cuts exist which render this method attractive even for certain sedimentological problems (cf. RITTMAN, 1929). An investigation of the clastic plagioclases in Permian graywackes clearly illustrates what can be achieved with this method in sedimentological research (see p.274).

Methods begun with cleavage planes

RITTMANN (1929) developed an identification technique beginning with the face poles [010] or [001]. This method is quicker, but slightly less reliable. He introduces his technique with the words: "The petrographer, in general, puts more weight on efficiency and security than on great accuracy during his practical work. For this reason the methods of Fouqué and Michel-Lévy still enjoy great popularity, although the results are often ambiguous or even incorrect". He writes further: "The most perfect method for plagioclase determination so far is doubtless that of Fedorov and Nikitin, because this technique is not only able to determine the *An*-content of a plagioclase, but also provides decisive answers about the twinning laws present at the same time. In its improved and simplified form the technique is now easily accessible to every petrographer, due to the clear and thorough presentation by Duparc and Reinhard. The fact that the petrographer faced with practical problems is afraid of losing too much time, by the application of this method to numerous thin sections, may explain why in spite of everything it is not more generally used".

Moreover, Rittmann's procedure offers a control on the Fedorov-Nikitin-Reinhard method. The above quotation saves us a discussion of the merits and the drawbacks of Rittmann's method. The identification scheme is known either as the *Rittmann-Ebert technique* or the *zone method*. The name of Ebert is added because he contributed some measurement data and a treatise on the system in 1932.

The procedure is rather simple, and will be treated here in some detail, as it may well suit the sedimentologist faced with the identification of plagioclases

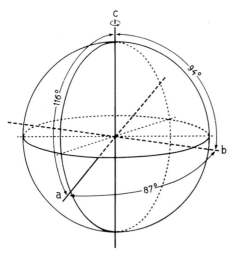

Fig.25. The orientation of the three crystallographic axes *a*, *b* and *c*, with reference to the projection plane normal to the *c* axis, through the centre of the sphere. In the stereographic projections of Fig.27, 29 and 30, only the upper hemisphere is taken into consideration.

in sediments and the need of doing some counting in order to obtain quantitative results. In particular, the determination of the chemical composition of plagioclases beginning with sections normal to the crystallographic *a* axis, one of the attractive details of the zone method, seems rather promising from a practical point of view.

THE ZONE METHOD; PROCEDURES AND REMARKS

Mounting of the thin section

Clean the thin section carefully. Grease or cement stains may cause all kinds of trouble. Firstly, the section may not move smoothly between the two glass hemispheres; secondly, the immersion liquid between hemispheres and thin section may not wet the surface of the section or the hemispheres in such a way that a continuous film of liquid will form. The second imperfection constitutes a particular nuisance. Air bubbles prefer to develop at these soiled sites, giving rise to total reflection of the incident light. Such bubbles not only prevent the study of a fragment of plagioclase situated above or just below them, but also produce stray light in the optical assemblages, for they behave like small mirrors. The importance of *cleaning* both section and hemispheres cannot be emphasized enough.

For the proper mounting of a thin section the following procedure is suggested. The section is washed with distilled water and then with ethanol. Take care that the glass is not touched after cleaning. The section is left to dry on a fresh paper tissue. The hemispheres are thoroughly cleaned with distilled water and then with ethanol. Take care that the glass parts move freely in the metal fittings. Hemispheres that are locked in the fittings and that cannot be rotated are either improper made or have fittings that have become foul through neglect. Such hemispheres must be soaked for a few days in a mixture of distilled water and ethanol. Hemispheres that are tightly locked in their mounts will show birefringence due to stress. The cleaned hemispheres are also laid flat face up on a fresh paper tissue. From this point on the glass parts are not touched at all. If this should accidentally happen, clean them thoroughly *again!* After drying, the parts are put in place, the lower hemisphere first.

Glycerine may be used as an immersion liquid. Take care that the glycerine is clean and that it does not contain too much water. Glycerine is hygroscopic and therefore the bottle must be closed after each use. It is even better to take a small beaker, covered with a watch-glass, and to fill it with the amount of glycerine needed for 1 day. The next day the beaker is cleaned and filled again. In this way the glycerine does not accumulate dust and water. With a glass rod a drop of glycerine is brought on the surface of the lower hemisphere and the thin section is laid on top of it, starting from one side. Subsequently starting again obliquely, the thin section is covered with glycerine and the upper hemisphere. If the universal stage is equipped with a central plate, the procedure for the central plate is the same as for the thin section.

If the apparatus is equipped with screws locking the assemblage of hemispheres, section and central plate, *one should take care not to fix these screws too tightly.* It may perhaps be noted that none of the screws of the universal stage should be fixed too tightly. It is found that universal stages used frequently by a number of people suffer, without exception, from stripped arresting screws and dirty bearings. Handbooks normally assume that the reader is fully aware of the fact that having clean apparatus and samples is one of the prerequisites for reliable results, and rightly so. For this reason they generally do not stress the inconvenience that may be avoided by putting this knowledge into practice . . .

If the various parts of the universal stage are in their proper positions, i.e., with the axes exactly normal to each other and the NS axis parallel to the direction of the analyser[1], we must control the position of the thin section. The mineral fragment must lie exactly in the plane of

---

[1] Some microscopes have analysers with the direction of vibration EW. For these microscopes the NS axis of the universal stage must be normal to the direction of the analyser.

Fig.26. A four-axes universal stage mounted on a polarizing microscope. The four axes: the inner vertical axis (A1), the north–south axis (NS), the east–west axis (EW), and the axis of the microscope stage (M) are clearly marked. The universal stage shown is one of the types which allow for orthoscopic and conoscopic observation. (Courtesy Carl Zeiss, Oberkochen, Germany.)

the EW and NS axis. The manual accompanying each instrument is sure to give the proper proce-dure. Another check before starting the measurements concerns the centering of the apparatus. The vertical axis or axes of the universal stage, the axis of the revolving stage of the microscope, the tube axis of the microscope, and the axis of the condensor must enter the same point in the thin section and they must coincide. For an illustration of the various parts of the universal stage mentioned in this text, see Fig.26. A procedure for achieving the centering of all these vertical axes of the assembled instrument is again to be found in the manual accompanying each instrument. It would be too complicated to give such procedures in this text because of the variety of constructions. Some instructions, especially for the Leitz apparatus, are to be found in WAHLSTROM (1960).

The measurement procedure

The apparatus is now ready for measuring plagioclase fragments. If these fragments are viewed with crossed polarizers, the universal stage in "zero-position", there are four possibilities:
(1) The fragment does not show cleavage traces nor traces of the presence of twins (p.117).
(2) The fragment shows the presence of cleavage traces but no twins (p.117).
(3) The fragment shows the presence of twins but no cleavages (p.121).
(4) The fragment shows the presence of twins as well as cleavages (p.125).
In the following sections it will be systematically shown how to proceed in the various cases.

(1) The fragment does not show cleavage traces nor traces of the presence of twins

The section is brought to a tilted position with the drum of the EW axis, e.g., the drum is turned counter-clockwise until one of the parts of the instrument is blocked. The section is now turned in the reverse direction with the same axis; simultaneously the section is rotated about the NS axis from time to time. The arresting screws of both axes are loosened during the operation. In this way the section is systematically observed from all possible orientations. As soon as a cleavage trace is observed, the positions of the EW and the NS axes are recorded. The systematic survey of the remaining orientations is repeated until the instrument does not allow for further rotation. If a cleavage trace is seen during this procedure, proceed as described in case 2; if a twin is seen proceed as in case 3; if both traces of cleavages and twins are seen proceed as in case 4.

If the absence of twins or cleavage traces in the region accessible for inspection is definitely ascertained, the true nature of the mineral must first be questioned. It may well be that the mineral under observation is an alkali feldspar or a quartz. If, however, there is sufficient indication that the mineral is a plagioclase, the only remaining possibility is to find other methods of identifying it.

(2) The fragment shows the presence of cleavage traces but no twins

One of the crystallographic axes is always found as the intersection line of two planes. The intersection of (010) and (001) $\rightarrow$ the a axis, (100) and (001) $\rightarrow$ the b axis, and (100) and (010) $\rightarrow$ the c axis. In plagioclases the forms (010) and (001) are usually well-expressed. Thus the chances are great that one of the visible cleavages is (010) or (001). In plagioclases the a-axis direction may therefore be found in some sections showing the traces of these two planes. Furthermore, it is possible that sections be encountered which are cut normal to the plane (001) or normal to the plane (010), although the section is obliquely cut to the a axis. Finally, sections cut parallel to the plane (010) or to the plane (001) can be expected. As the universal stage enables the analyst to rotate the section in a specific position that provides a better determination of various relations between the crystallographic frame and the indicatrix orientation, it can be seen that one of the three possible orientations listed below can always be obtained. This provides us with a useful scheme for a treatment of the measuring procedures.

(a) The fragment is cut in such a way that the section can be rotated in the position in which two cleavages (010) and (001) are parallel with the tube axis (p.117).

(b) The fragment is cut more or less parallel with the plane (001) (p.120).

(c) The fragment is cut more or less parallel with the plane (010) (p.121).

Ad (2a). The section is brought to a tilted position with the EW axis, and the systematic survey of the presence of other cleavages and twins is begun in much the same way as described in 1 (p.117). As soon as a twin is found, proceed as described in 4 (p.125). If a second cleavage is found proceed as follows:

One of the visible cleavage planes is brought into a position normal to the EW axis of the stage. This is done in two steps. The trace of the cleavage is rotated until it is parallel to the NS cross-hair of the objective. The small revolving stage within the inner ring is used for this manoeuvre, with the A1 axis (cf. Fig.26). Subsequently, the trace of the cleavage plane is rotated in such a position that it is as narrow as possible and does not wobble when being observed, while the tube of the microscope is moved up and down. This is achieved by slightly turning the sample about the NS axis until the proper position is reached. The cleavage plane is then normal to the EW axis of the universal stage.

The accurate orientation may be checked by tilting the sample with the EW axis. If the orientation is perfect the trace does not show lateral translation when viewed from the extreme N edge of the field of vision until the extreme S edge. A lateral translation due to steps in the plane obviously does not constitute an indication of improper orientation. It must be realized that such a tilted mount cannot be viewed at all sides at the same time, because the distance between parts of the object and the front lens of the objective varies. Finally the arresting screw of the NS axis is gently fixed.

After the orientation of the first cleavage plane, the second cleavage plane is brought into such a position that the pole of this plane is parallel to the plane of the EW and NS axes. In order to achieve this the EW axis is turned until the trace of this cleavage is rotated towards its narrowest appearance. Again the trace may not seem to wobble when the tube is moved upwards or downwards. Afterwards, the arresting screw of the EW axis is gently fixed. The position of the sample is read from the various graduated rings and arcs, and the values are recorded.

The NS cleavage-trace is now rotated clockwise to a 45° position with the revolving stage of the microscope with the M axis (cf. Fig.26). The parts of the universal stage are still not touched in the following phase.

If the polarizers have not already been inserted in the field of vision, this must be done now. The gypsum plate is brought in the optical system, and the "sign" of the 45° position of the fragment is determined. If the elongation is negative, the colour is yellow; if the elongation is positive, the colour is blue. The stereogram of Fig.27 should be consulted during further discussion. Fig.25 illustrates the orientation of the crystallographic axes and the projection plane as used in the Wulff

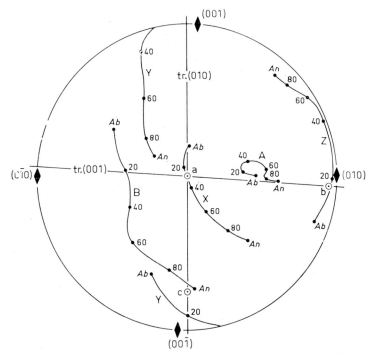

Fig.27. The indicatrix orientation of low-temperature plagioclases. The stereographic projection ⊥ *a*, of the upper hemisphere.

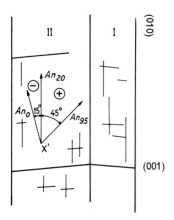

Fig.28. Diagram explaining Schuster's convention. The figure shows an albite twin cut perpendicular to the *a* axis. The parts *I* and *II* are the two twin lamellae. The cleavage plane (010) and (001) are also indicated. The extinction of $X' \wedge$ (010) is considered negative if X' passes through the obtuse angle between (001) and (010). If X' passes through the acute angle between the cleavage planes, the sign is positive.

net. It must be noted that the upper hemisphere alone is considered in the stereograms shown as Fig.27, 29 and 30. From Fig.25 it can be seen that the three axes are not normal to each other. This explains why the projections of these axes are not found on the circumference of the circle in the stereograms.

If the whole fragment is in the "substraction position", or if the fragment shows a yellow interference colour with the gypsum plate, which is the same, it is possible that the cleavage trace concerned belongs to the face (010).

Assuming that this is the case, we must consult the stereogram in order to get an insight into the optical behaviour of plagioclases in this orientation. The trace of (010) is seen as a NS line in the projection, the same direction as on the universal stage. Moreover, the stereogram shows Z to be more or less parallel to the horizontal plane of the instrument. The largest part of the curve of Z positions is quite near the EW axis. This explains why plagioclases in the orientation normal to the *a* axis show a negative elongation of the trace of (010) in the 45° position until about 70% An. This fact was noticed by RITTMANN (1929, p.28. Note the different orientation of the gypsum plate relative to the cleavage trace; the resulting colour is blue), and stressed again by TOBI (1963, p.157). Provided the chemical composition of our fragment is below this critical limit, it is proved that the face under observation is (010).

This having been established, the extinction angle of the feldspar in relation to the trace of (010) is measured in the conventional way, by turning the fragment first in the extinction position with the revolving stage of the microscope, and then in the position: trace (010) // cross-hair. The difference between the readings is entered in the graph of Fig.33. In order to get a somewhat better result the measurement should be repeated a few times and the average of these observations should be used for the rest of the determination[1]. If the extinction angle is smaller than 15°, the conventional plus or minus sign must be determined according to the following rules:

Trace of X' in the obtuse angle between the traces of (010) and (001); sign is *negative*, see Fig.28.

Trace of X' in the acute angle between the traces of (010) and (001); sign is *positive*, see Fig.28.

The use of the graph in Fig.33A will be demonstrated by the following example: supposing the extinction angle to be 5°, the conventional sign is found to be negative. Follow the solid line

---

[1] Bertrand's ocular, or Wright's biquartz wedge have proved very useful for an accurate measurement of extinction angles (cf. WAHLSTROM, 1960, p.193).

marked —5 from the upper side of the graph marked *Low-temperature*, down to the intersection with the solid line marked "section ⊥ *a*" at the left hand side of the graph. Proceed vertically downwards from this point to the lower side of the graph. Here the chemical composition is read as 17% An.

If the cleavage trace in the orientation parallel to the NS axis of the universal stage does not show a negative elongation, there are two possibilities. Firstly, the other visible trace is that of (010). This may be rapidly checked by reorientation of the mount. The procedure just described is then begun with this second orientation. Secondly, the An-content of the fragment is over 70%. In this case the sample will be rather near its extinction position in the 45° position, irrespective of which trace was originally in the NS direction, (010) or (001). If such a fragment is slightly rotated about the axis of the microscope itself, the elongation changes from "yellow" to "blue". This property of changing elongation, together with a large extinction angle, proves the presence of a calcic plagioclase. The trace (010) is selected from the two visible cleavage traces by the consideration that X′ ∧ (010) never exceeds 45°.

It is still theoretically possible that the two cleavage directions observed do not include (010). The only possible combination of planes in this case seems to be the presence of (001) and one of the planes (1̄10) or (110). The presence of this set of cleavages is considered rather exceptional. Moreover, the unexpected behaviour of the plagioclase in this orientation will certainly constitute a warning. The investigator always has some idea about the chemical composition of the fragment under study. As soon as his measurement results differ widely from these expectations he will carefully consider all the aspects of the measurement anew.

Ad (2b). If the section is cut parallel to the face (001), the only cleavage plane that can be observed must be (010). The stereogram of Fig.29 shows this orientation. In sections normal to the c axis the trace of (010) shows negative elongation. The section will show a small birefringence as indicated by the traces of X and B in the stereographic projection of Fig.29. Moreover, plagioclases have a

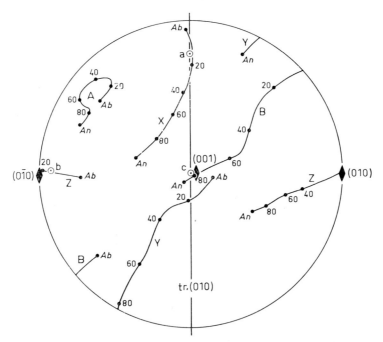

Fig.29. The indicatrix orientation of low-temperature plagioclases. The stereographic projection ⊥ *c*, of the upper hemisphere.

specific orientation showing the straight extinction of the trace (010), irrespective of the chemical composition. The pole of this particular section through a plagioclase is more or less parallel to the c axis.

For calcic plagioclases the section $\perp$ c can be distinguished from the section $\perp$ b by conoscopical observation. Calcic plagioclases will show an axial figure with a nearly centred optic axis (Fig.29). The extinction angle of a sodium-rich plagioclase in this position $\perp$ c is small. TRÖGER (1959, p.101) offers a graph according to a method of Schuster, from 1881, that can be used for these sections. It must be realized that these graphs were made for cleavage flakes. They assume the visibility of the trace of (100). If these graphs cannot be used, the Fedorow-Nikitin-Reinhard method will lead to a determination of the chemical composition. In this text graphs are given illustrating the behaviour of plagioclases in the zone normal to important cleavage planes. The graph in Fig.36B illustrates the zone (010). The curves given in this graph can also be used for a rough determination of the chemical composition. N.B. If the investigator has at his disposal modern universal stage equipment that allows for conoscopical observation, he should also consult paragraph *Ad (2b) and (2c)* on p.121.

Ad (2c). If the section is cut parallel to the face (010), the only cleavage trace that is visible is (001). The orientation under discussion is illustrated in Fig.30. It can be seen that the orientation $\perp$ b does not differ greatly from the position normal to the pole on (010). Such sections may show either positive or negative elongation.

The stereographic projection also shows that such sections will exhibit a considerable birefringence only for calcic plagioclases. Graphs for the determination of the chemical composition of plagioclase cleavage fragments with much the same orientation are again found in TRÖGER (1959, p.101), according to another method developed by Schuster in 1881. These curves have the same limitations as the ones discussed in the previous section. They assume the presence of a trace of (100). In this text the orientation under discussion, being one of the positions of the zone normal to (001), is given in Fig.32. The curves found in this figure may be used for a rough determination. Finally, the application of the Fedorov-Nikitin-Reinhard technique offers good possibilities. N.B. If the investigator has at his disposal a modern universal stage equipped for conoscopical observation, the next paragraph should also be consulted.

Ad (2b) and (2c). Another possibility exists for the determination of the chemical composition of some of the fragments in the position discussed in paragraphs *Ad (2b)* and *Ad (2c)*. The investigator must have a universal stage equipment that allows for conoscopical observation. If it is possible to rotate the section in a position showing an acute or an obtuse bisectrix figure, the method of FOUQUÉ (1894) can be used. Turn the section in such a position that the centre of the cross, seen conoscopically if Y is normal or parallel to the direction of vibration of the analyser, is exactly in the middle of the field of vision. In this position measure the extinction angle of the fragment with respect to the visible cleavage trace. This extinction angle can be used with the graph in Fig.31, that has been drawn according to the suggestions of Fouqué, but with data from A. Köhler (see TRÖGER, 1959). The graph originally given by TRÖGER (1959, p.101) has been slightly modified. The information concerning alkali feldspars has been omitted.

(3) The fragment shows the presence of twins but no cleavages

If the reader is not familiar with the various twinning laws of feldspars, it may be advisable first reading the chapter on twins in order to get a clear picture of the various possibilities. If he is slightly familiar with the subject, he can proceed with the concise description in the present chapter of the aspects of twins, which is necessary for an understanding of the following procedures.

For the application of the zone method it is necessary to know the difference between normal twinning and the other twinning laws. Furthermore, it is necessary to know the properties of albite twins, Carlsbad twins, and twins that may be confused with them.

A normal twin is characterized by a twinning axis that is the pole of the composition plane of the twin. The twinning axis may be described, for all practical purposes, as the axis about which one of the two members of a twin must be rotated in order to get exactly the same orientation as the other. The symmetry plane of a normal twin is its composition plane.

Other twins are either parallel twins or complex twins. Parallel twins are characterized by

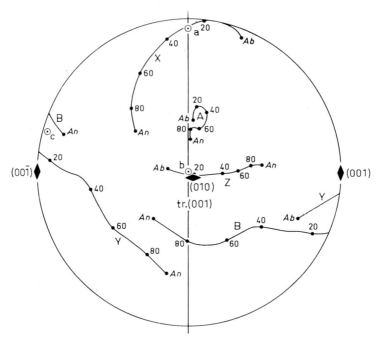

Fig.30. The indicatrix orientation of low-temperature plagioclases. The stereographic projection ⊥ *b*, of the upper hemisphere.

a twinning axis that lies in the composition plane and that coincides with a crystallographic axis. Complex twins have a twinning axis that is also situated in the composition plane, but which is the perpendicular direction on one of the crystallographic axes.

In the application of the zone method twins are only used for obtaining information on the orientation of a plagioclase with respect to one of the visible planes, in this case the composition plane of a twin. Therefore, the twins about the planes (010) and (001) are most important here. Albite and Carlsbad twins have (010) as the composition plane. Twins with (001) as the composition plane are rather scarce. The pericline twin, with the rhombic section as a composition plane, may be used for an indication of the (001) face, for this rhombic section is more or less parallel to (001) (see also p.142). The pericline twin may not be used for the orientation of a section in the position normal to the *a* axis.

One last remark before proceeding to the details of measuring such sections that show only twins. Fragments of plagioclases which show twins only, and no cleavage traces are rare. The text of this paragraph is written for the sake of completeness, and not because it is felt that this case will be observed frequently in practice when measuring plagioclases. Furthermore, the method given below is based on exactly the same aspects of the optical properties of plagioclases as the paragraph dealing with cleavage traces.

If a section shows only twins, with the universal stage in the "zero position", begin a systematical inspection of the accessible area for cleavage traces as described under 1. As soon as a cleavage trace is found, proceed as described under 4. If cleavages are not found in the course of this systematic survey, proceed as follows: make a sketch of the twinning stock. The behaviour of the twin lamellae is then recorded on this sketch. Needless to say, the polarizers should be crossed. For the systematic treatment three possible situations may be encountered:

(*a*) The fragment is cut in such a way that the plagioclase can be rotated in the position known as ⊥ *a*, at least for one of the twin members. The twin inventory in Table XII shows that albite twins, Carlsbad twins, Baveno twins and albite–Carlsbad twins may be seen in such a section (p.160–161).

(b) The fragment is cut approximately parallel to (001) for one of the twin members. The twin inventory, Table XII, shows the visibility of albite twins, Carlsbad twins, Ala-B twins and albite–Carlsbad twins (p.158).

(c) The fragment is cut approximately parallel to (010) for one of the twin lamellae. The twin inventory, Table XII, shows that the following twins may be observed. Manebach twins, Ala-A twins, acline-A twins and pericline twins (p.158).

Ad (3a). If it is evident from the general inspection of the plagioclase fragment that the section can be rotated towards the ⊥ a position, apply the following procedure. Because such fragments must show the presence of two sets of twins, which make an angle of not less than 60° with each other, we must select one of these sets to begin with. Bring the composition plane of this set in the direction of the NS axis. Rotate the section about this NS axis until the twinning seam is as narrow and clear as possible. The procedure is much the same as the one described under 2 for the orientation of a cleavage plane (see p.117).

For a good orientation of this composition plane consider the following property of a thin section: the section has a certain thickness. If it is possible to focus alternately on the lower part and on the higher part of the crystal section, then a well-oriented composition plane must show the images of the twinning seam in these two focus positions as coinciding.

As soon as the orientation is achieved, some information on the type of twinning is needed. If both parts of the twin about the composition plane show symmetrical extinction in all the possible rotation directions of the EW axis, the twinning type is normal and the twinning axis is parallel to the EW axis of the universal stage. It suffices to control this at two or three positions of the EW axis; equal birefringence of both parts of the selected twin in the remaining directions is satisfactory proof. For all practical purposes it may be assumed that if a normal twin is found, this twin is of the albite type. The other two possibilities, namely the Manebach or the Baveno twins, seldom occur. The Baveno twin is easily spotted because its trace is oblique (about 45°) to all other directions, and the composition face is (021). This face (021) is seen sharply in the orientation ⊥ a. The Manebach twin with (001) as the composition face, is seen in sections cut parallel to the form (010). Both twins, moreover, are simple twins, i.e., the fragments show only two parts, twinned according to these laws. This is a distinction from the multiple albite twin, which may show a number of lamellae next to one another.

If the presence is also established of another set of twins transverse to the set under study, it may allow for a useful orientation of this plagioclase fragment, irrespective of the nature of the set. The composition plane of this second set of twins is rotated towards the direction of the NS axis of the stage (A1). The composition plane is then turned in the position parallel to the tube axis (NS axis). Now the nature of the twins in this set is determined. If they show symmetrical extinction with respect to this composition plane in all possible positions of the EW axis, it is a set of normal twins. If the set does not show symmetrical extinction, the twins are either parallel or complex twins. The two sets of twins encountered can show the following combination possibilities:

(a) Both sets show normal twins.
(b) One set shows normal twins, the other set shows asymmetrical extinction.
(c) Both sets show asymmetrical extinction.

The case under a is exceptional, because a glance at the twin inventory of Table XII shows that this must be a combination of an albite and a Manebach twin. Manebach twins are not found frequently. The case under b is frequently observed and corresponds to a combination of albite twins with Ala, acline or pericline twins. The other possibility, i.e., a combination of a Manebach with one of the (010) twins, will be less common. The case described under c may point to the presence of Carlsbad twins, together with one of the more seldom twins with (001) as a composition face.

For all practical purposes a set of normal twins, especially when more than two lamellae are seen, may well be assumed to represent albite twins. This assumption may be checked as follows: bring the composition plane of the supposed albite twins in the NS direction (A1), and rotate until this plane is normal to the microscope stage (NS axis). Bring the other set of twins into such a position that the composition plane is normal to the microscope stage, by rotating the EW axis of the universal stage. This position must be more or less normal to the a axis of the albite twin lamellae. Therefore, the albite twin lamellae must show a negative elongation in the 45°

position for *An*-contents below 70%. If the *An*-content is higher they must be approximately in the extinction position for one half of the set; the other half is extinguished in the —45° position. The elongation is positive in these cases (see also p.161). Moreover, albite twins must show three characteristics simultaneously in any orientation of the fragment with the composition plane normal to the EW axis of the universal stage: symmetrical extinction, appreciable birefringence, and negative elongation. Twins with (001) as a composition plane, which are known to occur as multiple twins, never show these properties simultaneously (TOBI, 1961a, p.1485).

Such sets of two systems of twins, transverse to each other, always show a few albite twins. This enables an orientation normal to the *a* axis with (010) parallel to the NS direction. If pericline twins are the (001) twins in such a set, the orientation is only approximately ⊥ *a*. Still, extinction angles in such fragments with respect to (010) can be used for the evaluation of the approximate chemical composition, using the graphs in Fig.33.

A set of Carlsbad twins about (010) offers a second possibility. These twins are characterized by asymmetrical extinction in the position that is approximately ⊥ *a*. Moreover, the two members must show extinction on either side of the trace of the composition plane. If the two parts are in the extinction position at the same side of the composition plane, the twin is an albite–Carlsbad twin (TOBI, 1961a, p.1486). The extinction angles of a Carlsbad twin may be used, together with the graphs in Fig.33, for a determination of the chemical composition.

Ad (3b). If the fragment is cut parallel to (001), the orientation ⊥ *a* cannot be achieved. From the stereogram in Fig.29, it can be seen that such sections are more or less normal to the optical *B* axis for high Ca-contents. If it is possible to rotate the section in the position normal to the optical bisectrix *X*, a bisectrix figure is seen and the chemical composition can again be determined with the method of Fouqué, as in the graph of Fig.31. The advice just given is useful only if the twinned fragment shows albite twins exclusively.

If Carlsbad twins are also present a better method is available. In the section ⊥ *c* Carlsbad twins show equal extinction of the two parts of the twin at the same side of the composition plane; consequently the twin is invisible. Albite–Carlsbad twins behave differently in this section; the two individuals show symmetrical extinction. The orientation ⊥ *c* can be found with Carlsbad twins. It is the orientation at which they are not visible, while the plane (010) is normal to the EW axis of the universal stage. The extinction angle of the fragment in this particular position can be used together with the graphs in Fig.33. The extinction angle is followed to the line marked *section* ⊥ *c*. At the intersection of the solid line of the extinction angle and this line, the chemical composition is read.

From the graphs in Fig.33, it can be seen that the solid lines of the extinction angles are quite close to each other only for calcic plagioclases. Moreover, the solid lines are quite oblique to the *section* ⊥ *c* axis. Consequently accurate determinations are difficult. A better result can be obtained in the way described below. Determine the extinction angle of the two parts of a Carlsbad twin in the specific orientation ⊥ *c*. Take care that the twin is not visible while doing this. Then rotate the section over 20° with the EW axis of the universal stage. Determine the extinction position of the two lamellae again. The two lamellae are now clearly visible and the extinction angles are different. Enter these two values on the graphs in Fig.33, the smallest value following the dashed line, the largest following the solid line. The intersection of the two curves that indicate these two values lies exactly 20° from the line marked *section* ⊥ *c*. Connect this intersection with the value found for the extinction angle in the ⊥ *c* position. The connecting line is normal to the absciss of each graph. The intersection of this connecting line with the absciss indicates the chemical composition.

Ad (3c). If the section is cut parallel to (010) it is impossible to observe both albite twins and Carlsbad twins. The twin inventory of Table XII shows that pericline, acline-A and Ala-A twins may be seen in this section. The only normal twin seen in this section is the rather rare Manebach twin, characterized by the fact that it is a simple twin. As the Manebach twin is considered to be rare, such sections are easily recognized by the sole fact that they show only parallel or complex twins. Assuming that cleavage planes do not occur, it is clear that the chemical composition of plagioclases in this orientation is difficult to measure with the zone method.

For calcic plagioclases the orientation is such that a bisectrix figure can be seen with a cono-

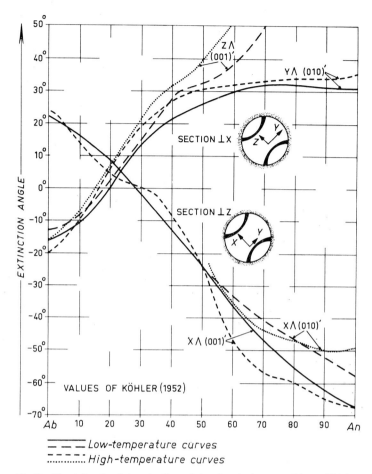

Fig.31. Chart for the determination of the chemical composition of high- and low-temperature plagioclases with conoscopically selected sections. The method has been devised by Fouqué (1894). The chart is from Tröger (1959). (Courtesy Schweizerbart'sche Verlagsbuchhandlung, Stuttgart, Germany.)

scopical observation technique. The method of Fouqué may therefore be of some use. Rotate the section until the cross of the bisectrix figure is exactly in the middle of the field of vision. This position is normal to the optical bisectrix. Measure the extinction angle on (001), the composition plane of acline or Ala twins. The pericline composition plane is not suitable for such measurements. The extinction angle will lead to the chemical composition with the graph of Fouqué, Fig.31.

Fragments that cannot be rotated towards the position necessary for Fouqué's method must be determined by using the Fedorov-Nikitin-Reinhard technique or the joined angle method.

(4) The fragment shows the presence of twins as well as cleavages

The case now under discussion may be assumed to represent the normally encountered situation. Plagioclase show both cleavages and twins in the majority of cases, with the exception of albite (see p.155). After having dealt with the cases in which only cleavages or twins are present, it follows that in the present situation the procedure is a mixture of the techniques mentioned earlier. Moreover, a number of difficulties encountered in sections 2 and 3 can now be solved quite easily.

Once again, three cases may be envisaged:

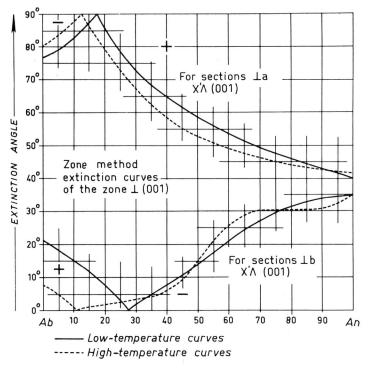

Fig.32. Chart for the determination of the chemical composition of high- and low-temperature plagioclases with sections normal to (001). The chart can be used with the zone method. The chart is from TRÖGER (1959). (Courtesy Schweizerbart'sche Verlagsbuchhandlung, Stuttgart, Germany.)

(a) The fragment is orientated in such a way that at least one, or several, lamellae can be brought into a position where two cleavages and a number of composition planes (010) and (001) are parallel to the tube axis (p.126).

(b) The fragment is cut in such a way that the face (001) is parallel to the cutting plane in at least a few lamellae (p.128).

(c) The fragment is cut in such a way that the face (010) is parallel to the plane of cutting in at least a few lamellae (p.128).

Ad (4a). If one or several twin lamellae of the fragment can be brought into the position known as normal to the a axis, two possibilities exist for the determination of the chemical composition of the fragment. A proper orientation of the section is brought about as described under 2 and 3. After the proper orientation of the fragment, the extinction angle X' ∧ (010) is measured in the twin lamellae that belong to a set of albite twins. Such albite twin lamellae show a number of transverse cleavages in the majority of cases. For the determination of the conventional plus or minus sign of the extinction angle smaller than 15°, see p.119 and Fig.28. Another reliable procedure

Fig.33. Charts for plagioclase determination with the aid of extinction angles X'∧ (010) in sections ⊥ (010) oriented vertically. Solid line: larger extinction angle of Carlsbad twin, also for section ⊥ a and maximum extinction angle. Dashed line: smaller extinction angle of Carlsbad twin, also for section // a.

A. Low-temperature optics. B. High-temperature optics. (Courtesy Dr. A. C. TOBI, 1963, and the *American Journal of Science*.)

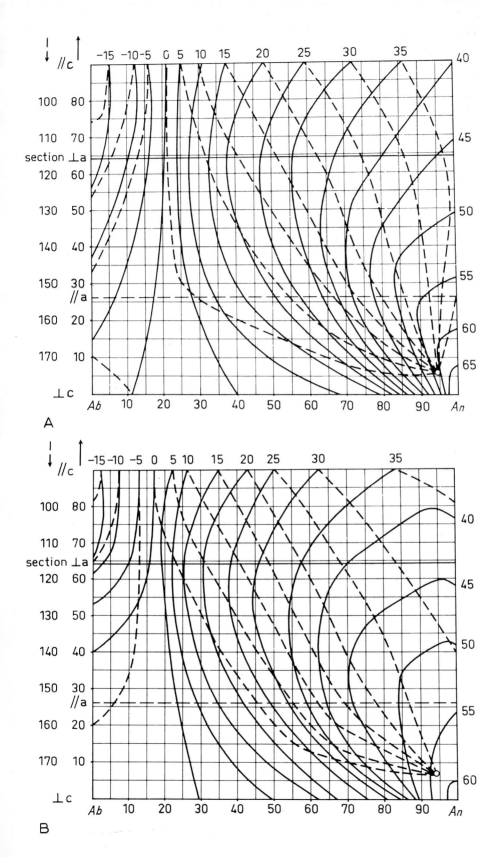

A

B

is the measurement of the extinction angles $X' \wedge$ (010) of a set of Carlsbad twin lamellae. The values obtained with these two techniques can be used, together with the graphs in Fig.33. Moreover, the first method can be checked by the second.

Ad (4b). In case the fragment is cut normal to (010) and parallel to (001), it is always possible to rotate the face (010) in a position normal to the EW axis of the universal stage (A1). We must here add the restriction that a twinned fragment is not cut entirely parallel to (001), due to the various orientations of the twinned parts. The introductory sentence is therefore meant to describe a fragment in which a number of the twinned parts have this specific orientation.

We must first establish that the face observed is indeed (010). If albite twins are present, the symmetrical extinction of the lamellae about the composition plane gives ample proof of this situation. Confusing albite twins with Manebach twins seems unlikely, because the composition plane of the latter is (001). If only parallel twins are observed in the section under consideration, it is rather evident that the cleavage plane observed is (001). If this is the case see paragraph 4c. Another helpful characteristic of the orientation normal to the crystallographic c axis is the following.

In plagioclases a certain section exists in which all the different members of this group of minerals show a straight extinction. The pole of this particular section is more or less parallel to the c axis. For this reason sections normal to the c axis are always rather dark, i.e., they show a rather low birefringence if (010) is parallel to the cross-hair of the eyepiece.

Carlsbad twins may render extinction angles that can be used for the identification of the plagioclase in these sections, although it follows from the graphs in Fig.33, that the extinction angles are rather inefficient in these very sections, a fact already noticed by RITTMANN (1929, p.33). If, however, the Carlsbad twins are rotated about the EW axis for 20°, the procedure on p.124, can be used. As an example we may assume the following case: in a section $\perp$ c the extinction angle of one of the parts of a Carlsbad twin is about —3°, the other about +5°. The section is rotated over 20° with the EW axis. The extinction angles are now +1° and +13°. A combination of these two measurements shows the fragment to have a chemical composition of 45% An.

Ad (4c). If the section is cut in such a way that the plane (010) of some lamellae is parallel to the cutting plane, we are in the situation presented in Fig.30, of sections normal to the b axis. Consequently, twins of the acline-A type, although they belong to the group of parallel twins, show identical extinction. Twins of the Ala-A type, with the twinning axis $\perp$ b in (001), show symmetrical extinction. Rittmann describes a method for measuring the chemical composition of plagioclases in this orientation.

With the EW axis the section is turned in the position where the two parts of a parallel twin show a symmetrical, or identical extinction position. The extinction angle $X' \wedge$ (001) is measured and entered in the graph of TRÖGER (1959, p.111). This graph is given here as Fig.32. Subsequently the chemical composition is determined.

Determination of the structural state

After the procedure just described it may be mentioned that until quite recently it was not quite possible to determine the structural state of plagioclases independently by this method. At present new diagrams for the zone method have been published by TRÖGER (1959), showing both high- and low-temperature curves. In addition, RITTMANN and EL-HINNAWI (1961) have developed a method for the determination of the structural state that is independent of chemical composition. Finally, for plagioclases with an *An*-content smaller than 40%, the axial angle may give information on the structural state (see p.96).

Let us first consider the suggestions made by RITTMANN and EL-HINNAWI

(1961). They began with the fact that the extinction angles of ordered plagioclases differ only slightly from those of disordered plagioclases. It is necessary to carry out more than two measurements on the same grain in order to reveal the course of the extinction curve for that specific fragment. The course of the extinction curve of a low-temperature plagioclase differs from that of a high-temperature plagioclase with exactly the same chemical composition. A comparison of the set of measurements will thus bring out the nature of the structural state.

An example will make this approach clear. Let us assume that a specific plagioclase shows an extinction angle $X' \wedge (010) = 40°$ in a section $\perp a$. If we enter this value in the low-temperature graph (Fig.33A) it is found that the feldspar in question has an An-content of 80%. Now we turn the section by rotating the EW axis of the universal stage over 30°. The extinction angle $X' \wedge (010) = 45°$. Consulting the chart at the 34° level, between the levels marked $\perp a$ and $// a$, the An-content of the section is seen to be approximately 76%. If, however, both values are entered in the graph of high-temperature structures (Fig.33B), the An-content for both cases is seen to be exactly the same, 70%. This result is a clear indication of the presence of a disordered structure, and consequently of a chemical composition of 70% An.

In order to establish the presence of ordered or disordered structures, Rittmann and El-Hinnawi suggested the following procedure.

Sections that can be rotated in the $\perp a$ position are prerequisite. Rotate the section in the position normal to the a axis as described on pp.117 and 121. Determine the extinction angle $X' \wedge (010)$. This extinction angle is designated E. Bring the section in its starting position, $(010) // $ "NS crosshair" of the eyepiece. Incline the section exactly 20° to the right (if still possible) by rotation about the NS axis. Determine the extinction angle $X' \wedge$ tr. (010) for this new position. Record the value, which will be called E'. Turn the stage back to its $(010) //$ "NS cross-hair" and rotate the section back to its starting position $\perp a$. Incline the section exactly 20° to the left (if still possible) and determine the extinction angle $X' \wedge$ tr. (010) in this new position, which will be called E''. Now calculate:

$$\Sigma = E' + E''$$
$$D' = E - E'$$
$$D'' = E - E''$$

Enter these three values in the graphs of Fig.34. The graphs are taken from the work of RITTMANN and EL-HINNAWI (1961). The results obtained with one of the two graphs can be checked by the outcome of the other. The use of the graphs is self-explanatory. As soon as the structural state is revealed, the measurement of the extinction angle E can be found in the high-temperature graph (Fig.33B) in order to determine the chemical composition.

Another possibility for the determination of the structural state of plagioclases is described in the paragraph on axial angles (see p.96 et seq.). It was shown here that the axial angles of plagioclases with a chemical composition of less than 40% An are a good indication of the degree of order of the phase under study. A procedure for such cases follows here.

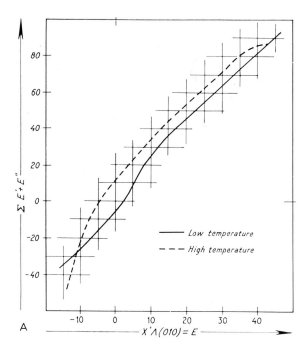

Fig.34. Two charts, A and B, for the determination of the structural state of plagioclases in sections ⊥ *a*. The charts have been devised by RITTMANN and EL-HINNAWI (1961). The use of the charts is explained in detail on p.129.

Determine the chemical composition of the fragment under consideration by one of the methods outlined earlier, assuming that an ordered phase is present. The determination with the low-temperature graphs must be well below 40% An. Then determine the axial angle with the universal stage, making use of a conoscopical technique if possible. As soon as the axial angle is not in accordance with the curve for low-temperature plagioclases (Fig.22), a disordered or partly disordered phase is present. In case such high-temperature plagioclases are found, re-determine the chemical composition making use of the available high-temperature curves. Such curves are given in this text (cf. Fig.31,32 and 33; TRÖGER, 1959).

In summary, the zone method offers numerous possibilities for the determination of the chemical composition of plagioclases, and is considered to be efficient enough for the identification of various plagioclases among detrital minerals in sediments, soils or other mineral aggregates. The reader may have received the impression that the method is complicated because of the number of pages dealing with the procedure. If so, he must realize that in these pages even the rare cases have been treated in detail. The normal case, described under heading *4* (The fragment shows the presence of twins as well as cleavages), is only a small part of this elementary text dealing with the operation of the universal

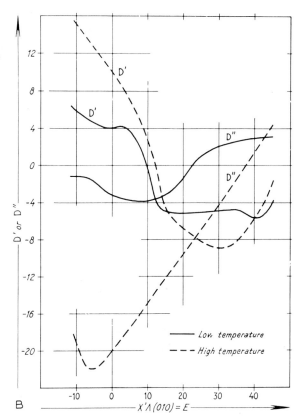

B

stage, the mounting of the thin section, and the identification of the cleavage planes and twins.

Although the method is comparatively easy, it is time consuming. If the investigator wants information on the feldspar composition of his sample, he is in most cases quite willing to measure a small number of crystal fragments. Such a small number, however, may not give sufficient information for drawing valid conclusions. He must be willing to select and measure a larger number of fragments. For special cases it might be useful to go through such an investigation, but in this event another requirement needs to be fulfilled. If the size of the crystal fragments is much smaller than about 50 μ the method is difficult to perform.

We should like to make one more concluding remark dealing with the practical applicability of universal stage measurements. It seems to be a firm belief that the use of a universal stage is a prerogative of academically trained people. This, however, has been proved a fallacy. It is not only possible to teach intelligent analysts without academic training how to perform the more currently used methods of analyzing heavy and light minerals, but they can also be taught successfully how to handle a universal stage.

METHODS REQUIRING A PETROGRAPHIC MICROSCOPE ONLY

It has been stressed on p.107 that the determination of the chemical composition of plagioclases in thin sections with the ordinary microscope is rather difficult. It goes without saying that the same physical properties of these minerals play a role here just as in the evaluation of the chemical composition with the universal stage. The features observed in thin sections are the result of a combination of the same effects.

First, we must consider the projection of the indicatrix axes on the plane of the section. The helicoidal rotation of this indicatrix within the structure of the mineral has been discussed earlier. The amount of rotation depends on the chemical composition and the structural state. Second, the presence of twins may well lead the observer astray (although it furnishes additional information), for parallel twins and normal twins behave in the same way in certain sections.

Consequently, the determination of the chemical composition of plagioclases with the ordinary petrographic microscope presumes the presence of a thorough understanding of all these various influences. With the universal stage the investigator can always try to avoid a difficult situation by rotating the section to another position. If a thin section is viewed with a microscope, the necessary information must be drawn from the available fragments of an unknown number of various plagioclases in a number of given orientations.

With an ordinary petrographic microscope, the only reliable method for the proper identification of detrital plagioclases is based on a selection of fragments with a useful orientation. Other fragments must be passed over. They can be classified on the basis of their relief according to a much coarser scheme.

Methods based on the maximum extinction angle observed in plagioclase fragments with albite twins, cut normal to (010), are useless in the case of detrital plagioclases. Such methods are only successful for plagioclases of igneous and metamorphic rocks as is shown by BALASANYAN (1963), among others. Such methods, advanced by DEER, HOWIE and ZUSSMANN (1963, p.137 and 138) and originally devised by Michel-Lévy in 1896, are not only based on the maximum extinction angle but also on a much more important property, discussed presently. Again, there is the implicit assumption that the mineral assemblage under study represents a system of phases in a state of equilibrium during the physical circumstances governing its genesis. Such assumptions are tacitly made by petrographers of igneous and metamorphic rocks. Clastic rocks do not meet these requirements. It must be realized that any plagioclase fragment observed in a sediment can have another chemical composition. Moreover, phases belonging to more than one structural state may well be present.

Although it certainly is beyond the scope of this text, it must be noted that the genetic circumstances of numerous igneous and metamorphic rocks are not always as simple as would be necessary for the validity of the above assumption.

Lately a number of workers in these areas of petrography have become aware of the fact that zonal structures, armoured relics, metasomatic replacement and crystals that are partly ordered in some domains and disordered in others, play a dominant role in a fair number of specimens of igneous and metamorphic rocks. The evidence clearly points to the presence of metastable phases in the course of transformation. The genetic history of such rocks may well be described as a concatenation of different metamorphic or igneous phases, each characterized by its own physical circumstances. Whether the identification methods based on these implicit assumptions provide reliable information in studying igneous or meta-morphic rocks, is left open for discussion, irrespective of BALASANYAN's (1963) findings.

Such methods, based on the genetic characteristics of a mineral assemblage, are not to be used for the identification of minerals in sediment rocks. Once more we repeat that the investigator must expect his sample to be composed of an unknown number of feldspar phases from an unknown number of unknown rocks. Therefore, the observer of such rocks must rely on selected sections.

A survey of the number of useful sections of a plagioclase fragment shows that quite a few possibilities remain. First of all, the sections normal to the crystallographic a axis, extensively discussed in the procedure of the zone method beginning on p.115, give highly reliable information on the chemical composition. Secondly, sections showing the presence of Carlsbad twins cut normal to (010) enable the use of the graphs in Fig.33. Thirdly, sections in which a bisectrix figure is seen when they are conoscopically observed enable the use of Fouqué's method (see Fig.31). Fourthly, the birefringence of plagioclases in quartz-rich thin sections can be accurately determined with a compensator. These sections provide an opportunity for the determination of their orientation if they are cut normal to a composition or a cleavage plane. Once the orientation is known, the chemical composition can be fairly well estimated with a number of graphs given in this text. Lastly the comparison of the relief of a plagioclase fragment with the refractive index of the immersion medium, or with that of adjacent quartz fragments, leads to a kind of chemical classification. Summarizing, the chemical composition of a large number of the fragments can at the worst be fairly well estimated. In the following sections the various cases will get brief treatment and the reader will find the necessary references.

(1) Sections $\perp$ a

In 1963, Tobi published a paper on plagioclase determination with the aid of extinction angles in sections $\perp$ (010). The section $\perp$ a is one of these. Consequently, a thorough discussion of all the possible difficulties is given in his paper. The charts in Fig.33 that are reproduced from this paper can be used equally well for all the sections of the zone normal to (010), as for the special case under discussion. In this book the recognition of sections $\perp$ a is treated in detail on p.117 and the following pages. Let us therefore consider the most important features only.

(a) The section must show two traces of cleavages or two composition planes of twins, or both. These faces are more or less at right angles (94°).

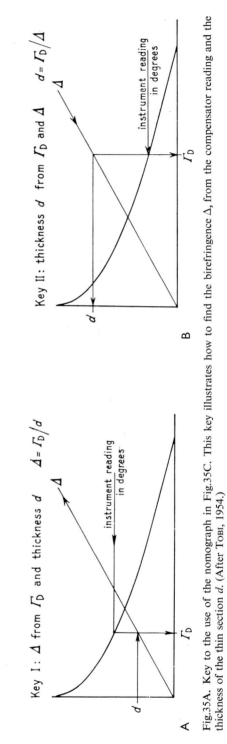

Fig.35A. Key to the use of the nomograph in Fig.35C. This key illustrates how to find the birefringence Δ, from the compensator reading and the thickness of the thin section d. (After Tobi, 1954.)

Fig.35B. Key to the use of the nomograph in Fig.35C. This key illustrates how to find the thickness of the section d, from the compensator reading and the birefringence Δ. (After Tobi, 1954.)

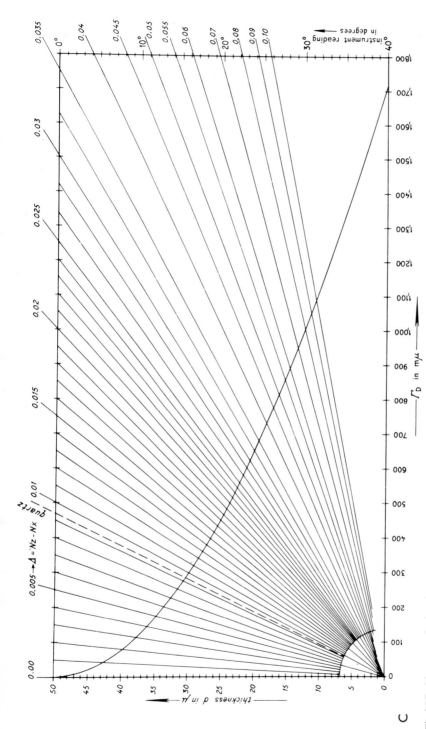

Fig.35C. Nomograph showing the relations between the compensator reading in degrees, the path difference Γ_D, the thickness of the thin section d, and the birefringence Δ. The curve pertains to the Ehringhaus compensator with quartz plates as produced by Carl Zeiss, Oberkochen, Germany. Curves for other compensators should be drawn in according to the specifications given by Tobi (1954).

(b) The plane (010) is characterized by a negative elongation in the 45° position for plagio-clases with an An-content below 70%. For An-contents over 70% the elongation may vary but the extinction angle $X' \wedge$ (010) is rather large.

(c) The extinction angle $X' \wedge$ (010) can be either positive or negative below values of 15°. The sign is conventionally chosen according to Schusters' rule (p.119, Fig.28).

As soon as the extinction angle is determined, the chemical composition is found at the intersection of the horizontal line marked $\underline{|}\ a$ and the solid curve of the corresponding extinction angle in the charts of Fig.33.

(2) Combined albite and Carlsbad twins in sections // (010)

According to TOBI (1963) such sections should fulfil the following requirements:

(a) The elongation of the composition plane (010) must be negative for An-contents below 70%.

(b) When turning the stage, the fragment showing both albite and Carlsbad twins must show at least three different extinction positions of X'.

(c) All twin individuals must show a distinct birefringence for An-contents below 80%.

(d) In order to control the exact position of the section, note the following. If lamellar albite twins are present and the section is exactly normal to (010), the composition plane of both albite and Carlsbad twins, the lamellae of the albite twins must be invisible when the trace of the composition plane is in the 0° or in the 45° position with regard to the direction of the analyser. This does not imply that the composition plane is invisible. The effect is such that the fragment at this orientation looks like a set of lamellar domains, each with the same birefringence, separated by parallel traces of planes, as illustrated in Fig.46B.

(e) The Carlsbad twin is a simple twin. In sections normal to the composition plane (010) the extinction positions of the two lamellae are usually asymmetrical. In the 0° and in the 45° position the lamellae are recognizable as twin lamellae due to the difference in birefringence as shown in Fig.47A. According to Tobi the difference is best observed in the 45° position.

Albite twins aid the investigator in properly recognizing the orientation of the fragment. They have no other function but the information they may give on a slightly tilted position. If the plane (010) is not exactly parallel with the axis of rotation of the stage they will show a slightly asymmetrical extinction of the lamellae. The true extinction angle in these cases can be found by averaging the two values measured. If the tilt is large this method may give wrong results. If in a stock of twins one of the lamellae, or a set of these, shows a position normal to the a axis, the method described in the section before is used. Carlsbad twins may in that case be used as a control.

(3) Sections showing an acute or an obtuse bisectrix figure

In the description of some aspects of the zone method attention has been repeatedly asked for the usefulness of the charts of Fouqué. They are going to be of help again. If a plagioclase fragment is cut in such a way that on conoscopical observation a bisectrix figure is seen, the extinction angle with respect to one visible cleavage or composition plane gives information on the chemical com-position. Four possibilities are to be distinguished, namely in sections $\underline{|}\ X$; $Z' \wedge$ (001) and $Y' \wedge$ (010); in sections $\underline{|}\ Z$; $X' \wedge$ (010) and $X' \wedge$ (001). The curves for these extinction angles run more or less parallel and are not too wide apart for large ranges. A disregard of the structural state may lead to errors that are not larger than about 10% An. A wrong assignment of the index to one of the traces of cleavages or twin seams is also not disastrous. The biggest errors that can occur must be expected in sections $\underline{|}\ X$. The order of magnitude may be as large as 40% An for fragments over An_{50}. These errors can be made, but there is no need to make them. The stereograms in Fig.27, 29 and 30 demonstrate the possible orientations of such sections. With the help of these figures wrong assignments are unnecessary.

For the sake of completeness one more remark will be made, though some readers may rightly find it superfluous. In searching the preparation for fragments that are suitable for the Fouqué method, the following fragments do not need to be checked: (a) fragments that remain dark or rather dark on turning the stage; (b) fragments that show the highest birefringence observed in the section. Only the fragments showing an intermediate birefringence will be possible "can-didates" for the proper orientation. It is self-evident that this remark applies only to thin sections that are neatly made. Concave thin sections or thin sections that are thicker at one side always confront one with difficulties, especially for these types of measurements.

(4) The relation between birefringence and orientation

In another paper TOBI (1961a) treats the relation between the orientation, the chemical composition and the birefringence of a plagioclase on the basis of three charts. These charts are given here as Fig.36B, 37B and 38. Each chart pictures 180° of a zone normal to a crystallographically important plane. The chart in Fig.36B shows the zone ⊥ (010). A comparison will show this chart to be similar to Fig.33A, though it is not folded along the symmetry plane of the Carlsbad twin. Fig.37B shows the behaviour of a plagioclase normal to the plane (001). Fig.38 shows the relationship between the extinction angle, the birefringence and the rhombic section. A similarity of the last two charts is a result of the fact that the rhombic section is more or less parallel with (001). These illustrations afford a clear insight into the optical aspects of a random fragment in a thin section. As soon as such a fragment is normally cut to a plane, whether a cleavage plane or a composition plane of a twin is irrelevant, the next considerations may help to get at the facts about the orientation of the fragment itself.

(a) Cleavage traces are either (010), (001) or, rarely, (021).

(b) Composition planes of twins are: in case of normal twins (010) and (001) or (021), at times; and in case of parallel twins (010) and (001). Other faces are rare, except the so-called rhombic section, the composition plane of pericline twins.

(c) The birefringence of plagioclases is never higher than approximately 0.008. (N.B. The maximum birefringence of quartz is 0.009.)

The birefringence of a particular plagioclase fragment can be accurately measured in thin sections with quartz crystals. If a Berek compensator or an Ehringhaus compensator is at hand one may proceed as given below.

Select a few quartz crystals surrounding the plagioclase fragment. These quartz fragments must show the maximum birefringence and consequently show the well-known "flash figure" on conoscopical observation. The thickness of a section can be calculated from the birefringence and the observed interference colour. The relations between these three properties are the basis of the Michel-Lévy chart known to everyone which deals with optical mineralogy. TOBI (1954) treats the aspects of this measurement in detail and he offers a graphical solution adapted to the Berek compensator. The chart that may be used for such problems has to be constructed by the investigator himself, because of the fact that the Berek compensator produced by Leitz (Wetzlar) has specific instrument constants which differ for any instrument. The chart for the use of the Ehringhaus compensator is principally the same. This chart is given here as Fig.35C. The Ehringhaus compensator produced by Carl Zeiss (Oberkochen) does not have such specific variable instrument constants. The chart reproduced here has been constructed according to the same instructions from Tobi. The use of the chart is self-evident. For the theory of this type of compensation the following papers may be consulted: EHRINGHAUS (1931, 1938, 1939) and BURRI (1953).

As soon as the thickness of the thin section has been established at the sites of the quartz fragments, the values are averaged and this average value is assumed to represent the thickness of the section at the site of the plagioclase fragment. N.B. The use of the instrument is adequately described in the accompanying manual. The same chart can now be used for an accurate measurement of the birefringence of the plagioclase fragment. The interference colour of the plagioclase in its 45° position is measured and the thickness of the fragment is assumed to be the same as that of the quartz fragments. A combination of these two occurrences leads to the birefringence. Together with the known birefringence of the fragment and the information about the visible planes, the approximate orientation of the plagioclase fragment can be found with the three charts in Fig.36B, 37B and 38 and if necessary with the additional help of the stereograms in Fig.27, 29 and 30. Moreover, the three charts just mentioned reveal information about the chemical composition of the plagioclase fragment under consideration.

If a Berek compensator or an Ehringhaus compensator is not available, a quartz wedge may be used in the manner described by WAHLSTROM (1960). A calibrated quartz wedge is preferred in these cases. If such a quartz wedge is not present either, the thickness of the section may be estimated from the interference colour of properly selected quartz fragments with the use of the Michel-Lévy chart reproduced in numerous textbooks. Wahlstrom's book shows such a chart on p.142, fig.11.

Although the various orientations of a plagioclase have been treated in detail in the parts of this book dealing with the zone method, it may be convenient to find them repeated in a concise form.

Sections ⊥ *(010) (Fig.36).* Negative elongation with regard to (010) characterizes this specific orientation of plagioclase fragments with less than 70% An. Calcic members show a central optic axis figure in some cases. Consequently, calcic plagioclases may show a rather small birefringence. In general the birefringence of these sections is appreciable. The aspects of twins in these sections is treated on p.123. Twins may be used for getting at the proper orientation of the section.

Sections ⊥ *(001) (Fig.37).* With regard to (001) these sections show variable elongation. A

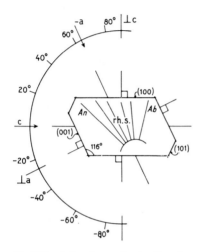

Fig.36A. A key for understanding the construction of Fig.36B. The arc shows part of the zone ⊥ (010) covered by Fig.36B. The twin axes and crystal axes lying in the plane (010) are indicated, as well as the traces of the rhombic section. Courtesy Dr. A. C. Tobi (1961a) and *The American Mineralogist.*

Fig.36B. This diagram shows the extinction angles $X'\Lambda$ (010) and the birefringences of plagio-clases in the zone normal to (010). The optical properties determined by a point in the diagram belong to a section through a plagioclase crystal with a specific chemical composition and a specific orientation. The chemical composition of such a section is given along the abscis, its orientation along the ordinate. Contrary to other diagrams, the orientation of the section is given in two ways. At the left side of the ordinate the orientation of the section is given as in Fig.33; at the right side one finds the direction of the perpendicular of the section, corresponding with the axes in Fig.36A. For instance, for oligoclase (An_{20}) cut ⊥ a, one has to consult the dia-gram at the intersection of the line An_{20} and the line marked *section* ⊥ a at the left side, $-a$ at the right side of the ordinate.

The two members of a normal twin (e.g., an albite twin) occupy one and the same point in the diagram. The sign of the extinction of the other member is found by reversal of sign. The two members of a parallel or a complex twin are represented by two points. These points are symmetrically situated on either side of the horizontal line indicated by the name of the relevant twin law in the right margin. If the name of the twin law is marked with a ⊕, these two points bear the correct sign. If the name is marked with a ⊖, one of the extinction angles should bear an opposite sign. This behaviour is clear after realizing that sections normal to the twinning axis are parallel with the symmetry plane of the twin. The angle of the rhombic section with (001) is indicated in degrees along the line marking this section. The position of the optic B axis is marked in the margin by (B). Courtesy Dr. A. C. Tobi (1961a) and *The American Mineralogist.*

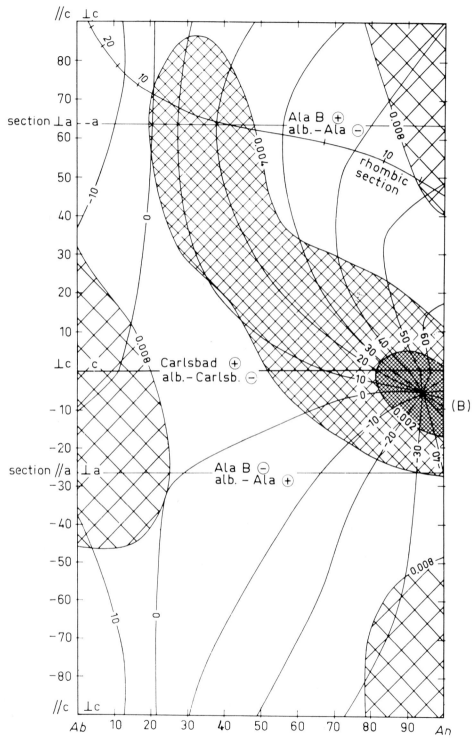

section ⊥a -a

Ala B ⊕
alb.-Ala ⊖

rhombic
section

⊥c c

Carlsbad ⊕
alb.-Carlsb. ⊖

(B)

section //a ⊥a

Ala B ⊖
alb. - Ala ⊕

Ab   10   20   30   40   50   60   70   80   90   An

Fig.36B. Legend see p.138.

large number of sections are expected to show a small birefringence, irrespective of their chemical composition. To understand this behaviour, Fig.37 may be consulted in combination with the stereograms ⊥ *a* and ⊥ *b*, given as Fig.27 and 30.

Sections normal to the rhombic section (Fig.38). These sections, not treated while discussing the zone method, may not be omitted here, because they constitute a useful increase of the number of fragments that can be incorporated in a counting procedure. For the applicability of the zone method such sections can be avoided because better procedures are then easily available.

The following remarkable feature of this specific orientation is mentioned here. One of the optic axes lies in the rhombic section for An_0 and for An_{20}. This particular interval between An_0 and An_{20}, where the optic B axis is near the rhombic section, is indicated as a black line in Fig.38B.

(5) The relief of plagioclase fragments, the Becke line method

If none of the afore-mentioned methods can be used with success, the relief of a plagioclase fragment may well give some information on its chemical composition. If relief is compared with the immersion plastic used to prepare the thin section or the grain mount, one must be careful. The refraction index of these plastics is never equal to that of Canada balsam. It may sound rather con-

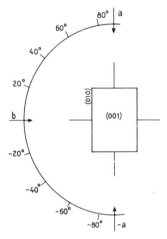

Fig.37A. A key for understanding Fig.37B. The arc shows part of the zone perpendicular to (001) covered by Fig.37B. This section shows the *a* and the *b* axes nearly at right angles. Consequently the perpendiculars of the axes cannot be distinguished from the other axes. Courtesy Dr. A. C. Tobi (1961a) and *The American Mineralogist*.

Fig.37B. This diagram shows the extinction angles $X'\wedge$ (001) and the birefringences of plagioclases in the zone normal to (001). The optical properties determined by a point in the diagram belong to a section through a plagioclase crystal with a specific chemical composition and a specific orientation. The chemical composition of such a section is given along the abscis, its orientation along the ordinate. The direction of the section is given in terms of the direction of the perpendicular of the section, corresponding with Fig.37A. For instance, for oligoclase (An_{20}) cut ⊥ *a*, one has to consult the diagram at the intersection of the line An_{20} and the line marked *a* or −*a*.

The two members of a normal twin (e.g., a Manebach twin) occupy one and the same point in the diagram. The sign of the extinction of the other member is found by reversal of sign. The two members of a parallel or a complex twin are symmetrically situated on either side of the horizontal line indicated by the name of the relevant twin law. If the name of the twin is marked with a ⊕, these two points bear the correct sign. If the name is marked with a ⊖, one of the extinction angles should bear an opposite sign. The position of the optic *A* axis and the optic *B* axis is marked in the margin by (*A*) and (*B*). Courtesy Dr. A. C. Tobi (1961a) and *The American Mineralogist*.

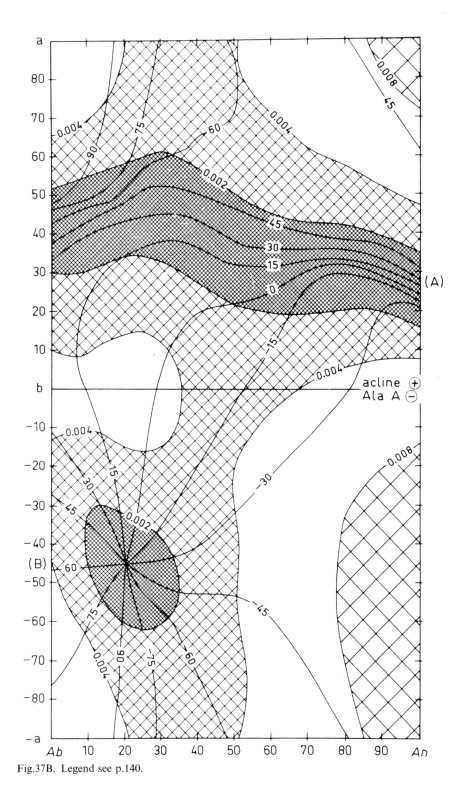

Fig.37B. Legend see p.140.

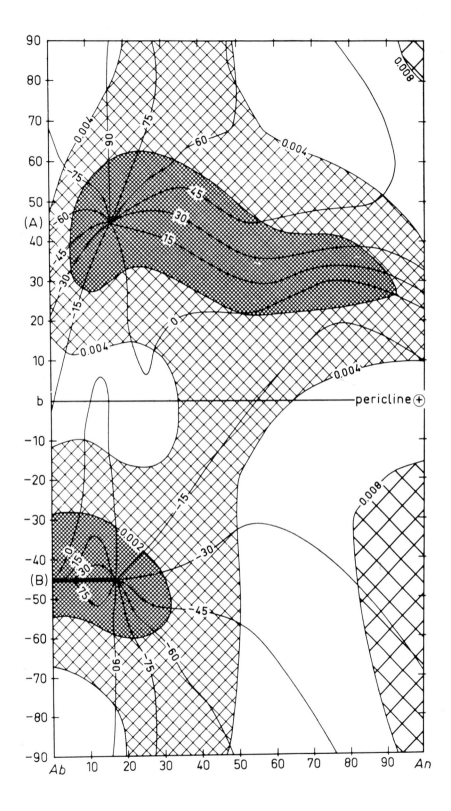

servative, but in my opinion there is no proper substitute for the "good old Canada balsam" with regard to its properties for distinguishing between plagioclase and alkali feldspar. Experience with Lakeside thermoplastic cement, with Vestopal and with Araldite taught that these are easier to handle and give better results, especially in impregnation of friable samples. But they are an outright nuisance in feldspar-identification work. For this reason sections used for petrofabric work, for a general description, and for studying the properties of minerals other than feldspars, are preferably made with one of these new cements. Samples especially prepared for feldspar studies are, if possible, made with Canada balsam. In case this is impossible they may be stained with cobaltinitrite before covering (cf. p.51).

If Canada balsam is used and it has received the proper treatment, its refraction index is about 1.534–1.540. A glance at the values in Table VIII shows that this is the range covered by the refractive indices of albite. Feldspars showing lower indices of refraction than the index of Canada balsam, therefore, are alkali feldspars. If all the visible indices are greater than that of the balsam, the plagioclase is frequently as calcic as an acid andesine.

If the plagioclase fragment is in touch with quartz, and the quartz fragment happens to be thus orientated that the Ne of quartz is parallel with the X of plagioclase, there the maximum index of quartz, being 1.55, enables us to tell whether the plagioclase is a calcic andesine or an acid andesine. If both refractive indices are similar and X plagioclase is parallel with e quartz the plagioclase is a calcic andesine. If Y plagioclase is parallel with e quartz the mineral is an acid andesine. Labradorite at least is present if the relief of the plagioclase is more than that of e quartz.

The maximum refractive index observed in a muscovite, namely 1.59, is about the same as the maximum index of anorthite. The lowest refraction index of calcite on the cleavage is about 1.56. This value may also be useful in rough estimates. It approximates the X of acid bytownite, the Y of labradorite and the Z of calcic andesine.

CONCLUSIONS

The chemical composition of plagioclases in thin sections of sediments, in grain mounts or in thin sections made of concentrates of minerals can be fairly well approximated. Provided they have the proper orientation, a number of fragments give highly accurate results. These orientations are $\perp a$, normal to the bisectrix figure or normal to (010) and they show Carlsbad twins. Others can be classified with such names as acid andesine or calcic oligoclases because a combination of birefringence and extinction angle on a specific plane allows for a rough approximation of the orientation. Sections of plagioclase fragments that do not meet the above requirements regarding their orientation still give some information on comparing the relief of the plagioclase fragment with that of the surrounding minerals or with the embedding medium.

Fig.38. The zone normal to the "rhombic section" of low-temperature plagioclases. This diagram shows the extinction angles $X'\Lambda$ "rhombic section" and the birefringences in the zone normal to the "rhombic section". The optical properties determined by a point in the diagram belong to a section through a plagioclase crystal with a specific chemical composition and a specific orientation. The chemical composition of such a section is given along the abscis, its orientation along the ordinate. The direction indicated by b along the ordinate refers to the perpendicular on the section. Consequently this section is cut $\perp b$.

The two members of a pericline twin are symmetrically situated on either side of the horizontal line indicated by "pericline $\oplus$". The points bear the correct signs of the extinction. The position of the optic A axis and the optic B axis is marked in the diagram by (A) and (B). Note the line at (B) discussed on p.140. Courtesy Dr. A. C. Tobi (1961a) and *The American Mineralogist*.

Chapter 9

TWINNING OF FELDSPARS

INTRODUCTION

It has been known for a long time that minerals of the feldspar group are often twinned. Even as early as 1807, Von Goethe wrote about twinning of the "rhombic feldspars" in the neighbourhood of Karlsbad. In a description of the mineralogical collection of Joseph Müller, Von Goethe mentions these typical twins as follows:

"Denn es gibt grosse Massen des Karlsbader Granits, worin man vollkommene Krystalle, und zwar von sehr complicirter Bildung antrifft. Es sind Doppelkrystalle, welche aus zwei in und über einander greifenden Krystallen zu bestehen scheinen, ohne dasz mann jedoch den einen ohne den andern einzeln denken könnte ... Kennen wir sie nun in ihrer einfachen Doppelgestalt, so finden wir sie auch miteinander auf vielfache Weise verbunden. Theils ist Tafel auf Tafel aufgewachsen, theils sind mehrere unregelmäszig zusammen gehäuft. Manchmal sind zwei solcher Doppelkrystalle in Kreuzform innig vereint."

Before considering the causes and the significance of twins, it does not seem superfluous to define the concept of twinning as used in crystallography and mineralogy. For this description we shall use BUERGER's definition (1945): "*a twin is a rational symmetrical intergrowth of the individual crystals of the same species*".

The intergrowth is rational because one of the two crystals may be assumed to represent a repetition of the other, brought about by some geometrical operation. This geometrical operation conforms to the requirements of a symmetry operation. The description of the specific aspects of such a geometrical operation is called a *twinning law*. For example, one may describe the so-called albite law as a rotation of one part of the crystal about the pole on the face (010). The pole on (010) is referred to as the *twin axis*, the face (010) is called the *composition plane*. The composition plane and the twin axis determine the twinning law.

Feldspar crystals have a number of important planes. Consequently one may expect a number of different twinning laws to occur. Before entering into a description of the various twinning laws it must first be clear that a classification of twins can be made on more than one basis.

CLASSIFICATION OF FELDSPAR TWINS

One may classify twins according to the aspects of the twinning laws, for example,

TABLE XII[1]

SELECTED LAWS OF FELDSPAR TWINNING

Composition plane	Normal twinning	Parallel twinning		Complex twinning (*Kantennormalen Gesetz*)	
		axis	*law*	*axis*	*law*
(010)	*albite* (often lamellar)	*a*	Ala-B	$\perp$ *a* in (010)	albite–Ala (albite–Esterel)
		c	*Carlsbad A*	$\perp$ *c* in (010)	*albite–Carlsbad* (Roc-Tourné)
(001)	Manebach (Four la Brouque)	*a*	Ala-A (Esterel)	$\perp$ *a* in (001)	= acline A
		b	acline A	$\perp$ *b* in (001)	= Ala-A (Scopi, Manebach–pericline, Manebach–acline A)
//b ~ (001) rhombic section		*b*	*pericline* (often lamellar)		
(100)	(X law)	*b*		$\perp$ *b* in (100)	X-pericline Carlsbad B cf., Burri (1962)
		c	Carlsbad B cf., Tobi (1961)	$\perp$ *c* in (100)	X-Carlsbad acline B
(021) (0$\bar{2}$1)	Baveno right Baveno left				
(110) (1$\bar{1}$0)	prism right prism left				

[1] Twinning laws in italics are very common, others are rather rare. The table was made up after consulting similar tables in BEREK (1924), WINCHELL and WINCHELL (1951), TOBI (1961a), BURRI (1962), and DEER, HOWIE and ZUSSMANN (1963).

according to the combinatory possibilities of planes and axes. One may also classify twins according to the genetical causes that have brought them about, or according to some morphological aspects of the twinning stock. In the following treatise it becomes evident that the three classifications just described all have attractive properties. For this reason they will be successively considered.

In order to understand the geometrical properties of the various twinning types, a classification according to the combinatory properties of planes and axes is most useful. The most important twinning axes and composition planes of feldspar twins are schematically given in Table XII. There are three categories:

twinning with an axis normal to a composition plane is called *normal twinning*; twinning with an axis parallel to a crystallographic axis is called *parallel twinning*; a third type of twinning can be visualized to be brought about by a combination of the earlier described "operations" and is therefore called *complex twinning*[1]. The latter may also be described as caused by the rotation about the axis, which is normal to a crystallographic axis and lies in the composition plane.

The twinning modes occurring in feldspars have long been known, but the identity of the investigator who first recognized and described a large number of these twinning types, with a full understanding of the laws that governed their structural and morphological properties, was until quite recently unknown. Professor Conrad Burri of Zürich brought the name of this intelligent petrographer and mineralogist in the limelight again. Gustav Eduard Kayser correctly described the twin laws known now, with a few exceptions, only 27 years after Von Goethe had written about the Carlsbad twins. In a paper issued in 1962, Burri reviews Kayser's thesis of 1834. In this chapter on twins we simply feel obliged to pay tribute to Kayser who, with rather limited technical means, so scholarly brought about the twinning laws of plagioclases, approximately 100 years before the importance of feldspar twins was fully recognized.

The list in Table XII is much shorter than the combined possibilities of the three important composition faces (010), (001) and (100), the three axes normal to these faces and the crystallographic axes *a*, *b* and *c*. The explanation is rather simple. Some twinning laws occur more often than others and a few hypothetical combinations do not seem to occur in nature. A few of the unlisted combinations have indeed been described from natural feldspars. For a more complete inventory of feldspar twins the reader is requested to consult a paper by BURRI (1962b). The list in Table XII also mentions the names of the twinning laws. These are in most cases named after the locality or after the mineral in which they are most frequently found.

Without giving a complete description of all the twin laws listed in Table XII, the following laws command special attention because they occur frequently: the albite law, a normal law with (010) as composition plane; the Manebach law, a normal law with (001) as composition plane; the Baveno law, a normal law with (021) as composition plane (the left and right laws, caused by aspects of the triclinic

---

[1] HARTMAN (1956) introduces a few arguments against the use of the term *complex twinning* in a paper about the morphology of growth twins. He re-introduced the term *Kantennormalengesetz* for the description of such twins. This term used by BEREK (1924), among others, is descriptive in mentioning the fact that the twin axis lies in the composition plane (hkl) and is normal to the edge, the "Kante", [uvw]. If these twins are described in such a way, the description accounts for the fact that the structure of the mineral that may form such twins needs to be centrosymmetrical.

The concept "complex twinning" does not take this restriction into account and may even cause confusion. If the need for an English term is felt instead of a German one, we may consider the term *antiparallel twinning*.

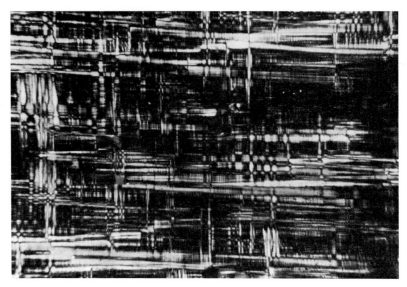

Fig.39. Twinning of microcline. Thin section no.1162, sample no.WR 693 II A, locality: Mitchell Mine, Va., U.S.A. Ocular 8×, objective 10×, crossed polarizers.

structure will be considered later in this chapter); the Carlsbad law, a parallel law with (010) as composition plane and an axis coinciding with the c axis; the pericline law, with a specific non-crystallonomic plane that contains the b axis and intersects (010), as composition plane, the axis is b; the albite–Carlsbad law, a complex law with (010) as composition plane and an axis normal to the c axis in (010) as twin axis.

A classification of twins according to some special morphological characteristics has attractive properties. Feldspars show in some cases lamellar sets of twins. These sets of twins—the property is called by different names, lamellar twinning, multiple twinning or polysynthetic twinning—are a special characteristic of plagioclases.

Alkali feldspars, especially microcline and "anorthoclase" sometimes show a cross grating of two twinning laws. This typical twinning pattern, illustrated in Fig.39, is rather indicative of microcline or, to be more precise, of triclinic alkali feldspars. It may function as an identification mark. Feldspars which show only two twin members are said to show "simple twins". Simple twins are an indication of the presence of one of a limited number of twinning laws. Manebach and Baveno twins are mostly simple twins. In this description the following classification more or less came about: (1) multiple twins, a characteristic of plagioclases; (2) cross grating twinning, a characteristic of triclinic alkali feldspars; (3) simple twinning, indicating the presence of one of a limited number of twinning types. This classification is not as strict as the first one, given in Table XII. It may even lead the investigator astray. The reason for this possible confusion is the fact that lamellar multiple twins, for example, though a characteristic of plagioclases, can also be observed in adularia (see Fig.40). Therefore, the exceptions to the "rule" are given here in detail.

The absence of the special "microcline twinning" in alkali feldspars is no proof for the absence of a triclinic phase (see Fig.41). A large number of authors, a.o., NABHOLZ (1945), GYSIN (1948), DOLAR MANTUANI (1952) and MARFUNIN (1961, p.100; table I, no.44 and 45), describe triclinic alkali feldspars without the typical cross grating twinning.

The absence of lamellar twinning is no proof that the feldspar in question is not an albite, or a plagioclase. Especially albites in greenschist facies rocks are untwinned. On the other hand, the presence of lamellar twins has also been noticed in alkali feldspars (BAMBAUER and LAVES, 1960). Such a set of parallel adularia twins occurring in an adularia from Vals, Graubünden, Switzerland is shown in Fig.40.

THE OCCURRENCE OF FELDSPAR TWINS

The occurrence of twins has a genetical cause. BUERGER (1945), in a paper on the genesis of twins, brings forward three genetical types. These types may function as the basis for the following genetical classification.

(1) Growth twins; these are caused by an accidental departure from equilibrium during growth of the crystals.

Fig.40. Lamellar twins in adularia. Thin section E 37, locality: Boden, Vals Platz, Graubünden, Switzerland. Ocular 8×, objective 2.5×, crossed polarizers.

Supersaturation seems to favour the inception of growth twins.

(2) Glide twins; these twins are caused by a specific type of shear in the course of plastic deformation of rocks (see Fig.42).

(3) Transformation twins; the origin of transformation twins is a consequence of the transformation of a high-temperature towards a low-temperature structure, hence the term transformation. In this special case the low-temperature phase should have a symmetry which is a subgroup of the symmetry of the high-temperature form.

There are sufficient indications for the assumption that the genesis of an igneous or metamorphic rock influences the assemblage of twinning types observed in the feldspars of these rocks. One of the most striking features is the frequent occurrence of Manebach and Baveno twins in igneous rocks, twins that are virtually absent in low-grade metamorphites. Therefore, the assemblage of twinning types of the feldspars in a sediment may give important information about the provenance of these sediments or of parts of these sediments. The presence of glide twins in sediments that are not tectonically influenced is ample proof for the assumption that the feldspars showing these twins derive from tectonites.

In order to take complete advantage of this knowledge the sedimentologist should be able to recognize the various types of twins. Moreover, he should possess further detailed knowledge about the frequency of certain twins in various groups of rocks. For these reasons the following paragraphs treat the aspect of twinning separately for alkali feldspars and for plagioclases; a discussion of twin recognition is given at the conclusion of this chapter.

Alkali feldspars

It is noteworthy that the typical microcline twinning, a combination of the albite law and the pericline law, occurs only in triclinic phases of alkali feldspars. Another particular characteristic of these microcline twins, or M-twins (a term borrowed from Smith and MacKenzie), is the fact that the composition plane of the albite member (010) is perpendicular to the twin axis of the pericline twin, being [010]. If the reader will consider the unit cell parameters of a triclinic alkali feldspar, given on p.29, he will soon realize that something is wrong with these microcline twins. In a triclinic alkali feldspar the *b* axis, being the same as [010] is not normal to (010)! This discovery was made by LAVES in 1950. He pointed out that a twinned microcline must have inherited this typical crystallographic property from a monoclinic phase. Hence the conclusion that the M-twinning is a transformation twinning caused by the alteration of a disordered alkali feldspar into an ordered phase, or in other words of a monoclinic alkali feldspar into a microcline. The twin is caused by the adjustment of the triclinic phase to the space and structure occupied by the original monoclinic crystal. Recently MARFUNIN (1962b, p.305) introduced two cases in which it is clear from observational evidence

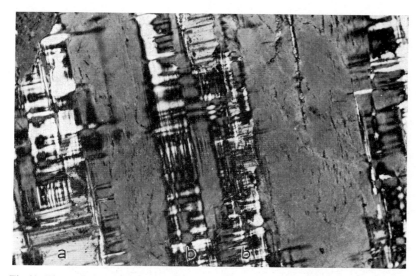

Fig.41. Photomicrograph of a coarse microcline perthite. The plagioclase phase, showing albite twinning is seen at *a*. The twinned microcline (*b*) is seen, among others, bordering the plagioclase domains. The gray zones in between these twinned domains consist of untwinned microcline. Thin section no.1164, sample no.WR 694, locality: Rutherford Pegmatite, Amelia district, Va., U.S.A. Ocular 8×, objective 10×, crossed polarizers.

that this ordering occurs in the solid state and that ordering does not occur if the initial formation temperature is too low.

In addition to this typical transformation twinning a number of other twinning types are observed in alkali feldspars. The Carlsbad twins described by Von Goethe are a common feature of alkali feldspars. Baveno twins (see Fig.43), are less frequently observed. The same may be said of Manebach twins. It is necessary to mention that the twinning laws observed in monoclinic phases may result in two different laws for the triclinic phases, a so-called left and right law, see Table XII. For example, the Baveno twin with composition plane (021) resolves in Baveno right with (021) and Baveno left with (0$\bar{2}$1) for triclinic alkali feldspars or plagioclases.

The record of the frequency of twinning types in a suite of feldspars from one type of igneous or metamorphic rocks may give information about the genesis of these rocks and may be considered to represent a characteristic property of such a rock type. Such a record of the quartz monzonites from near Beaverdell, B.C., Canada has been given by DOLAR MANTUANI (1952). Carlsbad and Manebach twins especially occur alongside microcline twins in the alkali feldspars of these rocks. The twinning record of a quartz latite sill from Texas has been given by INGERSON (1952). The frequency of untwinned feldspars in this igneous body is four to five times greater than that of the twinned crystals. Carlsbad twins are more frequent than Manebach or Baveno twins. It seems that microcline twins in the low-grade metamorphic rocks of the greenschist facies frequently show

Fig.42. Glide twins in plagioclase. The twins are albite twins. The plagioclase crystals occur in a gabbro. Thin section no.38, locality: unknown. Ocular $8\times$, objective $10\times$, crossed polarizers.

Fig.43. A Baveno twin in alkali feldspar. The numerous inclusions parallel to an important crystallographic direction mark the oblique character of the composition plane (021). Left: one polarizer, right: crossed polarizers. Thin section no.1180, sample no.WR 713 A, locality: Baveno, Italy. Ocular $10\times$, objective $10\times$.

albite, pericline and acline twins. The presence of Carlsbad twins, Manebach twins and Baveno twins points to an igneous origin. It must be kept in mind that the twinning pattern present in igneous rocks does not change much after metamorphism under greenschist facies conditions. A number of ortho-gneisses may well show the twinning pattern of the original igneous rock, as can be seen by studying the alkali feldspars of a number of gneisses from the Alpine regions of Switzerland.

One last remark about the meaning of microcline twins. DOLAR MANTUANI (1952) has shown that the absence or presence of microcline twins in triclinic alkali feldspars is not an indication of the temperature of formation, as has been suggested by some authors. Authigenic feldspars surrounding older detrital twinned microcline fragments clearly show a twinning pattern also.

From the foregoing it follows that the presence of certain twins in alkali-feldspar fragments of sediments or soils may be of importance in determining the provenance of such fragments. One limitation must be realized. The particle size of the feldspar fragments may be a reason for the obliteration of any trace of Baveno or Manebach twins. The twinned crystals of the original rock may have been rather large, whereas the average size of the fragments in the sand is small. This means that one may never draw conclusions based on negative evidence. The feldspars from a sand may well show themselves to be disordered but the presence of Carlsbad, Manebach or Baveno twins cannot be ascertained. If these sands originated as a result of the erosion of a rather coarse granite one can readily imagine that the chances of finding one of these twins is rather small, because precisely these three twin types are, generally, simple twins.

Plagioclase feldspars

The most common type of twinning observed in the group of plagioclase feldspars is the simple or polysynthetic albite twin (cf. Fig.44 and 45). This twin is so common that its absence may even lead the observer astray, as was shown by NABHOLZ (1945, p.28). Besides these albite twins all the twinning types listed in Table XII can be found in plagioclases, with the exception of the prism law.

Pericline twins have a specific useful property. The composition plane of these twins is a non-crystallonomic plane that contains the *b* axis and intersects (010). The intersection line is normal to the *b* axis. This irrational composition plane has a variable orientation with respect to the rational planes. The angle between this plane and (001) is always used as a reference. The orientation depends on the chemical composition and on the temperature of formation. A rather old identification method determines the chemical composition of plagioclases in sections ⊥ (010) by measuring the angle between pericline lamellae and the trace of (001) (see TRÖGER, 1959, p.98). LAVES and SCHNEIDER (1956) found that notable exceptions exist in this relation. It has been suggested that during an alteration of the plagioclase in the solid state, the position of the pericline composition plane

Fig.44. A simple albite twin in albite (*An₇*). The rock is a phengite gneiss produced by greenschist facies metamorphism. Thin section no.LP 152, sample no.LP 152, locality: Section DD, Vals Platz, Graubünden, Switzerland. Ocular $8\times$, objective $10\times$, crossed polarizers. (For further information see VAN DER PLAS, 1959.)

does not change. The orientation of the pericline twins, therefore, may give an indication of an alteration of a plagioclase after the genesis of these twins. The alteration may be either of a chemical or structural character. The observations of Laves and Schneider were confirmed by J. V. SMITH in 1958. This author gave a short treatment of the genetic aspects of twinning during the Oslo Feldspar Symposium of 1962.

The relation between twin type in plagioclase and rock genesis has been studied by a large number of authors. The most important contribution to a solution of this problem may well be ascribed to the Japanese petrographer GORAI (1950a, b, 1951). He classifies the possible twins in two groups, the group of lamellar twins, the A-twins and the other twinning types, the C-twins. The frequency of A- and C-twins in specific types of rocks, igneous or metamorphic, is plotted in a so-called UAC triangle; the symbol U stands for "Untwinned". The outcome shows that igneous rocks are characterized by an appreciable amount of C-twins. Moreover, the number of C-twins is governed by the *An*-content of the plagioclases. Calcium-rich plagioclases have a relatively high number of C-twins. Gorai's results meet with criticism; this criticism is not directed against the principal idea, but tries instead to refine the given tool. Such critical papers have been written by TOBI (1961, 1962), who argues that it would be advisable not to disregard the importance of the composition plane. According to Tobi the twins with (010) as composition plane are far more frequent than other twins. He concludes that in contact-metamorphic rocks the relative amount of twins is smaller than in igneous rocks. The frequency of (010)-twins in both types of rocks is about the same. Metamorphic rocks in the greenschist facies are characterized by the presence of a large number of untwinned crystals. Simple twins (cf. Fig.44) are more frequent in these greenschist facies rocks, and twins with a composition face other than (010) are "rigorously" absent. The rocks of the almandite–amphibolite facies have a large amount of the acline and pericline twins. In concluding Tobi proposes to distinguish the (010)-twin ratio next to Gorai's A- and C-twins.

In addition to these studies on the relation of twin type and rock genesis, others have studied the width of albite twins (DONNAY, 1940), the significance of polysynthetic twinning (EMMONS and GATES, 1943) and the difference between primary twinning and twinning brought about by stress (VANCE, 1961). Vance's conclusions about the origin of glide twins is somehow at variance with the ideas of LAVES (1952b). Vance ascribes the origin of glide twins to the deformation of rocks. Laves argues that the origin of twins in low albite needs a reorganization of the Si and Al in the structure. This rearrangement of Si and Al is known to be a rather slow process even under hydrothermal circumstances, whereas the origin of twins in high albite is a comparatively easy process.

This review on plagioclase twins is far from complete. Only the most important features have been touched upon. For the readers of this text the presence of a specific distribution of twin laws in plagioclase fragments from a specific sediment sample may give important information on provenance as witnessed by the results of MITZUTANI (1959) and PITTMAN (1962).

Fig.45. Typical lamellar albite twins in albite. Thin section no.1177, sample no.WR 700, locality: Rutherford Pegmatite, Amelia district, Va., U.S.A. Ocular 10×, objective 4×, crossed polarizers.

THE IDENTIFICATION OF FELDSPAR TWINS

The identification of the twinning laws observed in feldspars is rather difficult in a number of cases if a petrographic microscope is the only available instrument. With the universal stage, twin identification is reduced to a set of not too difficult operations.

In this text the properties of feldspars have been consistently treated separately for alkali feldspars and for plagioclases. The alkali feldspars were always treated first. In the case of twin identification it is practical to reverse this order. Plagioclase twins have received much more interest in the course of time than twins of alkali feldspars. Consequently, the general aspects of twin identification can be more clearly illustrated with the plagioclases as an example. Afterwards the methods can be modified for the identification of twins in alkali feldspars.

Plagioclase twins

For the identification of the twinning types in plagioclases we can rely for a large part on a paper recently written by TOBI (1961b). In this paper the author goes to great lengths in giving even the elementary aspects of the study of plagioclase twins. It is perhaps advisable to follow this text closely in the following treatise. A few of the elementary aspects in studying the properties of a twinned plagioclase have been treated previously in Chapter 8 (p.121 et seq.).

The identification of the twinning law starts from sections normal to the composition plane. The composition plane must have its proper label. Subsequently it must be established whether or not the twin belongs to the category of normal twins or to the other two categories, parallel twins or complex twins. Finally, one must conclude to which type of twinning law the twin under study belongs.

The information that can be drawn from a section normal to the composition plane is rather limited. We can determine the birefringence of the two members of a twin and the extinction position of the two. These properties are the result of the following three causes: (*1*) the optical orientation of the particular plagioclase, resulting from its chemical composition and structural state; (*2*) the twinning law; (*3*) the orientation of the section.

If the thin section is mounted on a universal stage, the fragment under investigation can be given a useful orientation. If an ordinary microscope is used, the sections with a useful orientation have to be selected from the available feldspars[1] in the thin section. Studying twins in grain mounts is to be discouraged,

---

[1] In this text it has been repeatedly stressed that for studying feldspars from sediments and soil a good concentration technique is a necessity. Investigators who have to rely on a petrographic microscope only for a study of twin-assemblages will grasp at once the attractive aspects of such a concentration technique. A mount will contain many more feldspars with a useful orientation if it is made of the feldspar fraction only.

because grain mounts do not have a uniform grain thickness and the interference colours of the grains are rather high.

Methods for the orientation of thin sections with a universal stage have been treated in detail in Chapter 8. The selection of fragments with a useful orientation from a thin section with the ordinary microscope starts from the same criteria. The trace of the composition plane should be seen as a sharp line and may not wobble when the tube of the instrument is moved slightly upwards and downwards. In addition, Tobi advises against the use of irregular composition planes.

The difference between symmetrical extinction and asymmetrical extinction is also treated in the former chapter. The most important features will be repeated here:

(1) symmetrical extinction; the member of a twin show equal illumination in the $0°$ and $45°$ position if the section is normal to the composition plane;

(2) asymmetrical extinction; the members of a twin show in at least one of either the $0°$ or the $45°$ position a different illumination in sections normal to the composition plane.

The determination of the extinction angle is a well-known operation. Still, it may be said that *reliable* measurements are obtained if the measurements are repeated a few times and the results averaged. Tobi mentions the importance of the sign of an extinction angle. In the meantime he argues that whatever the sign may be, it is reversed by turning the thin section upside down. For this reason he introduces a much more practical convention. If the signs of the two extinctions of a twin are compared they are either on the same side of the composition plane or on opposite sides. The convention says:

(1) if both members are considered and the angles are measured from the trace of the composition plane in *the same direction of rotation*, the signs of the extinctions are said to *agree*, i.e., they are either positive or negative depending on the absolute convention one prefers;

(2) if both angles of the members of a twin are measured from the trace of the composition plane in *opposite directions of rotation*, the signs of the extinction angles are said to be *opposite*, i.e., one of the signs is negative, the other is positive[1].

Another practical hint that can be found in the paper under discussion is the use of the gypsum plate in twin identification. If the twin is in the zero position, i.e., if the trace of the composition plane coincides with the direction of the NS cross hair of the eye piece, twin members showing symmetrical extinction will always show different colours with the gypsum plate inserted. This may be useful preliminary information about a fragment showing a composite set of twins.

---

[1] In sections ⊥ a, the Schusters convention, as pictured in Fig.28, and described on p.119, has nothing to do with this relative convention. In these sections the sign of the extinction angle can be determined in an absolute way, which does not change after the section has been turned upside down.

Recognition of the composition planes (010), (001) and the rhombic section in plagioclase fragments in thin sections has been discussed in Chapter 8. The most important characteristics will be concisely repeated for the sake of convenience.

Sections normal to (010). For an *An*-content less than 70%, these plagioclases show negative elongation and appreciable birefringence. For an explanation of these rules see p.119 et seq. and Fig.36.

Sections normal to (001). For *An*-contents up to about 50%, the sections may either show a negative or a positive elongation. Plagioclases cut normal to (001) show in most cases a small birefringence. They may even remain dark in these sections on turning the stage. For an explanation of these rules see p.121 et seq. and Fig.37.

Sections normal to the rhombic section. There is no simple rule for the identification of the rhombic section. Applicable rules depend on the chemical composition and the structural state of the crystal.

In Chapter 8 (p.140) the properties of this section are described in a concise manner. The properties discussed in this section follow from a study of Fig.38.

Sections normal to the a axis. Much has already been said on sections normal to the *a* axis. For a summary of the properties of this section turn to p.133.

As soon as the composition plane has its proper label, the identification of the twinning type can be established in a number of steps. These steps are described as follows. In order to obtain a more or less schematical treatment, the sections normal to the composition plane will first be treated, the sections normal to the *a* axis will be discussed later.

Twins in sections normal to the composition plane; normal twins

If a twin shows a symmetrical extinction of its members we may assume the probable presence of a normal twin. On the universal stage this can be easily controlled by rotating the fragment about the EW axis and determining the presence of symmetrical extinction in a few positions. With the ordinary petrographic microscope we can expect to observe a parallel or a complex twin, although the two members of the twin show a symmetrical extinction. The specific orientation pertinent to this problem is indicated in Fig.36, 37 and 38. In this respect the rules for "extraordinary extinctions" of parallel and complex twins given on p.159, command interest.

The three important laws of normal twins are the albite, the Manebach and the Baveno laws. The three are easily distinguished from one another. The albite law is characterized by its composition plane (010), by the general presence of lamellar twins and by a rather appreciable birefringence. Baveno twins are easily recognized by the special property of the composition plane (021). This plane is oblique to all the other features of the fragment. The Manebach twin may give rise to problems, although it is a twin with (001) as composition plane and in most cases developed as a simple twin. It may, under certain circumstances, get mixed up with a simple acline twin.

Twins in sections normal to the composition plane; parallel and complex twins
The ability to distinguish between the other twins not yet mentioned in sections normal to the composition plane is rather difficult if only a petrographic microscope is available. With the universal stage it is possible to study the same twin in more than one section normal to the composition plane by turning the EW axis of the stage. An attempt can be made to rotate until one of the "extraordinary sections" is brought in the position normal to the tube axis. The "extraordinary sections" of a twin are those sections in which both members of the twin display equal extinction or in which the members show a symmetrical extinction. From these orientations information can be obtained on the twinning axis; then the twinning type is determined. In the following example the details for such an operation are given. The characteristics of the two "extraordinary positions" are:

(*1*) sections *parallel to the twin axis*, perpendicular to the composition plane and to the symmetry plane of the twin show *symmetrical* extinction of the members of the twin;

(*2*) sections *normal to the twin axis*, coinciding with the symmetry plane, show *equal extinction* of the members of the twin at the same side of the composition plane.

Example
The sections normal and parallel to the twin axis are clearly marked on Fig.36, 37 and 38. In order to illustrate the use of these graphs let us take an Ala-B twin in plagioclase of 60% *An* as an example. The symmetry plane of the Ala-B twin is a plane normal to the twinning axis *a* (see Table XII). This plane is marked on Fig.36B, with the symbols ⊥ *a* and Ala-B⊖, along the ordinate. The intersections of the extinction curves with the line indicating this plane mark the extinction angles of one of the twin members in the section normal to the symmetry plane. According to the above rule *1*, the twin shows symmetrical extinction in this specific orientation. The extinction angle of the other twin member is therefore found by a reversal of the sign. It has the same numerical value. The necessity of a reversal of the sign, or the extinction angles being opposite as defined on p.157, is indicated by the ⊖ sign.

Let us now assume that the section is not normal to the symmetry plane. It follows from the construction of the graphs, described partly in TOBI (1963), partly in TOBI (1961b), that the extinction angles of the two members of the twin are found on horizontal lines situated at equal distances on either side of the line marking the position of the symmetry plane.

For this example we assume now that the section is normal to the *c* axis. One of the twin members has an extinction of about 8°, the other of about 17°. The signs of the extinctions of the two members are equal.

Consider the situation as pictured in Fig.36B. One of the twin members has an extinction angle as found on the line marked *c*, because the orientation of the fragment is given in this figure according to the rule: *the directions along the ordinate are the directions normal to the section whose optical properties are found on the absciss at that site.* The chemical composition of the fragment is fixed at 60% *An.* The extinction angle of one of the twin members is now found at the intersection of the line marked *c* and the ordinate of 60% *An.* If one wants to find the exact value of approximately 8° one can turn to the low-temperature graph given as Fig.33A. This graph is essentially similar to the graph in Fig.36B. This is easily understood as soon as the graph (Fig.33A) is unfolded along the ⊥ *c* line in such a way that the "square" holding the dashed lines is put below the "square" holding the solid lines. The solid lines in the top "square" are the prolongation of the dashed lines in the "square" below. The line marked *c* in Fig.36B is the same as the line marked ⊥ *c* in Fig.33A. The extinction angle of one of the members of the twin is therefore found at the intersection of the 60% *An* ordinate and the ⊥ *c* line in Fig.33A; its numerical value is 8°.

The extinction angle of the other member of the same Ala-B twin is found on a line parallel with the abscis and equally far from the line marked Ala-B$\ominus$ as the line marked c in Fig.36B, but in the opposite direction. The intersection of this line with the 60% *An* ordinate is found somewhere between the —50° and the —60° lines. The extinction angle is seen to be larger than 15° at least. The exact value can again be found in Fig.33A. The symmetry plane of the Ala-B twin in this figure coincides with the dashed line marked $//$ a. The twin members are found again at equal distances from this line. The intersection of the line, found as far away from the $//$ a line as the line marked $\perp$ c, with the 60% *An* ordinate is situated near the 50° absciss. The extinction angle (dashed line) is seen to be 17°.

The symmetry plane of a specific twinning law is marked with a $\ominus$ sign in Fig.36B, 37B and 38. The intersections of the extinction curves with this line give the extinction angle of one of the twin members in a section *normal* to the symmetry plane. The sign of the other twin member is *reversed*. Hence they show symmetrical extinction.

The plane marked with a $\oplus$ sign indicates the plane parallel with the twinning axis. The intersections of the extinction curves with this line give the extinction angle of one of the twin members in a section *normal* to the twinning axis. The signs of the twin members agree. Consequently, both twin members show equal extinction at the same side of the composition plane.

A characteristic feature of some twinning types is their lamellar character. The most important lamellar twins are the albite, the acline and the pericline twins (see Tobi, 1961). Albite twins are rather easy to distinguish because they always display the following properties: (*1*) appreciable birefringence, (*2*) negative elongation (the composition plane is (010)), (*3*) symmetrical extinction (normal twin), (*4*) a lamellar set of twins (not always present).

Tobi argues that these properties are never simultaneously present in acline or pericline twins. The reasons for this statement can be found in Fig.37 and 38.

With an ordinary microscope it is rather difficult to distinguish between acline and pericline twins. Only in sections $\perp$ b (the twinning axis of both types of twins) the distinction can be easily made. These sections show (001) cleavages and the rhombic section simultaneously. The fact that the trace of (001) is also visible without crossed polarizers may function as an identification mark of (001). The rhombic section is always rather vague.

With an ordinary petrographic microscope the distinctions between the other types of twins not yet mentioned in sections normal to the composition plane is intelligent guesswork in most cases. Fig.36 and 37 will be of some help.

Twins in sections normal to the a axis

For the identification of twins in sections $\perp$ a, Tobi (1961) gives the following possibilities.

(*1*) The composition plane of the twins is (010);

(*a*) the extinction is symmetrical;   albite twin

(*b*) the extinction angles are different and on   Carlsbad twin

either side of the composition plane, only one member
of the twin is $\perp a$;

    (*c*) the extinction angles are different and on the   albite–Carlsbad twin
same side of the composition plane, only one member
of the twin is $\perp a$.

    (*2*) The composition plane of the twins is (001);

    (*a*) the extinction of the members of the twins is   Manebach twin
symmetrical, the twin is a simple twin;

    (*b*) the extinction of the members of the twin is   pericline twin
symmetrical, the composition plane is rather vague,
while (001) is distinctly normal to the section, the twin
is lamellar;

    (*c*) the composition plane of the twins is (001),   acline twin
the extinction of the members of the twin is not symmetrical and the twin is lamellar;

    (*d*) although Ala twins have (001) as a compo-
sition plane they are not visible in these sections $\perp a$,
because the twinning axis is *a*. Consequently, they show
equal extinction.

    In order to illustrate the customary considerations in twin identification,
three figures are included. These figures show a plagioclase crystal with a number
of twins in a few extinction positions. They will be discussed below.

Fig.46 shows a set of twin lamellae in a plagioclase crystal. They occurred
in a trachyte from Kadersberg, Eifel, Germany. It has high-temperature optics.

The figure shows the fragment in four positions. The arrow is parallel with the NS cross-hair of
the eyepiece. The fragment shows a left and a right part, the left part consisting of a set of lamellar
twins, the right part is not twinned.
    The left part. This part has a comparatively high birefringence in the position B. It shows
two sets of cleavages more or less at right angles. In the position B the lamellar twins are not visible.
The presence of the two sets of traces of cleavage planes leads to the conclusion that this part is
cut $\perp a$. Upon turning the stage to the left, a set of lamellar twins is seen in the extinction position,
marked A. After turning the stage to the right, the other set of lamellar twins is seen in the extinction position D. The extinction angle is 27° in both cases. Turning the stage further to the right
(not shown), the left part again shows a high birefringence and the lamellae are invisible once more.
Insert the first-order-red compensator; the whole left part turns yellow. *Conclusion:* The lamellar
set of twins shows symmetrical extinction; the composition plane is (010). Hence it is a set of
lamellar albite twins. The *An*-content (see Fig.33B) is about 40%.
    The right part. In the position B, this part has a low birefringence; it shows one set of cleavage
traces only and it clearly stands out against the left part. The extinction position is shown in position
C. The extinction angle is 12°. *Conclusion:* This part forms a Carlsbad twin with the lamellae which
are in the extinction position at position A; it forms an albite–Carlsbad twin with the lamellae
which are in the extinction position at position C. The reasons for this conclusion are enumerated
in the above sections *1b* and *1c*. The two extinction angles 27° and 12° give an *An*-content of
approximately 40% with the chart of Fig.33B.

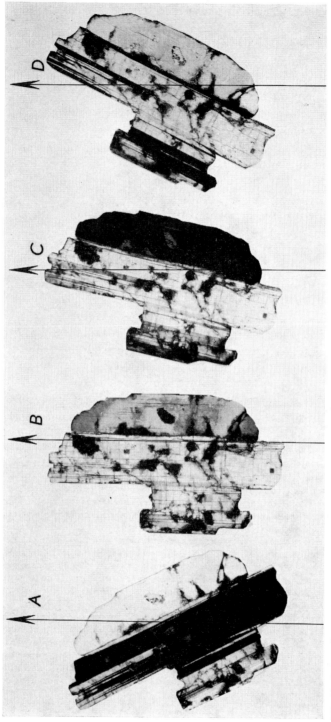

Fig.46. A set of twin lamellae in a plagioclase, An_{40}. The crystal occurred in a trachyte from Kadersberg, Eifel, Germany. For a discussion of the twinning pattern see p.161. Thin section and sample no.24. Ocular 8 ×, objective 2.5 ×, crossed polarizers.

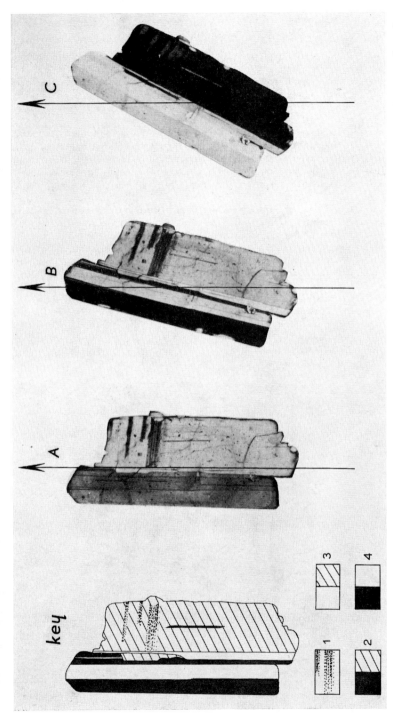

Fig.47. A set of twin lamellae in plagioclase An_{41-54}. The crystal occurred in a dacite from S. Télen, East Borneo, Indonesia. For a discussion of the twinning pattern see p.164. Thin section no.1263, sample no.93, collection Van der Kaaden. Ocular 8×, objective 2.5×, crossed polarizers. *1* = acline or pericline lamellae; *2* = albite–Carlsbad twins; *3* = Carlsbad twins; *4* = albite twins.

Fig.47 shows a set of plagioclase twins in a phenocryst. This sample has been described by VAN DER KAADEN (1951, p.80) and put at the disposal of the present author by the Geological Institute of the State University, Utrecht, The Netherlands.

The figure shows the fragment in three positions. The arrow is parallel with the NS cross-hair of the eyepiece. The fragment shows a left and a right part. The left part consisting of a set of lamellar twins parallel with the arrow and the right part showing two sets of twins approximately at right angles. A key explains the various aspects of the twinning laws.

The left part. This part has a comparatively low birefringence in the position A. It shows a set of cleavage traces parallel with the arrow. Upon turning the stage to the left and to the right, this part shows a set of lamellar twins with symmetrical extinctions. One of the extinction positions is shown at position B. In the 45° position this part is yellow after inserting the first-order-red compensator. Conclusion: The visible cleavage traces belong to (010). The set of lamellar twins follows the albite law.

The right part. This part has a comparatively high birefringence in the position A. It shows only one set of cleavage traces (010). Upon turning the stage to the right this part is seen in the extinction position at position C. The extinction angle is about twice as large as that of the left part. Moreover, in the position marked B a set of lamellar twins is seen at right angles to (010). The composition plane of this set is approximately parallel with (001). Conclusion: The right part forms a Carlsbad twin with the adjacent lamella of the left part, according to composition plane (010) and asymmetrical extinction, the extinction positions being opposite. With the other lamellae it forms an albite–Carlsbad twin; the extinction positions agree. The transverse twin lamellae form a set of either pericline twins or acline twins. Their proper nature is hard to tell in this particular case. The rhombic section of plagioclases, with about 40% An, coincides with (001).

The mineral given in Fig.48 is pure albite from the rather famous Rutherford

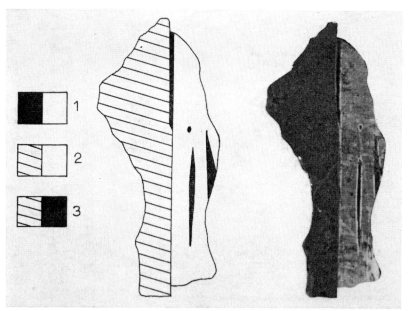

Fig.48. A typical Carlsbad twin in Amelia albite, with an albite–Carlsbad wedge. For further explanation see p.165. Thin section no.1174, sample no.WR 697, locality: Rutherford Pegmatite, Amelia district, Va., U.S.A. Ocular 8×, objective 2.5×, crossed polarizers. *1* = albite twin; *2* = Carlsbad twin; *3* = albite–Carlsbad twin.

Fig.49. A sample of albite crystals, showing the typical Clevelandite habit. This habit of albite is platy parallel to (010). The twinning that occurs in these plates is shown in Fig.48. Contact Carlsbad twins and albite twins are frequently observed. Sample no.WR 697; × 0.25.

pegmatite, Amelia district, Va., U.S.A. The hand-specimen consists of platy albite crystals with the typical Clevelandite habit, it is given in Fig.49.

The figure shows one extinction position only. The key explains the relations between the lamellae in terms of twin laws. The birefringence of the three parts is clearly different. The composition plane is (010). The laws that can be determined are the albite law, the Carlsbad law, and the albite–Carlsbad law. The wedge shaped lamella between the two parts of the crystal is especially characteristic to albite–Carlsbad twins. TOBI (1961a) showed, among others, that such wedge shaped albite–Carlsbad twins play an important role in the albite crystals of some metamorphic rocks.

Alkali-feldspar twins

The identification of twins in alkali feldspars is less complicated than that of plagioclase twins, because the labelling of the composition planes is easier. The indicatrix of the alkali feldspars does not rotate as much as the indicatrix of plagioclases with varying chemical composition. Furthermore, there is not very much difference between the indicatrix orientation of the monoclinic and the triclinic phases. The remaining procedures are similar to those described in the former paragraph.

The identification of twins in alkali feldspars begins with sections normal to the composition plane. The planes must be named and the twinning law must be established. Again we have to restrict ourselves to selected fragments; otherwise the thin section must be mounted on the universal stage. The rules for mounting and orienting the section are given in a former paragraph and in Chapter 8.

For the identification of the composition planes, the following general considerations are sufficient. The optical Z axis is parallel, or more or less parallel, to b. The optical X axis is always approximately parallel to the crystallographic a axis. There is an exception to this rule; the high sanidine, with a reversed axial plane, has $Y = b$. Although high sanidines are rare, they are a nuisance for sedimentologists, because these investigators have to work on fragments of crystals that are separated from the original rock. A petrographer of igneous or metamorphic rocks knows from the type of rock under study if high sanidines are to be expected. If one has only a crystal fragment without such a genetical label, a distinction between adularia, "orthoclase", low sanidine or high sanidine with optical methods is rather difficult, if at all possible. With X-ray powder methods, the distinction between these four phases is also either impossible or rather difficult. Fortunately, these high sanidines, or "reversed adularia", showing the same indicatrix orientation, are rather rare. The investigator, who assumes that his samples do not contain these phases, does not take a great risk of forming incorrect conclusions.

Beginning with the assumption that alkali feldspar have the orientation $Z = b$, the following criteria may be used for the identification of the composition planes.

(1) *Sections normal to (010)*. These sections always show negative elongation. The same, however, is true for sections showing (001) if they are more or less $\perp b$. Therefore, one may consider the fact that the sections normal to (010) must show an appreciable birefringence because $Y \approx c$. Upon conoscopical observation, sections normal to (010) show a flash figure or a central axis figure, but never a central axis.

(2) *Sections normal to (001)*. These sections show either negative or positive elongation. They show positive elongation in the same positions that a central axis may show on conoscopical observation. The sections are characterized by low birefringence or they even remain dark on turning the stage.

(3) *Sections normal to the a axis*. Sections normal to the a axis show two sets of cleavage planes more or less at right angles. The (010) cleavage trace in these sections shows negative elongation.

(4) *Sections normal to the a axis or normal to the c axis in monoclinic alkali feldspars*. These sections show straight extinction.

The identification of twins in alkali feldspars occurs in much the same way as in plagioclases. Normal twins show symmetrical extinction in sections normal to the composition plane. Because lamellar twins are exceptional in alkali feldspars, the properties of such twinning laws as the albite, acline or pericline twin, have to be determined without the help of these morphological characteristics.

Parallel twins, frequently observed in alkali feldspars, seem to be the Carlsbad and the pericline laws. They are easily distinguished by their composition planes. Little is known about the occurrence and identification of other twins in alkali feldspars. Graphs such as the ones Tobi constructed for plagioclases do not yet exist for alkali feldspars. Still, the identification of twins in these minerals can be made on the basis of the experience with plagioclase twins. If, under certain circumstances, a twin law cannot easily be found, it suffices to measure with the universal stage the position of both indicatrices with respect to the composition plane to find the twinning axis.

In summarizing the aspects of twin identification, it must once again be stressed that the universal stage gives better results. In a chapter on the use of the universal stage and its application on the *zone* method, it has been stated frequently that a universal stage is not a complicated instrument. On the contrary, modern universal stages are easily mounted and adjusted, and easy to operate. A sedimentologist, still trying to collect the necessary information with the ordinary petrographic microscope, is not only wasting his time but also denying himself the advantages of a powerful instrument, not to mention the pleasure of simply handling such an elegant tool. The more one thinks about it, the more one wonders why so many sedimentologists still adhere to the more difficult and less efficient methods developed for the use of a petrographic microscope without the available accessories.

In conclusion, the reader who would like to do more work on twin identification is advised to read the paper by TOBI (1961b).

Chapter 10

THE X-RAY POWDER PATTERNS OF FELDSPARS

INTRODUCTION

In this chapter it is assumed that the principles of X-ray analysis are known. A large number of excellent handbooks on X-ray analysis of single crystals and of polycrystalline materials exist. For this reason it is thought superfluous to deal with fundamental aspects of the different methods in current usage.

To enable the analyst to determine the various crystalline phases present in samples from soils or sediments, the methods generally advocated are those that inform him simultaneously about the nature as well as about the proportion of the different crystalline phases present in the sample. Feldspar fractions from soils or sediments are in most cases composed of a variety of crystalline phases "from an unknown number of unknown rocks". For this special purpose X-ray powder methods seem to be more efficient than single crystal methods. Still, it is imaginable that in a few cases it is interesting from a scientific point of view to identify one of the phases by single crystal methods. Afterwards the proportion of such a phase can be estimated by powder methods.

The results of the work of Taylor (1933) are of fundamental importance for the interpretation of X-ray diffraction patterns of feldspar phases. Taylor succeeded in proving the pseudocubic Schiebold-feldspar-structure-model to be at variance with a number of properties of the diffractogram of sanidine. The alternative structure model proposed instead is up until now successfully used in explaining the wealth of experimental results (see Chapter 2). A number of modifications have been suggested to meet the requirements of modern experimental results. This, however, does not distract from the importance of Taylor's suggestions. Taylor's feldspar model gave crystallographers, mineralogists and petrographers one of the most important tools for the achievement of progress in feldspar research during the last two decennia. In fact, so much information has been gathered in the last 20 years by the joint efforts of the three groups of workers just mentioned, that only a proper selection, classification and presentation of these results make them accessible to others not too familiar with feldspars.

The following is an attempt at such a presentation. The characteristic properties of the samples generally studied by pedologists and by sedimentologists are a first premise for a selection. The information these specialists look for in their samples may furnish further criteria for a presentation. For these reasons the results obtained by X-ray powder diffraction methods will be stressed.

As the structures of the various definite feldspar phases are more or less comparable and the unit-cell parameters of these phases show but small deviations from one another, it is to be expected that the X-ray powder patterns of these substances appear more or less similar. Consequently, a number of diffraction lines lie rather close to each other. Analytical results of practical value, therefore, can only be expected if well calibrated instruments with high resolving power are used, see Fig.50. An additional difficulty is formed by the fact that feldspars are in general rather transparent for X-rays, leading to long exposure times.

X-RAY POWDER METHODS

In this paragraph only those X-ray powder methods will be treated that have been preferred by the larger number of research workers because of good performance. The requirements earlier outlined limit the number of X-ray methods that can successfully be applied. These preferences and limitations will be given here.

The Debye-Scherrer arrangement

The principal features of the Debye-Scherrer arrangement are given below.

(*1*) The recording of diffraction effects is performed along a circle with the rod-shaped powder sample as its centre. Thus the diffracted rays striking the equator of recording, whether a film or a travelling counter, do so at normal incidence and travel the same distance from specimen to site of recording.

(*2*) The X-rays are always collimated in order to produce a narrow cone or ribbon of rays to fall symmetrically on the rod-shaped powder sample. The beam of X-rays hitting the specimen has a width not less than the specimen diameter.

(*3*) The X-rays used must be monochromatic.

Debye-Scherrer cameras must have a large diameter and a narrow collimating system in order to have high resolving power. Collimating systems need to be rather long, in order to produce a beam of X-rays with small divergence. The recording speed of the Debye-Scherrer arrangement is roughly proportional to the third power of the camera radius when the ratio of the aperture size of the collimating system to the radius of the camera is kept constant. Combining this with the information that feldspars are rather transparant for X-rays, one may conclude that the Debye-Scherrer arrangement is not the most suitable for recording powder diffraction patterns of feldspar samples. The truth of this statement is illustrated in Fig.50. This figure shows an X-ray powder pattern of Bucarischuna albite taken with an extremely accurate Debye-Scherrer camera (a so-called

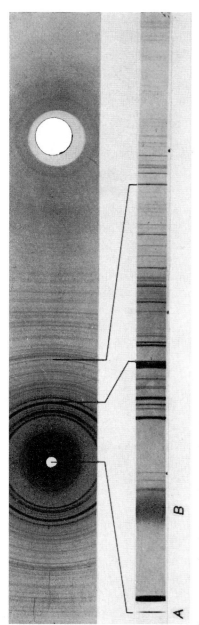

Fig.50. Comparison between a Debye-Scherrer photograph and a photographic powder pattern with a Guinier-De Wolff camera. The pattern shown is a low albite pattern of Bucarischuna albite. Top pattern: camera ∅ 55.3 mm, Co radiation, Fe filter, exposure time $2\frac{1}{2}$ h, 30 kV, 10 mA. Bottom pattern: Guinier-De Wolff camera, Co radiation, exposure time $2\frac{1}{2}$ h, 30 kV, 10 mA. The sample in the top photograph was filled in a Keesom capillary of 0.3 mm external ∅. At A the base line of the camera, at B the diffuse band caused by the grease used in sample preparation. Natural size.

Favejee camera, filled with H_2 gas and a Keesom capillary with known radius to hold the sample; cf. FAVEJEE, 1939), in comparison to the same pattern produced by a quadruple Guinier-De Wolff camera. The exposure time and the tube power were the same in both cases. Still in some cases Debye-Scherrer photographs are preferred above other powder diffractograms, see Chapter 11, p.272.

Focussing arrangements

The principal features of focussing arrangements are:

(*1*) The arrangement in space of the focus of the X-ray tube, the specimen and the recording device, whether a film or a counter, is such that the specimen uses the maximum available amount of X-rays. The diverging beam of monochromatic X-rays leaving the X-ray tube is in some way forced to become a converging beam of diffracted rays.

(*2*) The effect of focussing, i.e., the change from a diverging to a converging beam, is arrived at either by a special device such as a curved and ground crystal, or by a special arrangement of the X-ray tube-focus, the specimen and the recording device. In the last case the specimen is given a special shape as a rule.

The use of a crystal has additional advantages; such crystals diffract true monochromatic X-rays. The disturbing effect of $K\beta$ rays is thus entirely avoided. Two disadvantages of crystal monochromation are only of theoretical significance. In practical work they have never caused any problems. In the first place the high resolving power of the arrangement causes a splitting up of the $K\alpha_1$ and the $K\alpha_2$ diffraction lines in the region of larger values of ϑ. Secondly, it seems that harmonic rays of wavelength $\frac{1}{2}\lambda$ may be produced especially by quartz and LiF monochromators (see GOODYEAR and DUFFIN, 1964).

Two types of focussing arrangements will be discussed, because they are currently used in feldspar investigations.

The Bragg-Brentano para-focussing arrangement

This type of focussing arrangement, normally encountered in counter diffractometers is called a para-focussing arrangement by Arndt in PEISER et al. (1960), because it is a modification of a true-focussing system designed by Seeman and Bohlin. It combines the advantages of a more simple construction and a more simple specimen shape, with a rather good approximation of the geometrical requirements of a true focussing arrangement in the region of not-too-small scattering angles (cf. Arndt in PEISER et al., 1960, p.220).

A disadvantage of the counter diffractometers for the determination of tiny fractions of feldspars (e.g., isolated with a needle from stained samples of a sediment) is the fact that the diffractometer needs comparatively large amounts of sample. Moreover, the samples must be prepared in such a way that no preferred orientation occurs. This is rather difficult with feldspars because of the well-pronounced (010) and (001) cleavage. Finally, feldspars must be powdered to an extremely small grain size in order to give reproducible intensities with a diffractometer.

Traces of a counter diffractometer are hardly surveyable, especially because of the fact that in feldspar work rather large parts of the pattern are needed for a complete analysis of a sample composed of more than one phase. Such patterns are at least less surveyable than a powder photograph of about 17 cm, giving the largest part of the pattern. Finally, the accurate recording of a large portion of the diffractogram with a counter diffractometer is as time-consuming as the total recording of the diffractogram with a camera. This is especially the case with the quadruple Guinier-De Wolff camera recording 4 Co-patterns in $2\frac{1}{2}$ h, this being one diffractogram in 38 min.

The Guinier-De Wolff focussing system

This system, which generally uses film as a recording device, is equipped with a crystal monochromator, thus combining both the advantages of a focussing system and crystal monochromation. The crystal applied is a quartz plate, cut at an angle of 4.5° with (101) and bent ingeniously in order to approximate a logarithmic spiral. The details of a camera taking four photographs at the same time, based on these focussing principles, have been described by DE WOLFF (1948, 1950). The camera is made by the Nonius factory, Delft, The Netherlands. Recently, a number of radical improvements have been made which, as far as I know, are not yet published. These improvements provide the operator with the necessary means for more rapid and better adjustments of the monochromator and the camera. Investigators acquainted with the old type will find these improvements highly satisfactory. A skilled operator can now adjust the camera within 1 or 2 days; it is clear that the camera is not everyman's friend. The camera should preferably be handled by one person. Only then high resolution, short exposure times and a minimum diaphragm are reached. It goes without saying that the apparatus is not suitable for a combined task, such as instruction for students and research. In this case two cameras are necessary because the instrument is rather easily dis-arranged and readjustment is time-consuming. On the other hand, a well-adjusted camera can be used for months at a stretch without the need of a slight readjust-ment. After this tirade the reader may feel inclined to leave it at that and use another camera or a diffractometer. To this reader I wish to say that whatever the case may be, the Guinier-De Wolff camera is the most powerful tool ever given to investigators faced with a routine analysis of feldspars, and much more powerful than any other instrument available at present. The newest instrument is shown in Fig.51.

LAVES (1954) and GOLDSMITH and LAVES (1961) used the Nonius quadruple Guinier-De Wolff camera in feldspar research. The camera is known to be used by a large number of workers in this field of mineralogy and the newest type is,

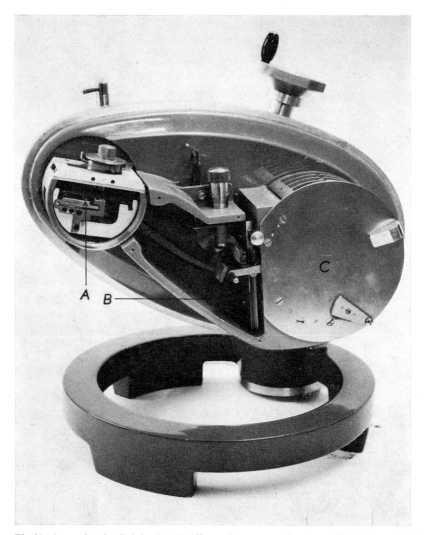

Fig.51. A quadruple Guinier-De Wolff powder camera for use with horizontal and vertical X-ray tubes. The present illustration shows the camera in its vertical position. At *A* the quartz monochromator without its covering lid. *B* points to the quadruple sample holder. The film holder (not shown) fits the frame with four slits shown at *C*. The motor moving the sample holder is fixed behind the camera base. Courtesy N.V. Nederlandsche Instrumentenfabriek "Nonius", Delft, The Netherlands.

among others, one of the important tools in the Mineralogical Department of the Earth Science Institute of the Wageningen Agricultural University.

Calibration

One of the disadvantages of focussing arrangement is the rather difficult calibration and the recording of the true intensity ratio of the diffraction lines. To illustrate the difficulties of calibrating a counter diffractometer we may point to the remarks by J. V. Smith (1956) on the calibration of Donnay and Donnay (1952). In most commercially-made counter diffractometers calibration is done by the manufacturer. A standard specimen enables a control or a correction. For highly accurate work this calibration is not satisfactory and other methods have to be used. In most cases the admixture of a pure crystalline substance in a known proportion will suffice.

Using film as a recording device, one is faced with a choice between a careful calibration of the camera and the fitting of calibration marks in the camera to be simultaneously recorded with the diffraction pattern, or the admixture of a standard substance. This problem is even more important if one wishes to make quantitative estimates of the chemical composition of feldspar samples or if one wishes to estimate the obliquity of microclines. With the Nonius quadruple Guinier-De Wolff camera one has the advantage of four diffraction patterns at the same time. One of these may be the standard substance. Substances used in connection with feldspar work are ammonium allun or precipitated lead or silver nitrate. A calibration method for this camera has been described by Fisher (1956).

Comments on the type of target of the X-ray tube

Investigators using powder methods seem to prefer the copper tube, judging from the number of papers reporting the use of a copper target. A large number of these investigators, however, seem to use an X-ray diffractometer both for rapid qualitative information and for the necessary highly reliable quantitative information. In those cases the reason for using a copper target is quite clear. The older diffractometers generally give a better performance with copper tubes than with any other type of target.

One of the main difficulties with the copper tube is the exciting of fluorescent radiation on iron-bearing samples. With a modern diffractometer this difficulty can be overcome. Presently the electronic circuits of diffractometers are equipped with a discrimination unit and with special counters. The combination of these two items enables the operator to "filter" the fluorescent radiation.

If one prefers to use a camera for qualitative work and for a part of the quantitative work, as the author does, the use of a copper tube is a nuisance with a large number of samples because of these fluorescent rays. The samples must be de-ironed to result in clean photographs. A number of investigations, however, have to be performed on samples that did not receive any treatment before the X-ray analysis. In those cases another target has to be used.

In order to avoid all these difficulties and to be free to choose either the diffractometer or one of the available cameras for an analysis of even iron-bearing samples, an increasing number of investigators is changing from copper to cobalt radiation. Apart from avoiding iron fluorescence, cobalt radiation has other advantages. Its longer wave length gives better resolution.

The longer exposure time may constitute a disadvantage. Using a Guinier-De Wolff camera hardly constitutes a difference in exposure time, because this camera produces one pattern in about 38 min with cobalt radiation and one pattern in about 25 min with copper radiation. X-ray diffractometers, provided they are well-adjusted, give good performance with cobalt radiation. This statement, as we experienced, does not hold for every type of modern equipment now on the market. It holds true only for apparatus equipped with a cobalt tube, with a line focus and mica-beryllium windows, with a well-stabilized generator, a proportional counter probe and a pulse-height analysis unit. In our laboratory we have had good experience with apparatus produced by Philips.

The shape of the target is also important in camera work. It goes without saying that a point focus should be used with Debye-Scherrer cameras. We operate the Guinier-De Wolff camera with a line focus with excellent results.

Comments on sample preparation

For the general aspects of sample preparation for X-ray analysis we must refer to the numerous textbooks on the X-ray analysis of polycrystalline materials. Still, some special feature may be considered here. For instance, feldspars have to be powdered with great care in order to obtain an average grain size well below 8 μ. Coarse-powdered samples lead to useless films and irreproducible traces. Moreover, the amount of sample for X-ray analysis isolated from a sediment will be rather small in a number of cases. Such samples must be powdered carefully in order not to spill a part. If such a small number of grains is powdered in an agate mortar under a rapidly evaporating liquid such as acetone, the grains do not shoot away and sample loss is reduced to a minimum.

The sample holder of the quadruple Guinier-De Wolff camera is a square metal plate with four rectangular windows. The windows can be filled with a cake or the sample can be smeared on a sheet of film. In the case of feldspar powders we prefer to cover the windows with "Melinex" film (a Philips product, code: PW 1526). The powdered feldspar is smeared on this film with stopcock grease. The preferred orientation that may occur during this application of the sample is disturbed by scratching the smear with a needle in order to produce a kind of grating pattern on the Melinex film.

Making films of feldspars with a Debye-Scherrer camera is rather easy, although some comments may be of help. In our laboratory the cameras are always filled with H_2 gas. Thus the blackening of the film in the region surrounding the beam catcher is totally avoided, without the troubles experienced with evacuated cameras. Such problems are the exploding of the sample tube, the buckling of the film and a remaining black smear around the beam-catcher hole because of imperfect evacuation. The use of Keesom capillaries, though a rather old-fashioned technique, is still practiced in our laboratory. One of the advantages of Keesom capillaries is that the capillary is used for more than one sample, thus providing for equal sample diameter in a number of films. This equality of experimental circumstances is rather important if quantitative results are to be obtained from films. The use of Keesom capillaries as well as the type of camera we use for this work has been described by FAVEJEE (1939).

If only two or three feldspar grains have been isolated from a sediment sample by handpicking, these grains can be used for a powder pattern applying the method of HIEMSTRA (1959). This method is performed as given below.

Take two object glasses. Clean them thoroughly. Put three or four fragments on one glass. Place the other on top of it. Then crush the grains by pressing the two glass plates with the three grains inbetween tightly. As soon as the crushing has been done, separate the two plates. Put a very small drop of fresh solution (used for repairing the inner tubes of bicycles) on one of the glasses. The drop should be minute, i.e., not larger than 0.2 or 0.3 mm in diameter. Collect the powdered fragments in the drop by moving the upper plate with a circular movement over the lower one. In this way powdering can be perfected also. Separate the plates again and allow to dry for 10 sec. Bring again together. Now, by gently moving one plate of glass over the other, the solution with the mineral powder covering the plates is turned into one small sphere. Take care to collect all the solution in this small sphere.
    After this has been done, a Debye-Scherrer camera is prepared for taking a photograph. The small sphere is mounted on top of a Lindemann glass capillary and this capillary is mounted in the camera in such a way that the solution sphere is seen in the centre of the line which runs through the collimator and the beam catcher. It should be perfectly centred! The camera is then loaded and operated as if a normal photograph is going to be made. Exposure time is longer. We apply about 3 h instead of 2 h with Co radiation, 10 mA, 30 kV. The result is a perfect Debye-Scherrer photograph clearly showing the pattern of the mineral in question, in addition to a diffuse band due to the solution. If this band is too dark, the analyst has used too much solution.

Although feldspar analysis with a Debye camera is less efficient, the type of feldspar can at least be established. Some measurements can even be made if the photograph is slightly enlarged in the measuring apparatus. And if this is the only possible method a rough estimate is always better than nothing.

Summary

In summarizing the properties of the three powder methods considered, it is clear that the author, at least, is an ardent advocate of the quadruple Guinier-De Wolff camera for feldspar work. Especially for the purpose of determining tiny fractions of feldspars isolated from sediments or soils, as well as for the recording of the entire diffractogram of the light fraction, this camera is superior to a diffractometer. For an identification of micas or clay minerals this camera can also be used, but is not superior to the Debye-Scherrer camera. As soon as intensities have to be accurately recorded the diffractometer has advantages over cameras, provided the sample preparation avoids preferred orientation. In conclusion it can be stated that the sedimentologist must make use of a proper combination of a

Debye-Scherrer camera, a Guinier camera and a diffractometer in order to reach satisfactory results in the quantitative mineralogical analysis of the light fraction of a sediment or a soil. No one of the instruments just mentioned is alone capable of covering the whole range of problems one may encounter.

SPACE GROUPS AND UNIT-CELL PARAMETERS OF FELDSPARS

The structure of a number of feldspars has been accurately determined with the aid of single crystal X-ray methods. MEGAW (1961) has just recently prepared a small bibliography of papers reporting structural analyses of feldspars in terms of detailed coordinates. From this list it can be inferred that the structure of the following phases is rather well established: sanidine, "orthoclase", microcline, albite, bytownite, anorthite and celsian.

Monoclinic alkali feldspars belong to the space group C 2/m, microcline to the space groups C $\bar{1}$. Both high and low albite have space group C $\bar{1}$. Anorthite is shown to have space group P $\bar{1}$, by KEMPSTER et al. (1962) and MEGAW et al. (1962).

The lattice parameters of feldspars are a function of the approximate unit cell parameters:

$$a = 8.6 \text{ Å} \qquad b = 13.0 \text{ Å} \qquad c = 7.0 \text{ Å}$$
$$\alpha \cong 90° \qquad \beta \cong 116° \qquad \gamma \cong 90°$$

Monoclinic feldspars consequently have two angles of 90°. In triclinic phases the values of all the angles differ from 90°. In microcline the value of γ can be as small as approximately 87° (cf. GOLDSMITH and LAVES, 1954, p.116). The value of α as a rule does not differ much from 90°. In albites the values of the angle α are approximately 94°; the values of γ vary from 88° for low albite to 90° for high albite. The structure of anorthite differs from the above approximate values in two respects. Firstly, the length of the c axis is doubled, viz., about 14 Å. Secondly, the values of the three angles are larger than 90°, being approximately 93°, 116°, and 91°.

From the given values it is possible to calculate a theoretical powder pattern for the different phases, taking into account the so-called "extinction conditions" following from the different space groups. These "extinction conditions" are for the lattice type C: only reflections for which h + k = 2 n are present, and for the lattice type P: no restrictions, all possible combinations are generally present.

From the structure of feldspars in general, and from the structure of specific phases in particular, it follows that a change in chemical composition, being a change in the proportion of the cations, has an important influence on the length of the a axis. For high-temperature alkali feldspars this has been observed by

DONNAY and DONNAY (1952), for microclines the same feature is assumed to exist (GOLDSMITH and LAVES, 1961). The change of the proportion Na/Ca in the group of plagioclase brings about a change in the Si/Al ratio; consequently, a more complicated influence on the structure is expected. This has been observed by a number of authors and the influences to be recorded in powder patterns have been described by GOODYEAR and DUFFIN (1953), J. V. SMITH (1956) and J. V. SMITH and GAY (1958).

A change from the low- to the high-temperature phases has a certain influence on the angles of the unit cell. This is clear at once for alkali feldspars because a change from triclinic to monoclinic symmetry is involved. In plagioclases, however, a comparable tendency may be observed.

From the details of the structure mentioned previously, it can at least be theoretically deduced which reflections do not promise to give an indication about chemical composition or structural state. First of all, reflections of high values of h, k, or l will certainly show considerable variations with varying chemical composition or a change in structural state. They tend, however, to have comparatively high values of ϑ, and therefore are rather difficult to record.

In plagioclase-feldspar patterns an additional difficulty is observed. The still rather complex albite pattern becomes even more intricate in the presence of a large calcium content. A number of additional weak reflections may be observed in the powder pattern of these plagioclases with a so-called intermediate structure (Fig.61).

As a result of these considerations it is to be expected that only a small number of diffraction lines are of practical value. This has indeed been found to be true by the investigators who tried to unravel the feldspar powder patterns in an attempt to draw something useful from them. Their investigations proved that in general the reflection with a rather important a-axis component, i.e., a reflection with a value of h, deviating largely from the values of k and l, may give information on the chemical composition. In the following sections the different aspects of the powder patterns of the various feldspar phases will be discussed. As a result a set of more or less practical methods will be advocated which may enable the sedimentologist and the pedologist to arrive at some analytical results after an evaluation of these powder patterns.

In the field of X-ray powder methods for identification, a number of excellent papers exist which give the experimental details. Some of these papers have one drawback only, a drawback observed in a large number of papers on feldspars; they are often addressed to the "igneous and metamorphic petrographer" and leave the investigators of the "dirty part" of geology for what they are. Therefore it is necessary to discuss these methods in the light of the special features of sediments and soils.

POWDER PATTERNS OF ALKALI FELDSPARS

Before starting this discussion we may recall the fact that in the group of alkali feldspars two different structures exist. One of these is monoclinic; the triclinic phase is of widespread occurrence. Some of these triclinic phases show a cross-grating twinning. A number of the alkali feldspars is pseudo-monoclinic. Reference has already been made to the work of HAFNER and LAVES (1956, 1957), BRUN et al. (1960) and MARFUNIN (1961, 1962a, b). A number of these pseudo-monoclinic phases have axial angles larger than $44°$. The X-ray powder pattern or the single crystal X-ray photograph reveals that these pseudo-monoclinic phases are triclinic. Some pseudo-monoclinic phases are monoclinic, also with respect to the X-ray analysis. In this case other techniques reveal that in fact an ordered phase has been studied.

In order to keep the following description as clear as possible, the powder patterns of alkali feldspars will be discussed in three sections: disordered monoclinic phases; ordered or partly ordered homogeneous triclinic phases; and the concept of "obliquity".

It has been described in Chapter 3 that a large number of alkali feldspars are unmixed in a sodium-rich and in a potassium-rich phase, the so-called perthites or antiperthites. The specific aspects of the powder patterns of these aggregates will be treated separately in the last section.

Disordered monoclinic phases

DONNAY and DONNAY (1952) studied a series of synthetic alkali feldspars of composition varying from pure *Or* to pure *Ab*. A number of these showed monoclinic symmetry (see Table XIII). Phases with more than 70% *Ab* were triclinic. Apart from a calculation procedure to arrive at unit-cell parameters from powder patterns, a number of selected patterns and the unit-cell parameters of eleven alkali feldspars with varying *Ab*-content are reported in their paper. J.V. SMITH (1956) showed the powder data of Donnay and Donnay to be systematically $0.025°$ $2\vartheta_{Cu}$ too low. Still, we did not correct these data as given in Tables XIII, XVI, XVIII, XIX and XX, because we felt that information on how to apply this correction was enough. The only solution to more reliable data seems to be a new program of research on synthetic phases. The values of the observed reflection 111 show a decreasing d_{111} with increasing *Ab*-content. BOWEN and TUTTLE (1950) observed the same effect for $d_{\bar{2}01}$. GOLDSMITH and LAVES (1961) used the values of Donnay and Donnay for a calculation of the values of d_{400}, which showed the same effect as the other reflections just mentioned. The result of this calculation of d_{400} against chemical composition is shown in Fig.52.

It has been argued on p.179 that diffraction lines with d_{hkl} values where h differs largely from k and l give the best information about the chemical composition. Consequently, the line with d_{400} is more suitable for such a measurement

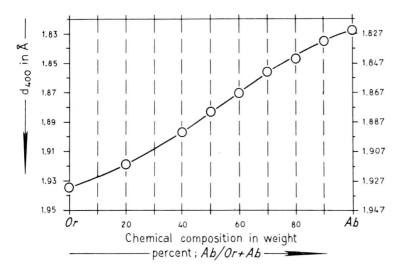

Fig.52. The relation between the 400 spacing (left ordinate) and the chemical composition of
high-temperature synthetic alkali feldspars, data derived from DONNAY and DONNAY (1952).
As the absolute values of d_{400} may be approximately 0.025° $2\vartheta_{Cu}$ too high, this correction has
been applied in the right ordinate. The figure is after GOLDSMITH and LAVES (1961, p.82).

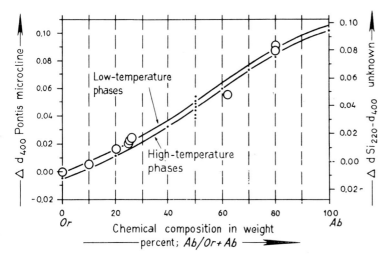

Fig.53. The relation between the 400 spacing and the chemical composition of low-temperature
alkali feldspars. The left ordinate lists the value of the 400 spacing of Pontis microcline minus the
400 spacing of the phase under investigation. The right ordinate lists the 220 spacing of silicon
minus the 400 spacing of the phase under investigation. The curve of Fig.52 for high-temperature
phases is also drawn for reasons of comparison. Microcline with intermediate obliquity would
fall on intermediate curves. The reference values are plotted as circles and a dashed line. After
GOLDSMITH and LAVES (1961, p.83).

TABLE XIII

LATTICE PARAMETERS OF SELECTED ALKALI FELDSPARS

	State[1]	Or	Ab	An	a	b	c	α	β	γ	V[2,3]	Source
1	H.T.S.	100	—	—	8.617	13.030	7.176	90.00	116.07	90.00	723.7	Donnay and Donnay (1952)
2	H.T.	92	8	—	8.564	13.030	7.175	90.00	116.00	90.00	719.6	Cole et al. (1949)
3	H.T.S.	80	20	—	8.537	13.026	7.173	90.00	115.94	90.00	717.3	Donnay and Donnay (1952)
4	H.T.S.	60	40	—	8.445	13.001	7.168	90.00	116.04	90.00	707.1	Donnay and Donnay (1952)
5	H.T.S.	50	50	—	8.389	12.990	7.164	90.00	116.10	90.00	701.1	Donnay and Donnay (1952)
6	H.T.S.	40	60	—	8.335	12.970	7.159	90.00	116.60	90.00	694.5	Donnay and Donnay (1952)
7	H.T.S.	37	63	—	8.316	12.977	7.163	90.63	116.32	90.10	692.6	Laves (1952)
8	H.T.S.	35	65	—	8.310	12.964	7.154	90.00	116.20	90.00	691.5	Donnay and Donnay (1952)
9	H.T.	35	65	—	8.308	12.981	7.166	91.18	116.35	90.10	692.3	Laves (1952)
10	H.T.S.	30	70	—	8.279	12.949	7.149	91.31	116.26	90.11	687.1	Donnay and Donnay (1952)
11	H.T.	23	73	4	8.260	12.950	7.157	92.28	116.43	90.18	684.4	Laves (1952)
12	H.T.S.	20	80	—	8.243	12.927	7.140	92.15	116.28	90.30	681.5	Donnay and Donnay (1952)
13	H.T.	19	79	2	8.239	12.940	7.147	92.53	116.38	90.20	681.6	Laves (1952)
14	H.T.S.	—	100	—	8.172	12.884	7.123	93.65	116.45	90.19	669.7	Donnay and Donnay (1952)
15	H.T.S.	—	100	—	8.115	12.871	7.127	93.55	116.50	89.98	663.6	Laves (1952)
16	L.T.	85	13	2	8.578	12.960	7.211	89.70	115.58	90.87	722.8	Bailey and Taylor (1955)
17	L.T.	89	11	—	8.568	12.964	7.216	90.00	116.08	90.00	719.9	Laves (1952)
18	L.T.	90	10	—	8.577	12.967	7.223	90.65	115.93	87.70	721.9	Laves (1952)
19	L.T.	92	8	—	8.562	12.996	7.193	90.00	116.06	90.00	718.6	Cole et al. (1949)
20	L.T.	—	100	—	8.156	12.773	7.170	94.32	116.67	87.62	665.6	Laves (1952)
21	L.T.	—	100	—	8.135	12.788	7.154	94.23	116.52	87.72	664.1	Cole et al. (1951)

[1] Explanation of abbreviations: H.T.S. = high-temperature synthetic phase; H.T. = heat treated natural phase; L.T. = natural low-temperature phase.

[2] V = volume of the unit cell in Ångstrom units.

[3] The volume of the unit cell of all the data not derived from Donnay and Donnay (1952) is calculated by the present writer.

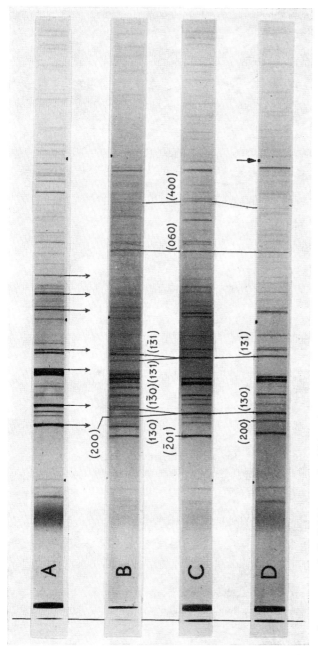

Fig.54. X-ray powder patterns of alkali feldspars. A. Albite of Bucarischuna, Graubünden, Switzerland. B. Perthitic microcline showing both low-temperature alkali feldspar spacings as well as low albite spacings (indicated with arrows). C. Adularia of Selkingen, Austria. D. Sanidine of the Drachenfels, Germany. Spacings discussed in the text are marked on the photographs. N.B. The small dots at the edge of the patterns are calibration marks; one of them is indicated by an arrow. The powder patterns were made with a quadruple Guinier-De Wolff camera, Co radiation, 30 kV, 10 mA; exposure time 2½ h.

than lines with d_{111} or $d_{\bar{2}01}$. The diffraction lines 400 of disordered potassium feldspar and of pure albite are about 0.1 Å apart, corresponding with approximately 1.65° ϑ or 6.60° 4ϑ for cobalt radiation in that particular region of the diffraction pattern. Values of 4ϑ are given here because on films taken by a Guinier-De Wolff camera 1 mm corresponds with 0.25°ϑ. The values of 111 for pure potassium feldspar and pure albite are only 0.59°ϑ or 2.4° 4ϑ apart for cobalt radiation, although in this region this difference corresponds with 0.17 Å. From a comparison of these data it follows that the chemical composition of an alkali feldspar can be more accurately measured over a range of 6.6° than over a range of only 2.4°.

For a practical application of this measurement technique the reader may find the following considerations of some help. The intensity of 400 is weak in comparison with 111 or $\bar{2}01$. Moreover, the two last mentioned lines are easier to find. In this connection the following considerations may help to locate 400. The spacing of 200 in Ångstrom units is exactly two times the value of 400 in Ångstrom units. 200 is easily found. In sanidines 200 is close to 130, and this line is marked on the X-ray powder photograph of Drachenfels sanidine Fig.54D. Note that 200 has a smaller angle than 130 for pure potassium sanidine, is of about the same angle as 130 in sanidine with approximately 60% Ab and is too weak to be detected between $1\bar{3}0$ and 130 in high albite. Together with the d_{hkl} values of alkali feldspars listed in Tables XV–XXIII, and the powder patterns of Fig.54, the reader will be able to find 400 without too much difficulty. For a determination of the sodium content of disordered feldspar phases the values of d_{400} are given in Fig.52, taken from GOLDSMITH and LAVES (1961). The method is reliable and quite promising. One objection, however, must be made.

If a sedimentologist has prepared a sample of alkali feldspars with the methods described in Chapter 6, this fraction seldom contains disordered phases exclusively. Apart from some other minerals, this fraction is in most cases a mixture of different alkali feldspars. In the case where disordered phases are in the minority, the powder pattern of the total fraction only enables the analyst to decide that both monoclinic and triclinic phases are present by the detection of the 131 of the monoclinic phase inbetween the 131–$1\bar{3}1$ pair of microcline, as shown in fig.7 in the paper by GOLDSMITH and LAVES (1954). Unless other separation techniques are developed in order to divide the alkali-feldspar fraction again in a number of fractions containing closely related phases exclusively, this property of sediment samples will certainly prove to be an obstacle in the extraction of further information.

Partly ordered or completely ordered homogeneous triclinic phases

The chemical composition and the "obliquity" of microcline have proved to be of importance for petrological purposes. The chemical composition will first be considered, the "obliquity" will be treated later.

GOLDSMITH and LAVES (1961) suggest in detail the only practical non-destructive method for the determination of the sodium content of microcline with X-ray diffraction. Again the relationship between d_{400} and the chemical composition is of importance. The curve presented as Fig.53 is a tentative curve constructed by the authors just mentioned. The shape of this curve is similar to the sanidine curve but slightly shifted towards higher values. The method is applicable also in the presence of albite or oligoclase lines in the powder pattern. This situation is often encountered with perthites. Especially in the normal microcline perthites with a subordinate amount of a plagioclase phase, the plagioclase lines do not constitute a problem because they are too weak to be noticeable in this part of the pattern.

For a practical application of this method the following remarks will certainly help the reader who is not familiar with this part of X-ray methods. To begin with, the curve of Fig.53 lists only relative values. The values are expressed in relation to an ideal microcline from the Pontis dolomites. As this sample is not available to large numbers of investigators, the right-hand side of the same curve lists the values in relation with the d_{220} line of pure silicon. The exact value of this spacing is 1.9200 Å. The 400 spacing of the Bucarischuna albite of Fig.61A is found at a value of 117.88° 4ϑ for cobalt radiation corresponding to 1.8184 Å. The chemical composition of this sample is practically pure $NaAlSi_3O_8$, the amount of Or and An being approximately 1%. According to GOLDSMITH and LAVES (1961) the 400 spacing of microcline is found at 110.44° 4ϑ for cobalt radiation or at 1.930 Å. On the microcline perthite pattern of Fig.54B the 400 is indicated. As soon as this microcline perthite is heated at about 900°C for 10 h the albite lines disappear. The 400 is seen to shift to the right for about 2 mm, or 0.5ϑ for cobalt radiation. This shift is due to the migration of the sodium ions into the microcline structure. The microcline phase becomes rich in sodium and the 400 spacing will show a larger value of ϑ. The above-mentioned authors stress the fact that in microcline perthites and in homogeneous microclines with a maximum obliquity, i.e., with a maximum distance between 130 and $1\overline{3}0$ or between 131 and $1\overline{3}1$, the amount of sodium in solid solution is always remarkably small. More than 5% Ab seems to be exceptional. In microclines with an intermediate obliquity the amount of sodium in solid solution can be much higher.

The diffraction line 400 of a fraction from a sediment or a soil will in most cases show a certain diffuseness. The reason for this diffuseness is the fact mentioned previously, that the alkali-feldspar fraction is a mechanical mixture of an "unknown number of unknown phases". The average position of this line can be determined in a number of cases, which leads to a coarse estimate of the chemical composition of the alkali feldspars in the sample. One point in favour of this technique is the fact that most microclines have a chemical composition ranging from about 0% to about 25% Ab. This observation may help in determining an average chemical composition. Methods for surmounting the difficulty of analysing

TABLE XIV

$2\vartheta_{Cu}$ AND $2\vartheta_{Co}$ VALUES FOR PLAGIOCLASES[1]

$2\vartheta_{Cu}$ values for plagioclases

indices	20Ī	1Ī1	111	1̄30	130	Ī12	11̄2	040	002	220
Unheated										
Amelia[2]	22.057	23.071	23.538	24.306	24.155	26.418	25.392	—	—	—
BM 1940, 27[3]	22.042	23.03	23.567	24.19	24.19	26.427	25.445	—	—	—
81822[4]	22.013	22.981	23.586	24.078	24.248	26.428	25.486	—	—	—
103086[5]	22.00	22.958	23.60	23.988	24.275	26.435	25.508	—	—	—
97490[6]	21.983	22.918	23.612	23.922	24.302	26.435	25.542	—	—	—
152[7]	22.01	22.925	23.655	23.88	24.36	26.458	25.565	27.84	28.032	28.365
64[8]	21.99	22.865	—	—	24.39	26.455	25.625	27.80	28.04	28.44
144[9]	22.015	22.895	—	—	24.375	26.45	25.575	27.815	28.035	28.37
24[10]	21.967	22.862	—	—	24.369	26.435	25.644	27.80	28.037	28.374
Heated										
Amelia[2]	22.00	22.915	—	—	24.46	26.445	25.63	27.785	28.095	28.525
BM 1940, 27[3]: 12 days	22.02	22.97	—	—	24.33	26.42	25.52	27.84	28.005	28.315
BM 1940, 27[3]: 24 days	22.012	22.92	—	—	24.397	26.435	25.57	27.827	28.047	28.44
81822[4]	21.998	22.863	—	—	24.44	26.44	25.61	27.773	28.053	28.483
103086[5]	21.985	22.88	—	—	24.435	26.42	25.60	27.75	28.04	28.47
97490[6]	21.99	22.855	—	—	24.427	26.45	25.652	27.775	28.045	28.465
152[7]	21.988	22.868	—	—	24.460	26.47	25.655	27.797	28.057	28.477
64[8]	21.988	22.848	—	—	24.435	26.455	25.625	27.782	28.027	28.442
Synthetic										
An0	22.005	22.885	—	—	24.465	26.48	25.65	27.80	28.085	28.53
An10	22.025	22.875	—	—	24.475	26.47	25.66	27.805	28.075	28.53
An30	22.025	22.855	—	—	24.455	26.43	25.67	27.795	28.04	28.485
An50	22.02	22.805	—	—	24.47	26.46	25.675	27.81	28.03	28.46

TABLE XIV (*continued*)[1]

2ϑ_{Cu} values for plagioclases

indices	$1\bar{3}1$ $\alpha_1 + \alpha_2$	131 $\alpha_1 + \alpha_2$	$\bar{1}32$ α_1 only	$24\bar{1}$	$\bar{2}41$	060	222	113	$20\bar{4}$
Unheated									
Amelia[2]	30.148	31.210	33.946	34.996	36.757	42.507	48.118	50.548	51.118
BM 1940, 27[3]	30.04	31.295	33.908	35.108	36.557	42.425	48.193	50.614	51.168
81822[4]	29.941	31.346	33.876	35.202	36.42	42.363	48.235	50.666	51.273
103086[5]	29.838	31.363	33.833	35.270	36.223	42.31	48.245	50.69	51.288
97490[6]	29.782	31.377	33.799	35.319	36.125	42.285	48.32	50.722	51.337
152[7]	29.73	31.465	33.815	35.43	36.065	42.275	48.385	50.765	51.40
64[8]	29.65	31.49	33.76	—	—	42.22	48.42	50.79	51.455
144[9]	29.71	31.46	33.81	—	—	42.24	48.37	50.77	51.415
24[10]	29.649	31.462	33.772	—	—	42.235	48.354	50.752	51.452
Heated									
Amelia[2]	29.62	31.61	33.74	—	—	42.19	48.57	50.91	51.46
BM 1940, 27[3]: 12 days	29.81	31.435	33.82	—	—	42.305	48.40	50.73	51.33
BM 1940, 27[3]: 24 days	29.665	31.47	33.76	—	—	42.225	48.49	50.835	51.385
81822[4]	29.60	31.54	33.735	—	—	42.18	48.49	50.85	51.45
103086[5]	29.59	31.52	33.66	—	—	42.15	48.46	50.81	51.43
97490[6]	29.58	31.492	33.69	—	—	42.16	48.425	50.79	51.435
152[7]	29.587	31.535	33.75	—	—	42.18	48.46	50.828	51.463
64[8]	29.562	31.525	33.72	—	—	42.185	48.47	50.793	51.453
Synthetic									
An$_0$	29.59	31.62	33.75	—	—	42.19	48.54	50.92	51.475
An$_{10}$	29.605	31.585	33.735	—	—	42.19	48.56	50.91	51.47
An$_{30}$	29.59	31.52	33.735	—	—	42.18	48.475	50.83	51.48
An$_{50}$	29.55	31.525	33.735	—	—	42.195	48.395	50.815	51.515

Footnotes are given on p.190.

TABLE XIV (*continued*)[1]

$2\vartheta_{Co}$ values for plagioclases

indices	$20\bar{1}$	$1\bar{1}1$	111	$\bar{1}30$	130	$\bar{1}12$	$11\bar{2}$	040	002	220
Unheated										
Amelia[2]	25.6699	26.8556	27.4020	28.3009	28.1241	29.5728	30.7754	—	—	—
BM 1940, 27[3]	25.6524	26.8077	27.4359	28.1651	28.1651	29.6349	30.7860	—	—	—
81822[4]	25.6185	26.7504	27.4582	28.0340	28.2330	29.6830	30.7871	—	—	—
103086[5]	25.6033	26.7235	27.4746	27.9287	28.2646	29.7087	30.7953	—	—	—
97490[6]	25.5834	26.6767	27.4886	27.8514	28.2962	29.7486	30.7953	—	—	—
152[7]	25.6149	26.6849	27.5389	27.8022	28.3641	29.7755	30.8223	32.4437	32.6691	33.0601
64[8]	25.5916	26.6147	—	—	28.3993	29.8458	30.8188	32.3968	32.6785	33.1482
144[9]	25.6208	26.6498	—	—	28.3817	29.7873	30.8129	32.4144	32.6726	33.0660
24[10]	25.5647	26.6112	—	—	28.3747	29.8681	30.7953	32.3968	32.6750	33.0707
Heated										
Amelia[2]	25.6033	26.6732	—	—	28.4812	29.8517	30.8071	32.3791	32.7431	33.2480
BM 1940, 27[3]: 12 days	25.6266	26.7375	—	—	28.3290	29.7228	30.7777	32.4437	32.6374	33.0014
BM 1940, 27[3]: 24 days	25.6173	26.6790	—	—	28.4074	29.7814	30.7953	32.4284	32.6867	33.1482
81822[4]	25.6009	26.6124	—	—	28.4578	29.8283	30.8012	32.3651	32.6938	33.1987
103086[5]	25.5857	26.6322	—	—	28.4519	29.8165	30.7777	32.3381	32.6785	33.1834
97490[6]	25.5916	26.6030	—	—	28.4426	29.8775	30.8129	32.3674	32.6844	33.1776
152[7]	25.5892	26.6182	—	—	28.4812	29.8810	30.8364	32.3932	32.6985	33.1917
64[8]	25.5892	26.5948	—	—	28.4519	29.8458	30.8188	32.3756	32.6632	33.1506
Synthetic										
An0	25.6091	26.6381	—	—	28.4871	29.8751	30.8481	32.3968	32.7313	33.2539
An10	25.6325	26.6264	—	—	28.4988	29.8869	30.8364	32.4026	32.7196	33.2539
An30	25.6325	26.6030	—	—	28.4754	29.8986	30.7895	32.3909	32.6785	33.2011
An50	25.6266	26.5445	—	—	28.4929	29.9044	30.8247	32.4085	32.6668	33.1717

TABLE XIV (*continued*) [1]

$2\vartheta_{Co}$ values for plagioclases

indices	$\bar{1}31$	131	$\bar{1}32$	$2\bar{4}1$	$\bar{2}41$	060	222	113	$20\bar{4}$
Unheated									
Amelia[2]	35.1557	36.4054	39.6310	40.8713	42.9546	49.7886	56.5122	59.4439	60.1335
BM 1940, 27[3]	35.0286	36.5055	39.5861	41.0036	42.7178	49.6908	56.6025	59.5237	60.1940
81822[4]	34.9122	36.5655	39.5483	41.1148	42.5556	49.6169	56.6531	59.5866	60.3211
103086[5]	34.7911	36.5856	39.4976	41.1951	42.3224	49.5536	56.6651	59.6156	60.3393
97490[6]	34.7252	36.6020	39.4574	41.2531	42.2065	49.5238	56.7554	59.6543	60.3986
152[7]	34.6641	36.7057	39.4763	41.3843	42.1355	49.5119	56.8337	59.7063	60.4749
64[8]	34.5700	36.7351	39.4114	—	—	49.4463	56.8759	59.7366	60.5415
144[9]	34.6406	36.6998	39.4704	—	—	49.4701	56.8156	59.7124	60.4931
24[10]	34.5689	36.7021	39.4256	—	—	49.4642	56.7964	59.6906	60.5379
Heated									
Amelia[2]	34.5348	36.8764	39.3878	—	—	49.4105	57.0566	59.8817	60.5476
BM 1940, 27[3]: 12 days	34.7582	36.6703	39.4822	—	—	49.5477	56.8518	59.6640	60.3902
BM 1940, 27[3]: 24 days	34.5877	36.7116	39.4114	—	—	49.4523	56.9602	59.7910	60.4568
81822[4]	34.5113	36.7940	39.2934	—	—	49.3986	56.9602	59.8092	60.5355
103086[5]	34.4995	36.7704	39.3288	—	—	49.3628	56.9240	59.7608	60.5113
97490[6]	34.4877	36.7375	39.3996	—	—	49.3747	56.8819	59.7366	60.5173
152[7]	34.4960	36.7881	39.3642	—	—	49.3986	56.9240	59.7825	60.5512
64[8]	34.4666	36.7763		—	—	49.4045	56.9361	59.7402	60.5391
Synthetic									
An_0	34.4995	36.8882	39.3996	—	—	49.4105	57.0204	59.8938	60.5658
An_{10}	34.5171	36.8470	39.3819	—	—	49.4105	57.0445	59.8817	60.5597
An_{30}	34.4995	36.7704	39.3819	—	—	49.3986	56.9421	59.7850	60.5718
An_{50}	34.4525	36.7763	39.3819	—	—	49.4165	56.8458	59.7668	60.6142

Footnotes are given on p.190.

a mineral assemblage of monoclinic, pseudo-monoclinic and triclinic phases of varying chemical composition can be developed to a certain extent, and some additional suggestions will be found in the section on perthites.

The concept "obliquity"

Before starting this discussion of the measurement of the "obliquity" of microclines we may recall the discussion of such terms as intermediacy index, obliquity index, triclinicity and others used to indicate the degree of order observed in the triclinic structure of a feldspar on p.96. It has been stated that the degree of order in feldspars is of petrological significance. It has been shown that the degree of order is reflected by the optical axial angle. It has been discussed that particularly in alkali feldspars the order–disorder relations are of importance, because in this group of minerals the true structure of the homogeneous domains may well be concealed by sub-X-ray twinning or sub-X-ray perthites. It has been argued that the term "triclinicity", quite often used for the description of the degree of order of microclines, is a misnomer because a structure is either monoclinic or triclinic. In order to avoid a term that may suggest properties of concepts not incorporated in the symmetry theory, it is preferable to use a purely descriptive term. The term "obliquity" is meant to describe a structure more inclined than another without reference to the symmetry aspects of such a structure.

Obliquity is a term used to describe the deviation of the triclinic structure of microclines from the monoclinic structure observed in low sanidine. Consequently, it is a conventional term describing the deviation of the angles α and γ from $90°$. The "obliquity index" is an expression in percentages of the obliquity of a structure of a specific microcline in relation to the monoclinic structure with zero obliquity and the structure of maximum microcline, with a 100% obliquity.

---

[1] The values in this table were calculated from the values for Cu radiation of these samples given by J. V. SMITH (1956, p.52, table III), and listed here too. For calculation an I.B.M. computer was used. The conversion factor is based on the relation $\lambda_{Co}/\lambda_{Cu} \cdot \sin \vartheta_{Cu} = \sin \vartheta_{Co}$.

[2] Pegmatite. Amelia, Va., U.S.A. Weight %: An 0.0; Ab 98.2; Or 1.8 (KRACEK and NEUVONEN, 1952).

[3] Pegmatite. Kenya. Weight %: An 10.9; Ab 86.5; Or 2.6 (GAME, 1949).

[4] Pegmatite. S.C., U.S.A. Weight %: An 17.7; Ab 81.0; Or 1.3 (KRACEK and NEUVONEN, 1952).

[5] Pegmatite. Hawk Mine, N.C., U.S.A. Weight %: An 22.1; Ab 74.4; Or 3.5 (KRACEK and NEUVONEN, 1952).

[6] Little Rock Creek, Mitchel County, N.C., U.S.A. Weight %: An 29.9; Ab 66.5; Or 3.6 (KRACEK and NEUVONEN, 1952).

[7] Granodiorite. Spanish Peak, Calif., U.S.A. Weight %: An 35.9; Ab 62.6; Or 1.5 (EMMONS, 1953, no.6).

[8] Dacite. San Luis Obispo, Calif., U.S.A. Weight %: An 36.1; Ab 60.7; Or 3.2 (EMMONS, 1953, no.7).

[9] Granodiorite. Crestmore, Calif., U.S.A. Weight %: An 38.0; Ab 60.0; Or 2.0 (EMMONS, 1953, no.8).

[10] Anorthosite. Essex, N.Y., U.S.A. Weight %: An 49.0; Ab 47.2; Or 3.8 (EMMONS, 1953, no.9).

Maximum microcline is characterized conventionally by a γ angle of $87°48'$. The effect of a changing γ in powder patterns is clearly shown in fig.13 and 14 in the paper by GOLDSMITH and LAVES (1954b). The same aspects are shown in Fig.54 of this book, showing the reflections 130 and $1\bar{3}0$ as well as 131 and $1\bar{3}1$ in a microcline, whereas in a monoclinic structure these reflections are not visible and only 130 and 131 are seen. Goldsmith and Laves have studied a number of phases with the spacings 130–$1\bar{3}0$ and 131–$1\bar{3}1$ clearly apart, but not as far apart as in maximum microcline. From their fig.14 on p.110 of the above paper it is clear that principally four types of powder patterns of microcline can be expected.

The first one is the pattern of pure maximum microcline with the 130–$1\bar{3}0$ and the 131–$1\bar{3}1$ far apart or in values for cobalt radiation $130 = 54.06° \, 4\vartheta$; $1\bar{3}0 = 55.94° \, 4\vartheta$; $131 = 68.77° \, 4\vartheta$ and $1\bar{3}1 = 70.62° \, 4\vartheta$.

The second pattern is a microcline pattern with the spacings $1\bar{3}0$–130 and 131–$1\bar{3}1$ distinct and less far apart, a microcline with an intermediate obliquity.

The third pattern belongs to a microcline with numerous small domains of different obliquity indexes, resulting in a smeared-out region between the extreme values of the spacings, described by GOLDSMITH and LAVES (1954b) in table 1, p.105, no.4.

The fourth pattern, described in the same table as no.7, 11, 15, 16 etc., shows a broadened 131 spacing suggesting that a triclinic phase is present but that the deviation from a monoclinic structure is rather small.

The powder patterns of Fig.54 and 55 will enable the reader to find the spacings considered, the values of maximum microcline given above will enable him to determine the obliquity index of microclines in his own samples. It is certainly advisable to begin such determinations with a few large microcline samples from a geological collection before applying them to the crystals isolated from sediments or soils.

Varying proposals exist for the measurement of the obliquity index. MAC-KENZIE's proposal (1952, 1954) is based on 130, Goldsmith and Laves propose to use 131. Still others advocate the use of 111. The fact that the obliquity index measured on one of these three spacings is not exactly the same as the ones measured on the other spacings is confusing. As long as the authors report exactly what they measure this will not constitute a real problem and large deviations are generally not expected. The reader is advised to try the measurements on 131.

If sedimentologists or pedologists should ever find use for this concept which proved to be of some value for petrological consideration, they must again keep in mind the fact that they are generally studying mechanical mixtures of an unknown number of feldspar phases derived from an unknown number of unknown rocks.

Powder patterns of perthites

It is common experience that the powder patterns of microclines and other alkali feldspars from igneous or metamorphic rocks show the diffraction lines of sodium-rich plagioclases. This experimental observation is due to the perthitic nature of these minerals. Homogeneous triclinic alkali feldspars are even rare. For the evaluation of the chemical composition of such feldspar aggregates X-ray powder methods can be used. The intensity of a strong sodium feldspar line may give information about the amount of plagioclase present in the exsolution phases. Meanwhile the sodium retained in the alkali feldspar lamellae can be measured with the use of the 400 spacing as described on p.185. Such intensity measurements should be performed with sensitive counting circuits or with a photodensitometer on carefully made X-ray photographs.

In order to make such measurements possible the investigator has to prepare a number of standard samples by mixing pure albite and pure microcline or pure sanidine, in known proportions. But pure microcline is generally not available, because these very minerals are more often than not found as perthitic aggregates. Therefore other methods must be found. In a paper from 1961, p.89, GOLDSMITH and LAVES describe microcline perthites and microclines in contact with $NaAlSi_3O_8$-glass which homogenize on heating without a notable change of obliquity. Such homogenized microclines may be used in the preparation of standard samples. With the aid of such standard samples the influence of varying amounts of albite on the total perthite pattern can be investigated. The standard films and standard traces thus obtained can be of help in further research. The standard samples themselves cannot be kept for a long time, because in some cases homogenized microcline perthites unmix again after some time.

In a treatise by KUELLMER (1959, 1960), heating of perthites plays an important role. Such a heat treatment causes one of the two phases present in a perthite to vanish. The ultimate result is one homogeneous alkali feldspar phase of intermediate obliquity or of monoclinic structure. This effect, observed by SPENCER (1937) and discussed by numerous others, was also considered to be of importance for the understanding of the properties of the feldspar structure in Chapter 3. Upon heating, the intensity ratio between the plagioclase and the alkali feldspar lines of a perthite changes and the plagioclase lines finally disappear (see Fig.55). The measurement of the chemical composition before and after heating may give information about the amount of plagioclase present.

In some cases it is necessary to heat for rather long periods, because some perthites persist even after long and intensive heating, as was shown by KUELLMER (1961).

Kuellmer's methods of studying perthites are not only concerned with the determination of bulk composition. He discusses an identification technique giving information about the structural properties of the two phases of a perthite. Perthites containing more than two phases are not treated. The reflections used in these papers are the $20\bar{1}$ spacing of alkali feldspars and the $20\bar{1}$ spacing of sodium-

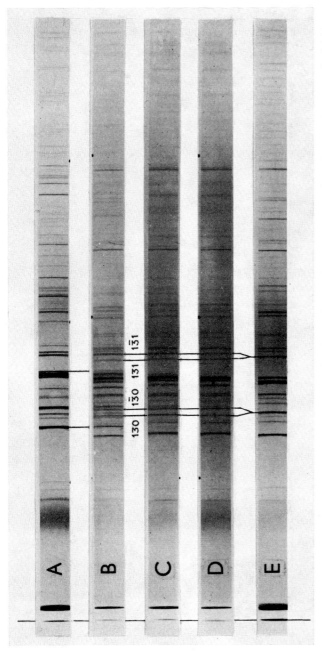

Fig.55. The results of heating a perthite. A. Albite of Bucarischuna, Graubünden, Switzerland. B. A perthitic microcline showing both alkali feldspar and albite spacings, compare B with A. C. The same microcline perthite after heating the powder 10 h at 900 °C, the albite lines have partly vanished. D. The same microcline perthite after heating the powder 40 h at 900 °C. E. Adularia of Selkingen with monoclinic symmetry. The powder patterns were made with a quadruple Guinier-De Wolff camera, Co radiation, 30 kV, 10 mA, exposure time 2½ h. Note the change of chemical composition of the potassium-rich phase; shifting of lines to the right with increasing sodium content. Note the slight change in obliquity, the distance between 130 and 1̄30 is decreasing. Note the absence of albite lines in D.

rich plagioclase[1]. The 1960 paper advances a cut-and-dried technique for such measurements. Even the details of sample preparation, sample purification and intensity measurements are not forgotten.

Enough about Kuellmer's methods. In samples from sediments or soils perthites are quite often present. The following consideration may now be used for an identification and eventually for a determination of the chemical composition of the alkali-feldspar fraction of such samples.

If the concentration technique for the extraction of the alkali-feldspar fraction from soils and sediments is of such a reliability that only alkali feldspars and perthites are present and pure albite as well as plagioclase fragments are rigorously absent, the powder pattern of this fraction will show: (*1*) the presence of alkali-feldspar phases, (*2*) the presence of albite, and (*3*) the relative importance of albite in the alkali-feldspar fraction. The presence of albite diffraction lines may, under these circumstances, be solely ascribed to the presence of perthites. The total amount of albite can be estimated by the method already advocated.

Microclines have been proved to consist of practically pure potassium feldspar in case the obliquity is near to 100% (see LAVES and GOLDSMITH, 1961, p.92). Such microclines are often perthitic and the sodium-rich phase is close to pure albite in most cases. If in the alkali-feldspar fraction of a sediment only such maximum microclines are found the above property may be used for an approximate determination of the amount of albite, or sodium-rich plagioclase. The intensity of the plagioclase spacings determines the sodium content.

If the alkali feldspar phases are of intermediate obliquity or even close to a monoclinic structure the amount of plagioclase can still be determined by the intensity of the plagioclase spacings. The amount of sodium in the alkali-feldspar phases may in these cases be comparatively important. The position of the 400 reflection indicates the approximate value of this amount of sodium.

Finally, the specific property of alkali feldspars to absorb large amounts of sodium during heating was used by HAFNER and LAVES (1957). They tried to prepare a number of standard samples of alkali feldspars with a known admixture of sodium in solid solution. Mechanical mixtures of fine powders of microcline and albite with known chemical compositions were pressed at 10,000 atm. The tablets obtained were heated for 48 h at 1,000 °C.

X-ray patterns of this material showed that a homogeneous phase was obtained with the sodium previously present in the admixed albite phase, now in solid solution in the potassium phase. Infrared patterns indicated the presence of still highly ordered phases. The structure of the microcline and of the albite did not suffer largely from the treatment.

A modification of this experimental technique may be useful for sedimentologists and soil scientists. Grind the alkali-feldspar fraction obtained by the

---

[1] Kuellmer writes $\bar{2}01$ instead of $20\bar{1}$, which is entirely the same for all practical purposes.

separation methods treated in Chapter 6 to a suitable grain size in an agate mortar under acetone. Subject this powder to a pressure of 10,000 atm. Treat the tablet thus obtained for 48 h in a furnace at 1,000 °C. Prepare an X-ray powder pattern of this material and determine the bulk chemical composition by the method described on p.185. If the 400 spacing is not sharp or hardly visible, one of the other less affected reflections suitable for such measurements may be used.

POWDER PATTERNS OF PLAGIOCLASE FELDSPARS

The discussion in Chapter 2 pictures the different high- and low-temperature structures found in plagioclases. Moreover, in the group of low-temperature plagioclases, the change of the C$\bar{1}$ structure of low albite to the P$\bar{1}$ structure of anorthite, due to an increasing amount of Ca and an increasing amount of Al in the framework, also leads to a number of different structures. The complexity encountered is discussed for instance by GAY (1953, 1954, 1956), GAY and BOWN (1956) and BOWN and GAY (1958). It is schematically illustrated in Fig.9.

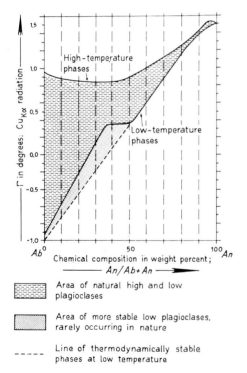

Area of natural high and low plagioclases

Area of more stable low plagioclases, rarely occurring in nature

Line of thermodynamically stable phases at low temperature

Fig.56. The variation of $\Gamma = (2\vartheta_{131} + 2\vartheta_{220} - 4\vartheta_{1\bar{3}1})$ with the chemical composition of low- and high-temperature plagioclases. The figure expressing Γ in values for Cu radiation has been modified after J. V. SMITH and GAY (1958, p.749).

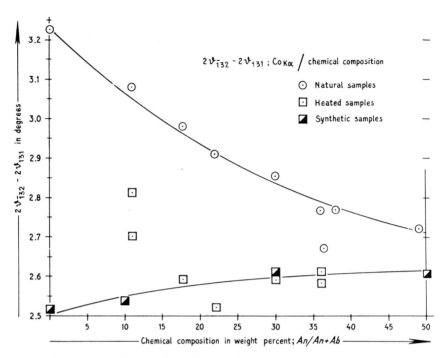

Fig.57. The values of $2\vartheta_{\overline{1}32} - 2\vartheta_{131}$ of low- and high-temperature plagioclases plotted against the chemical composition. (After J. V. SMITH, 1956.) The data are listed in Table XIV. The curve is valid for measurements with Co radiation. For Cu radiation turn to the original paper; d values are not listed because these are useless in this case as has been argued on p.200.

At present we are fortunate that at least two excellent papers on the powder patterns of plagioclases have been written by J. V. SMITH (1956) and J. V. SMITH and GAY (1958). These papers describe thoroughly and clearly the different aspects of the powder patterns of plagioclases, and address themselves also to readers with a limited crystallographic background. Sedimentologists who want to try an evaluation of the chemical composition of plagioclases with X-ray powder methods are strongly advised not to begin with the summarizing comments in this book, but also to consult the original papers.

Although it has been mentioned previously, it is not superfluous to state again that the characteristics of the various structures of plagioclases have been established by making use of single crystal X-ray techniques. The measurements to be obtained from single crystal X-ray patterns generally give much more information than can be found in powder patterns. The specific characteristics of the powder method are responsible for this fact. Especially in the case of plagioclases the differences of both these X-ray diffraction methods are rather important. Smith and Gay discuss this aspect in detail and conclude that of the six lattice parameters of plagioclases only one is effectively useful in powder work. Consequently, in certain ranges of the group of plagioclases only *one* of the two variables, chemical composition and structure, can be determined with a powder pattern, provided the other is known. In Fig.56, modified after a figure published by the above-mentioned authors, it is illustrated that the error can be theoretically about 60% *An* if only the powder pattern is used for the determination. Such errors will never occur in practice, because of the presence of some helpful additional information. Such information bears upon the genesis of the rock or the association of minerals in such a rock if the plagioclase under investigation has been isolated from an igneous or a metamorphic rock. In other cases the index of refraction or the specific gravity might be known. A combination of such data with those drawn from the powder analysis will certainly lead to a useful conclusion, although J. V. SMITH and GAY (1958) are rather pessimistic about the practical application of powder methods in this special case.

The methods of Smith and Gay are divided into three groups. One group is applicable to sodium-rich plagioclases, the other to intermediate plagioclases and the third to calcium-rich plagioclases. As the high-temperature phases of this group of feldspars are thought to be less frequently encountered in sediments or soils, we may emphasize the identification of low-temperature phases.

Plagioclases with less than 20% An

The high-temperature phases of the composition between An_0 and An_{20} do not

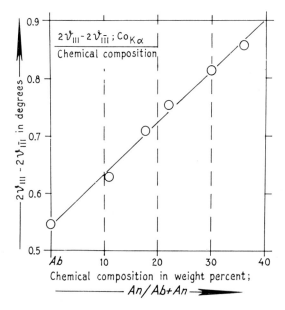

Fig.58. The values of $2\vartheta_{111} - 2\vartheta_{1\bar{1}1}$ plotted against chemical composition for natural low-temperature plagioclases. (After J.V. SMITH, 1956.) The data are listed in Table XIV. The curve is valid for Co radiation, for Cu radiation turn to the original paper.

show a large change in lattice parameters with an increase of the calcium content. Even a substitution of sodium by 50% *An* is hardly detectable. Consequently, the identification of high-temperature plagioclases with X-ray powder methods in this range looks rather hopeless, the more so because slight admixtures of potassium produce about the same change in the pattern as those due to large admixtures of calcium. Moreover, according to SEN (1959) these high-temperature plagioclases in particular are comparatively rich in potassium in some cases. It is at least helpful that the pattern of a high-temperature phase is rather different from the pattern of a low-temperature plagioclase, as can be seen from Table XXI and XXII which list data of high- and low-temperature Amelia albite. The values in these tables are given in 4ϑ cobalt radiation and in Å units. The values were recalculated with the formula on p.202, from values for $2\vartheta_{Cu}$ given by J. V. SMITH (1956, p.50, table II).

The low-temperature phases show a considerable change in lattice parameters with increasing calcium content. According to J. V. SMITH (1956) the separation between $\bar{1}32$ and 131 gives the best estimate of the chemical composition. In Fig.57, the relations of these spacings with the structural state and the chemical composition is given for $2\vartheta_{Co}$. The graph has been reconstructed on the basis of a graph from J. V. SMITH (1956, p.65, fig.4) listing values of copper radiations. The spacings $\bar{1}32$ and 131 occur at $33.85° \pm 0.1$ and $31.4° \pm 0.15$ $2\vartheta_{Cu}$ or at 2.654–2.638 and 2.860–2.833 Å or at $79.04° \pm 2.4$ and $73.26° \pm 3.4$ $4\vartheta_{Co}$, respectively.

If low-temperature structures prevail in the plagioclase concentrate, a fact that can be made plausible by a comparison of the chemical composition obtained by a measurement of the refractive index and the composition determined from the powder pattern, the determination can be checked by measuring the separation between 111 and 1$\bar{1}$1. These spacings are found at $23.6° \pm 1.0$ and $23.0° \pm 1.0$ $2\vartheta_{Cu}$ or at 3.782–3.751 and 3.880–3.847 Å or at $54.97° \pm 2.5$ and $53.55° \pm 2.3$ $4\vartheta_{Co}$, respectively. A graph showing the curve of 111–1$\bar{1}$1 plotted against the chemical composition as given in Fig.58, is again adopted from Smith but recalculated for $2\vartheta_{Co}$. Investigators who prefer or are obliged to work with copper radiation can use the values and the graphs in the paper by Smith.

In case the phases in the sample have a high-temperature structure the separation of 131 and 1$\bar{3}$1 is measured instead and compared with the graph in Fig.59, which lists this separation against the chemical composition expressed in ϑ-values for cobalt radiation. Again Smith's paper furnished the basis for this graph.

If the values obtained from the three graphs do not match, the possibility must be considered that intermediate phases are present. With "intermediate" we mean to indicate phases with an intermediate structure. Smith believes the chemical composition found with the combination of the $\bar{1}32$–131 and 111–1$\bar{1}$1 separations to be more reliable than the value arrived at with the 131–1$\bar{3}$1 separation.

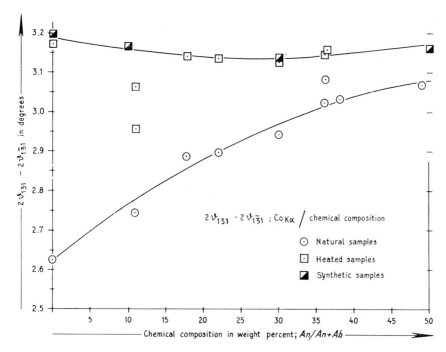

Fig.59. The values of $2\vartheta_{131} - 2\vartheta_{1\bar{3}1}$ of low- and high-temperature plagioclases plotted against the chemical composition. (After J. V. Smith, 1956.) The data are listed in Table XIV. The curve is valid for measurements with Co radiation. For Cu radiation turn to the original paper.

Plagioclases with more than 20% An, but less than 40% An

If phases with a chemical composition between An_{20} and An_{40} are present in the sample, Smith advises the use of the separation of 131 and $1\bar{3}1$. The relation between these two spacings and the chemical composition is shown in Fig.59. The two spacings just mentioned occur at 31.4° ± 0.15 and 29.9° ± 0.25 for $2\vartheta_{Cu}$, or at 2.860–2.833 and 3.010–2.942 Å, or at 73.26° ± 3.4 and 70.08° ± 7.2 $4\vartheta_{Co}$, respectively. According to Smith the separation of these spacings is not to be used for peristerites.

Other reflections, such as $2\bar{2}0$, $\bar{1}32$, $24\bar{1}$ and $\bar{2}41$, have also been used for the determination of the chemical composition. According to Smith these spacings meet with serious objections in certain regions of the whole range of plagioclases. For this reason we will not treat these reflections in this book. This does not imply that in certain circumstances these spacings cannot be very useful. The interested reader is advised to consult the paper by Goodyear and Duffin for information on these methods. It must be mentioned that the indexing of the powder patterns published by Goodyear and Duffin (1954) is not flawless and is met with criticism. The patterns themselves are considered reliable and a number of these are reported in Tables XXIII–XL in order to fill the gap between well-indexed albite and well-indexed anorthite patterns.

Plagioclases with more than 40% An

J. V. SMITH and GAY (1958) developed a procedure for the evaluation of the chemical composition of plagioclases with more than 40% *An*. They measured the relation between two variables Γ and B (based on certain structure parameters) and the chemical composition. The expression of these variables in terms of ϑ is given below:

$$\Gamma = 2 \cdot (\vartheta\ 131 + \vartheta\ 220 - 2\vartheta\ 1\bar{3}1)$$
$$B = 2 \cdot (\vartheta\ 1\bar{1}1 - \vartheta\ 20\bar{1})$$

There is a definite drawback in using a set of variables that are dependent on the wave-length of the X-rays. Moreover, converting values of 2ϑ for Cu radiation towards values of 2ϑ for Co radiation with the tables that are currently used,

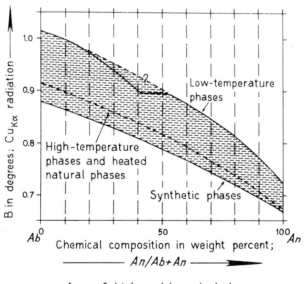

Area of high and low plagioclases, synthetic phases included

Limiting boundary of natural high temperature plagioclases and heated natural plagioclases

Fig.60. The variation of B ($2\vartheta_{1\bar{1}1} - 2\vartheta_{\bar{2}01}$) with the chemical composition of low- and high-temperature plagioclases. The figure expressing B in values for Cu radiation has been simplified after J. V. SMITH and GAY (1958, p.754).

L. van der Plas THE IDENTIFICATION OF DETRITAL
FELDSPARS
Elsevier Publishing Company, Amsterdam, 1966

ERRATUM

Fig.59 (p.199):

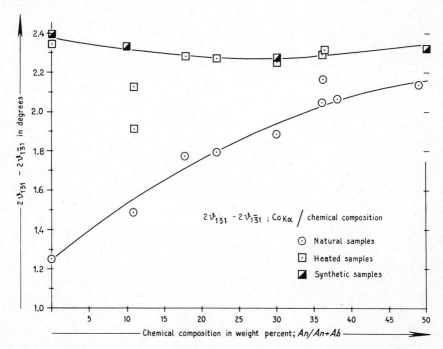

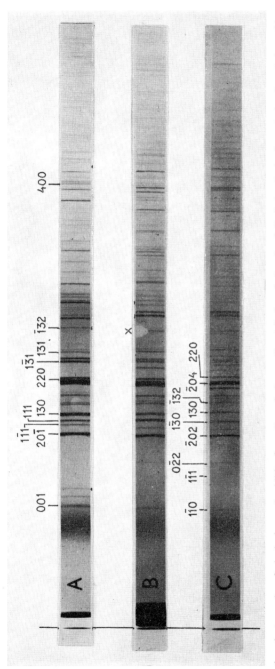

Fig.61. Powder photographs of plagioclases. A. Albite from Bucarischuna, Graubünden, Switzerland. B. Labradorite from Labrador. C. Anorthite from Kragero, Norway, cf. A.S.T.M. card 12-301. Quadruple Guinier-De Wolff camera, Co radiation; 30 kV, 10 mA, exposure time $2\frac{1}{4}$ h. Note the difference between the albite pattern, the intermediate plagioclase pattern and the anorthite pattern. The most important lines are indexed. NB. The shadow marked with a cross in pattern B is a calibration mark.

leads to inaccuracies that are large in comparison with the small differences to be measured, so large in fact that such converted data are useless. The only possible conversion that is accurate enough is found in the application of the following relation:

$$\sin \vartheta_{Co} = \frac{\lambda_{Co}}{\lambda_{Cu}} \cdot \sin \vartheta_{Cu}$$

The values of $\sin \vartheta$ have to be found in tables with more than five decimals, or may be calculated by a computer. The present author uses a simple computer program to convert values of 2ϑ or ϑ directly via the above relation. The paper by Smith and Gay gives data and charts in values of $2\vartheta_{Cu}$.

A recalculation of the values necessary to draw the charts of Γ and B for cobalt radiation is not possible, because Smith and Gay published the separations and the sums of these spacings only. According to Dr. P. Gay (personal communication, 1963) the absolute figures were never measured and are not available elsewhere. The values listed in table III of the paper by J.V. SMITH (1956) may function instead, but in this table the 220 values of only four samples are given. Consequently, the graph for Γ versus chemical composition cannot be constructed. With the same table a rough reconstruction of the B graph is possible. The values of Smith's table III were recalculated for cobalt radiation and are given in this book as Table XIV (pp.186–189). With these values the interested reader can make such a rough graph himself. Fig.60 giving the B graph from Smith and Gay; as well as Fig.56, giving the Γ graph of these authors, may function as an example.

CONCLUDING REMARKS

After this treatment of the analysis of powder patterns of feldspars, some remarks must be made concerning the applicability of these methods to samples of sediments and soils. We will concentrate on deposits of erosion products. Consequently, such sediments as tufaceous deposits will be left out. The treatment of feldspars in the latter types of sediments is much the same as the feldspar analysis of igneous and metamorphic rocks.

For an X-ray analysis of feldspars from sedimentary rocks, it is necessary to concentrate the feldspars, at least to a certain extent. Consolidated sediments have to be crushed in order to perform such a concentration. In crushing such rocks one must take care that the average particle size of the crushed material is of the same size as the original feldspar grains in these rocks. In some cases the matrix of such sediments allows for another process of fragmentation. Calcareous rocks, for instance, can be treated with an acid in order to obtain the noncalcareous fragments. Some sandstones can be rubbed for the loosening of single fragments. Other sediments will fragmentate by a treatment with an organic solvent or with gasoline or kerosene. Whatever the case may be, the samples must undergo such a treatment that the feldspars become available as single grains.

Afterwards the ground product or the unconsolidated sample can be subjected to flotation for a first concentration of the feldspars. This concentrate can be treated with heavy liquids for a coarse separation in alkali feldspars, albite, oligoclase and more calcium-rich plagioclases. The resulting fractions can be subjected to X-ray methods after powdering to a suitable grain size. In some cases it is useful to select a number of apparently similar grains from the fraction with a stereo microscope or with a petrographic microscope. The selected grains can be powdered under acetone and the powder can be used for an X-ray powder diagram with the Guinier-De Wolff camera. If only two or three grains are handpicked out of a fraction, the Guinier-De Wolff camera is not suitable for the preparation of an X-ray photograph. In this special case, HIEMSTRA's method (1959) can be used with good results (see p.177).

Some comments on the usefulness of the methods described in the foregoing paragraphs may be given also. The feldspar fraction of a large number of sediments contains a limited number of important phases. It is the author's opinion that only in a small number of cases more than four different feldspars occur in about equal quantities in such samples. Old and frequently reworked sediments are devoid of calcium-rich plagioclases because these phases weather more easily. Sediments with a small and nearby region of provenance may furnish such complex samples as previously anticipated. These sediments may hold a mineral assemblage composed of an important fraction of the local igneous and metamorphic rocks and of a number of minerals of older sediments. In fact, such feldspar assemblages may be rather difficult to unravel. On the other hand, the efficiency, the accuracy and the reliability of X-ray powder methods is in most cases higher than of other information-seeking methods generally used by sedimentologists. Finally, the additional information provided by the specific properties of the concentration techniques is of great help in drawing the right conclusions from powder patterns.

CONCERNING THE TABLES

This book contains a number of tables giving powder data of some feldspars taken from literature. For the reader's convenience the spacings are given in values of $2\vartheta_{Co}$, $4\vartheta_{Co}$ and Ångstrom units. The data were mostly recalculated from values for Cu-radiation or values in Å units. When available these original values are also given.

In fact, the author is a fervent advocate of using Ångstrom units in reporting X-ray powder patterns. In feldspar work, however, the differences of the spacings are often so small that they can only be reliably measured on diffractometer traces or on Guinier-De Wolff photographs. A transformation of such values expressed in degrees with the currently used tables into Ångstrom units leads to inaccurate values in comparison with the measurements[1]. The powder patterns of alkali feldspars are listed in Tables XV–XXIII, those of plagioclases in Tables XXI–XL.

N.B. In these tables values calculated by the present author are always given in four decimals if they were the result of applying the formula of p.202. It goes without saying that the last two decimals may have no practical meaning.

Finally, we ask the readers' attention for the existence of X-ray powder data card files. Such card files contain a large number of X-ray powder patterns of various crystalline substances. The section on minerals of the A.S.T.M. X-ray Powder Data File, for instance, contains a number of reliable feldspar patterns. Feldspar patterns not taken from literature, but purposely prepared for the system are also found. The file mentioned here is published by the American Society for Testing Materials. It seems that a comparable file of excellent quality is issued by a Russian institute. The author could not trace more details of this file because the information reached him after the present text was finished.

---

[1] Of late new graphical tables (PARRISH and MACK, 1963) have become available. As the author has not yet been able to verify these tables, they are to be excluded from the ones mentioned in this sentence.

TABLE XV[1]

X-RAY POWDER PATTERN OF A SYNTHETIC HIGH-TEMPERATURE ALKALI FELDSPAR

$2\vartheta_{Fe}$	$2\vartheta_{Co}$	$4\vartheta_{Co}$	hkl	d Å
16.8	15.5156	31.0312	110	6.63
17.1	15.7923	31.5846	020	6.51
17.2	15.8846	31.7692	001	6.47
19.0	17.5448	35.0896	$11\bar{1}$	5.86
24.4	22.5211	45.0422	021	4.58
26.4	24.3624	48.7248	$20\bar{1}$	4.24
28.4	26.2024	52.4048	111	3.95
29.0	26.7542	53.5084	200	3.87
29.6	27.3059	54.6118	130	3.789
31.0	28.5927	57.1854	$13\bar{1}$	3.623
31.6	29.1439	58.2478	$22\bar{1}$	3.555
32.5	29.9706	59.9412	$11\bar{2}$	3.460
33.7	31.0723	62.1446	220	3.340
34.3	31.6230	63.2460	$20\bar{2}$	3.283
34.6	31.8983	63.7964	040	3.255
35.0	32.2653	64.5306	002	3.219
37.7	34.6407	69.2814	131	3.004
38.5	35.4736	70.9472	$22\bar{2}$	2.936
38.9	35.8399	71.6798	041	2.907
39.2	36.1146	72.2292	022	2.886
40.2	37.0300	74.0600	201	2.817
40.4	37.2130	74.4260	$31\bar{1}$	2.803
41.0	37.7619	75.5238	$13\bar{2}$	2.764
43.6	40.1386	80.2772	$31\bar{2}$	2.606
44.0	40.5039	81.0078	221	2.584
44.0	40.5039	81.0078	$24\bar{1}$	2.584
44.7	41.1430	82.2860	112	2.545
45.0	41.4168	82.8336	310	2.529
45.8	42.1468	84.2936	240	2.488
46.2	42.5116	85.0232	150	2.467
47.1	43.3322	86.6644	$15\bar{1}$	2.423
47.7	43.8789	87.7578	$33\bar{1}$	2.394
48.2	44.3344	88.6688	$20\bar{3}$	2.370
49.4	45.4269	90.8538	$11\bar{3}$	2.316
49.5	45.5179	91.0358	$24\bar{2}$	2.328
50.0	45.9729	91.9458	042	2.290
50.5	46.4276	92.8552	$33\bar{2}$	2.270
51.5	47.3367	94.6734	$22\bar{3}$	2.228
51.5	47.3367	94.6734	132	2.228
51.8	47.6093	95.2186	330	2.216
52.1	47.8818	95.7636	151	2.204
53.0	48.6990	97.3980	060	2.170

[1] The chemical composition of this synthetic high-temperature phase is $KAlSi_3O_8$. The values for Fe radiation have been calculated from unit cell parameters by GOLDSMITH and LAVES (1954). The other values were added by the present author. In this and in the following tables ϑ values are always given in four decimals if they were calculated by the formula of p.202; it goes without saying that the last two decimals have no practical meaning.

TABLE XVI[1]

X-RAY POWDER PATTERN OF A SYNTHETIC HIGH-TEMPERATURE ALKALI FELDSPAR

$2\vartheta_{Cu}$	$2\vartheta_{Co}$	$4\vartheta_{Co}$	hkl	$d\ \text{Å}$
13.31	15.4684	30.9368	110	6.65
13.59	15.7943	31.5886	020	6.51
13.74	15.9690	31.9380	001	6.44
15.095	17.5468	35.0936	$11\bar{1}$	5.80
19.37	22.5313	45.0626	021	4.58
20.945	24.3704	48.7408	$20\bar{1}$	4.24
22.54	26.2346	52.4692	111	3.941
22.98	26.7492	53.4984	200	3.867
23.485	27.3400	54.6800	130	3.785
24.565	28.6042	57.2084	$13\bar{1}$	3.621
25.05	29.1722	58.3444	$22\bar{1}$	3.552
25.76	30.0041	60.0082	$11\bar{2}$	3.455
26.79	31.2117	62.4234	220	3.325
27.13	31.6105	63.2210	$20\bar{2}$	3.284
27.35	31.8686	63.7372	040	3.258
27.66	32.2324	64.4648	002	3.222
29.795	34.7405	69.4810	131	2.996
30.43	35.4874	70.9748	$22\bar{2}$	2.935
30.73	35.8404	71.6808	041	2.907
30.93	36.0758	72.1516	022	2.889
31.75	37.0413	74.0826	201	2.816
31.91	37.2298	74.4596	$31\bar{1}$	2.802
32.34	37.7365	75.4730	$13\bar{2}$	2.766
34.315	40.0667	80.1334	$31\bar{2}$	2.611
34.67	40.4860	80.9720	221	2.585
34.96	40.5097	81.0194	$24\bar{1}$	2.584
40.89	47.8616	95.7232	151	2.205
41.55	48.6476	97.2952	060	2.171
41.76	48.8979	97.7958	313	2.161
50.64	59.5551	119.1102	062	1.8010
50.87	59.8334	119.6668	043	1.7934
50.87	59.8334	119.6668	$20\bar{4}$	1.7934
50.94	59.9180	119.8360	$17\bar{1}$	1.7911

[1] The chemical composition of this synthetic high-temperature phase is $KAlSi_3O_8$. The values for Cu radiation have been measured by DONNAY and DONNAY (1952). The indexing of the pattern is also adopted from the afore-mentioned authors. Other values were added by the present author.

FOOTNOTE TO TABLE XVII
[1] The chemical composition of this natural low-temperature phase is practically pure $KAlSi_3O_8$. The powder pattern has been calculated from the reciprocal lattice parameters recently published by FINNEY and BAILEY (1964). Calculated values of a comparable phase have previously been published by GOLDSMITH and LAVES (1954a, b) for Fe radiation. The material was derived from the Pontis limestone, Switzerland. The same material has been used as a standard by GOLDSMITH and LAVES (1961), and is consequently used as a standard in Fig.53.

TABLE XVII[1]

X-RAY POWDER PATTERN OF A NATURAL LOW-TEMPERATURE ALKALI FELDSPAR, AN AUTHIGENIC MAXIMUM MICROCLINE

$2\vartheta_{Co}$	$4\vartheta_{Co}$	hkl	$d\ \text{Å}$	$2\vartheta_{Co}$	$4\vartheta_{Co}$	hkl	$d\ \text{Å}$
15.2604	30.5207	110	6.736	43.3049	86.6098	$33\bar{1}$	2.4241
15.7914	31.5829	$1\bar{1}0$	6.511	43.9510	87.9019	$\bar{1}51$	2.3903
15.8399	31.6798	001	6.491	44.0839	88.1679	$20\bar{3}$	2.3834
15.8782	31.7564	020	6.476	44.9888	89.9777	$\bar{3}31$	2.3379
17.3609	34.7219	$11\bar{1}$	5.926	45.0059	90.0117	$24\bar{2}$	2.3370
17.7148	35.4296	$\bar{1}11$	5.809	45.0879	90.1758	$11\bar{3}$	2.3330
22.4079	44.8157	021	4.603	45.1381	90.2762	$\bar{1}13$	2.3305
22.5935	45.1871	$02\bar{1}$	4.566	45.7352	91.4705	042	2.3017
24.4737	48.9473	$2\bar{0}1$	4.220	45.8270	91.6541	$33\bar{2}$	2.2973
25.9611	51.9221	111	3.9820	46.1308	92.2616	$04\bar{2}$	2.2830
26.3640	52.7281	$1\bar{1}1$	3.9222	46.1997	92.3995	$\bar{2}42$	2.2798
26.8552	53.7103	200	3.8518	46.7713	93.5426	132	2.2535
27.0119	54.0239	130	3.8298	46.9004	93.8008	$22\bar{3}$	2.2476
27.9363	55.8727	$1\bar{3}0$	3.7055	46.9483	93.8966	330	2.2454
28.3581	56.7162	$13\bar{1}$	3.6515	47.2955	94.5910	$\bar{3}32$	2.2299
28.7961	57.5922	$22\bar{1}$	3.5971	47.3853	94.7706	$\bar{2}23$	2.2260
29.0244	58.0488	$\bar{1}31$	3.5694	47.4396	94.8792	151	2.2235
29.7493	59.4987	$11\bar{2}$	3.4843	47.6430	95.2859	$13\bar{2}$	2.2146
29.8127	59.6254	$\bar{2}21$	3.4771	48.6344	97.2688	$15\bar{1}$	2.1721
29.8923	59.7846	$\bar{1}12$	3.4680	48.6451	97.2901	$31\bar{3}$	2.1717
30.8001	61.6002	220	3.3681	48.6751	97.3502	$33\bar{0}$	2.1704
31.5473	63.0946	$20\bar{2}$	3.2904	48.8332	97.6664	003	2.1638
31.8932	63.7864	$2\bar{2}0$	3.2556	48.9472	97.8945	241	2.1591
31.9930	63.9861	002	3.2457	48.9582	97.9164	060	2.1586
32.0719	64.1439	040	3.2379	49.0698	98.1397	$\bar{3}13$	2.1540
34.3218	68.6436	131	3.0314	50.0157	100.0314	$40\bar{1}$	2.1159
35.1372	70.2745	$22\bar{2}$	2.9632	50.0769	100.1538	$15\bar{2}$	2.1134
35.2561	70.5121	$1\bar{3}1$	2.9536	50.1629	100.3258	$40\bar{2}$	2.1100
35.7868	71.5737	022	2.9112	50.5389	101.0777	$\bar{1}52$	2.0953
35.8405	71.6810	041	2.9070	50.6227	101.2454	$24\bar{1}$	2.0921
35.8716	71.7433	$\bar{2}22$	2.9045	50.9253	101.8506	$13\bar{3}$	2.0805
36.0292	72.0583	$02\bar{2}$	2.8922	50.9570	101.9141	311	2.0794
36.0825	72.1650	$04\bar{1}$	2.8881	51.0626	102.1253	$\bar{1}33$	2.0753
37.0408	74.0815	201	2.8159	51.0738	102.1476	202	2.0749
37.1365	74.2729	$31\bar{1}$	2.8089	51.5407	103.0814	023	2.0573
37.5204	75.0408	$13\bar{2}$	2.7812	51.5494	103.0988	$3\bar{1}1$	2.0570
37.7793	75.5585	$\bar{3}11$	2.7629	51.6475	103.2950	061	2.0533
37.8692	75.7385	$\bar{1}32$	2.7565	51.8124	103.6248	$02\bar{3}$	2.0473
39.9208	79.8415	$31\bar{2}$	2.6202	51.9188	103.8377	$06\bar{1}$	2.0433
39.9845	79.9691	$24\bar{1}$	2.6161	52.1405	104.2810	$42\bar{1}$	2.0353
40.0365	80.0730	221	2.6129	52.3283	104.6566	$42\bar{2}$	2.0285
40.4714	80.9429	$3\bar{1}2$	2.5860	53.3899	106.7797	222	1.9911
40.7557	81.5114	112	2.5687	53.4789	106.9578	$\bar{4}21$	1.9879
41.0209	82.0418	$2\bar{2}1$	2.5528	53.5751	107.1503	$\bar{4}22$	1.9847
41.0812	82.1625	$1\bar{1}2$	2.5492	53.8433	107.6866	$33\bar{3}$	1.9754
41.2775	82.5550	310	2.5377	54.2703	108.5406	$2\bar{2}2$	1.9611
41.4566	82.9132	240	2.5271	54.4143	108.8287	$35\bar{1}$	1.9563
41.5092	83.0184	$\bar{2}41$	2.5240	54.5644	109.1288	$26\bar{1}$	1.9513
41.9198	83.8397	$3\bar{1}0$	2.5004	55.0231	110.0461	$\bar{3}33$	1.9363
42.2025	84.4051	150	2.4845	55.1167	110.2334	$24\bar{3}$	1.9333
43.1464	86.2928	$2\bar{4}0$	2.4326	55.3470	110.6940	400	1.9259
43.1774	86.3547	$15\bar{1}$	2.4309	55.6916	111.3832	260	1.9150
43.2501	86.5003	$1\bar{5}0$	2.4270	55.7578	111.5157	$40\bar{3}$	1.9128

Footnote is given on p.206.

TABLE XVIII[1]

X-RAY POWDER PATTERN OF A SYNTHETIC HIGH-TEMPERATURE ALKALI FELDSPAR $(Na_{61}K_{39})$ $AlSi_3O_8$

$2\vartheta_{Cu}$	$2\vartheta_{Co}$	$4\vartheta_{Co}$	hkl	$d\ \text{Å}$
13.655	15.8700	31.7400	020	6.48
13.67	15.8875	31.7750	110	6.47
13.78	16.0155	32.0310	001	6.42
15.27	17.7507	35.5014	$11\bar{1}$	5.80
19.45	22.6246	45.2492	021	4.56
21.585	25.1182	50.2364	$20\bar{1}$	4.11
22.915	26.6732	53.3464	111	3.877
23.77	27.6735	55.3470	130	3.740
23.79	27.6969	55.3938	200	3.737
24.745	28.8149	57.6298	$13\bar{1}$	3.595
25.63	29.8517	59.7034	$22\bar{1}$	3.473
25.83	30.0861	60.1722	$11\bar{2}$	3.445
27.49	32.0329	64.0658	$20\bar{2}$	3.242
27.51	32.0564	64.1128	040	3.239
27.53	32.0799	64.1598	220	3.234
27.77	32.3615	64.7230	002	3.209
30.14	35.1463	70.2926	131	2.963
30.79	35.9110	71.8220	$22\bar{2}$	2.902
30.86	35.9934	71.9868	041	2.895
31.04	36.2053	72.4106	022	2.879
32.45	37.8662	75.7324	$13\bar{2}$	2.757
32.55	37.9841	75.9682	201	2.748
33.00	38.5147	78.0294	$31\bar{1}$	2.712
35.14	41.0415	82.0830	$31\bar{2}$	2.552
35.20	41.1124	82.2248	$24\bar{1}$	2.547
35.445	41.4021	82.8042	221	2.530
35.59	41.5735	83.1470	112	2.521
36.64	42.8161	85.6322	150	2.451
36.65	42.8279	85.6558	240	2.450
36.67	42.8516	85.7032	310	2.449
37.30	43.5979	87.1958	$15\bar{1}$	2.409
38.09	44.5345	89.0690	$20\bar{3}$	2.361
38.535	45.0624	90.1248	$33\bar{1}$	2.334
38.895	45.4898	90.9796	$11\bar{3}$	2.313
39.35	46.0302	92.0604	$24\bar{2}$	2.288
39.455	46.1549	92.3098	042	2.282
40.42	47.3022	94.6044	$33\bar{2}$	2.230
40.64	47.5640	95.1280	223	2.218
40.82	47.7782	95.5564	132	2.209
41.245	48.2843	96.5686	151	2.187
41.75	48.8859	97.7718	060	2.162
41.78	48.9219	97.8434	330	2.160
42.16	49.3747	98.7494	003	2.142
50.87	59.8334	119.6668	062	1.7934
51.00	59.9907	119.9814	$20\bar{4}$	1.7891
51.07	60.0754	120.1508	043	1.7690

[1] The values for Cu radiation have been calculated by DONNAY and DONNAY (1952). The indexing of the pattern is also adopted from the afore-mentioned authors. Other values were added by the present author.

TABLE XIX[1]

X-RAY POWDER PATTERN OF A SYNTHETIC HIGH-TEMPERATURE ALKALI FELDSPAR $(Na_{71}K_{29})$ $AlSi_3O_8$

$2\vartheta_{Cu}$	$2\vartheta_{Co}$	$4\vartheta_{Co}$	hkl	$d\ \AA$
13.67	15.8875	31.7750	$1\bar{1}0$	6.47
13.68	15.8991	31.7982	020	6.47
13.815	16.0563	32.1126	001	6.41
13.83	16.0737	32.1474	110	6.40
15.22	17.6925	35.3850	$11\bar{1}$	5.82
15.40	17.9021	35.8042	$\bar{1}11$	5.75
19.23	22.3679	44.7358	$02\bar{1}$	4.61
19.75	22.9748	45.9496	021	4.49
21.715	25.2701	50.5402	$20\bar{1}$	4.09
22.87	26.6205	53.2410	$1\bar{1}1$	3.885
23.19	26.9949	53.9898	111	3.832
23.71	27.6033	55.2066	$1\bar{3}0$	3.749
23.97	27.9076	55.8152	200	3.712
23.995	27.9368	55.8736	130	3.706
24.625	28.6744	57.3488	$13\bar{1}$	3.612
24.975	29.0843	58.1686	$\bar{1}31$	3.562
25.71	29.9455	59.8910	$11\bar{2}$	3.464
25.73	29.9689	59.9378	$22\bar{1}$	3.459
25.78	30.0275	60.0550	$\bar{2}21$	3.453
26.02	30.3088	60.6176	$11\bar{2}$	3.422
27.54	32.0916	64.1832	$2\bar{2}0$	3.236
27.565	32.1209	64.2418	040	3.233
27.57	32.1268	64.2536	$20\bar{2}$	3.232
27.84	32.4437	64.8874	002	3.202
27.865	32.4731	64.9462	220	3.199
29.91	34.8758	69.7516	$13\bar{1}$	2.985
30.59	35.6757	71.3514	$04\bar{1}$	2.920
30.63	35.7227	71.4454	131	2.916
30.685	35.7874	71.5748	$22\bar{2}$	2.911
30.78	35.8992	71.7984	$02\bar{2}$	2.902
31.06	36.2288	72.4576	$\bar{2}22$	2.877
35.255	41.1774	82.3548	$31\bar{2}$	2.544
35.295	41.2247	82.4494	$24\bar{1}$	2.541
35.36	41.3016	82.6032	$\bar{3}12$	2.536
35.37	41.3134	82.6268	$\bar{2}41$	2.536
35.375	41.3193	82.6386	$2\bar{2}1$	2.535
35.56	41.5381	83.0762	$1\bar{1}2$	2.532
40.99	47.9806	95.9612	$\bar{2}23$	2.200
41.80	48.9455	97.8910	$3\bar{3}0$	2.159
41.84	48.9932	97.9864	060	2.157
42.615	49.9175	99.8350	$15\bar{2}$	2.120

[1] The values for Cu radiation have been calculated by DONNAY and DONNAY (1952). The indexing of the pattern is also adopted from the afore-mentioned authors. Other values were added by the present author.

TABLE XX[1]

X-RAY POWDER PATTERN OF A SYNTHETIC HIGH-TEMPERATURE ALBITE

$2\vartheta_{Cu}$	$2\vartheta_{Co}$	$4\vartheta_{Co}$	hkl	$d\ \text{Å}$
13.72	15.9457	31.8914	$\bar{1}10$	6.45
13.78	16.0155	32.0310	020	6.42
13.92	16.1785	32.3570	001	6.36
14.15	16.4463	32.8926	110	6.25
15.155	17.6167	35.2334	$11\bar{1}$	5.84
15.68	18.2284	36.4568	$\bar{1}11$	5.65
18.905	21.9886	43.9772	$02\bar{1}$	4.69
20.35	23.6754	47.3508	021	4.36
21.975	25.5740	51.1480	$20\bar{1}$	4.04
22.87	26.6205	53.2410	$1\bar{1}1$	3.885
23.695	27.5857	55.1714	$\bar{1}30$	3.752
23.745	27.6442	55.2884	111	3.744
24.345	28.3466	56.6932	200	3.653
24.455	28.4754	56.9508	130	3.637
24.485	28.5105	57.0210	$13\bar{1}$	3.632
25.475	29.6701	59.3402	$\bar{1}31$	3.493
25.575	29.7873	59.5746	$11\bar{2}$	3.479
25.95	30.2267	60.4534	$22\bar{1}$	3.431
26.115	30.4202	60.8404	$\bar{2}21$	3.409
26.445	30.8071	61.6142	$\bar{1}12$	3.374
27.64	32.2089	64.4178	$2\bar{2}0$	3.225
27.765	32.3557	64.7114	$20\bar{2}$	3.210
27.77	32.3615	64.7230	040	3.210
28.055	32.6961	65.3922	002	3.178
28.515	33.2363	66.4726	220	3.128
29.56	34.4642	68.9284	$1\bar{3}1$	3.019
30.24	35.2639	70.5278	$04\bar{1}$	2.953
30.44	35.4980	70.9960	$0\bar{2}2$	2.934
30.56	35.6404	71.2808	$2\bar{2}2$	2.923
31.57	36.8293	73.6586	131	2.831
31.63	36.9000	73.8000	$\bar{2}22$	2.826
31.64	36.9118	73.8236	$13\bar{2}$	2.825
32.09	37.4419	74.8838	041	2.787
32.275	37.6599	75.3198	022	2.771
33.245	38.8037	77.6074	201	2.692
33.63	39.2580	78.5160	$\bar{3}11$	2.664
33.75	39.3996	78.7992	$31\bar{1}$	2.653
33.755	39.4055	78.8110	$\bar{1}32$	2.653
35.375	41.3193	82.6386	$2\bar{2}1$	2.535
35.51	41.4789	82.9578	$31\bar{2}$	2.526
35.535	41.5085	83.0170	$24\bar{1}$	2.524
35.62	41.6090	83.2180	$1\bar{1}2$	2.518
35.79	41.8101	83.6202	$\bar{2}41$	2.507
35.815	41.8397	83.6794	$\bar{3}12$	2.505
41.96	49.1363	98.2726	$3\bar{3}0$	2.151
42.01	49.1959	98.3918	$15\bar{2}$	2.149
42.16	49.3747	98.7494	060	2.142
42.455	49.7266	99.4532	$31\bar{3}$	2.127

[1]The values for Cu radiation have been calculated by DONNAY and DONNAY (1952). The indexing of the pattern is also adopted from the afore-mentioned authors. Other values were added by the present author.

TABLE XXI[1]

X-RAY POWDER PATTERN OF NATURAL AMELIA ALBITE

I_{Cu}	$2\vartheta_{Cu}$ obs.	$2\vartheta_{Cu}$ calc.	hkl	$2\vartheta_{Co}$ obs.	$2\vartheta_{Co}$ calc.	$4\vartheta_{Co}$ calc.	d Å
75	13.86	13.855	001	16.1087	16.1028	32.2056	6.38
—	—	13.89	020	—	16.1436	32.2872	6.37
2	14.9	14.98	11$\bar{1}$	17.3197	17.4129	34.8258	5.91
4	15.85	15.86	$\bar{1}$11	18.4264	18.4381	36.8762	5.58
60	22.057	22.055	20$\bar{1}$	25.6699	25.6676	51.3352	4.026
20	23.071	23.07	1$\bar{1}$1	26.8556	26.8545	53.7090	3.853
85	23.538	23.54	111	27.4020	27.4044	54.8088	3.776
70	24.155	24.155	130	28.1241	28.1241	56.2482	3.681
50	24.306	24.27	13$\bar{1}$	28.3009	28.2588	56.5176	3.663
—	—	24.335	1$\bar{3}$0	—	28.3349	56.6698	3.653
5	25.185	—	002β	29.3303	—	—	—
35	25.392	25.40	11$\bar{2}$	29.5728	29.5822	59.1644	3.504
5	25.57	25.565	22$\bar{1}$	29.7814	29.7755	59.5510	3.482
20	26.418	26.415	$\bar{1}$12	30.7754	30.7719	61.5438	3.371
360	27.915	27.92	002	32.5318	32.5376	65.0752	3.193
—	—	27.99	040	—	32.6198	65.2396	3.185
—	—	28.12	220	—	32.7724	65.5448	3.171
30	28.325	28.325	2$\bar{2}$0	33.0132	33.0132	66.0264	3.148
30	30.148	30.145	1$\bar{3}$1	35.1557	35.1521	70.3042	2.962
—	—	30.225	22$\bar{2}$	—	35.2462	70.4924	2.954
50	30.48	30.51	02$\bar{2}$	35.5462	35.5815	71.1630	2.928
—	—	30.54	04$\bar{1}$	—	35.6168	71.2336	2.925
20	31.210	31.23	131	36.4054	36.4290	72.8580	2.862
3	31.47	31.505	13$\bar{2}$	36.7116	36.7528	73.5056	2.837
3	32.11	32.105	022	37.4655	37.4596	74.9192	2.785
—	—	32.155	041	—	37.5185	75.0370	2.781
15	33.946	33.94	$\bar{1}$32	39.6310	39.6239	79.2478	2.639
20	34.996	34.995	24$\bar{1}$	40.8713	40.8701	81.7402	2.562
3	35.34	35.32	31$\bar{2}$	41.2779	41.2543	82.5086	2.539
4	35.72	35.70	1$\bar{1}$2	41.7273	41.7036	83.4072	2.513
2	35.95	35.945	2$\bar{2}$1	41.9994	41.9935	83.9870	2.496
2	36.5	36.495	221	42.6503	42.6444	85.2888	2.459
7	36.757	36.76	$\bar{2}$41	42.9546	42.9582	85.9164	2.443
5	36.95	36.955	15$\bar{1}$	43.1832	43.1891	86.3782	2.431
5	37.35	37.305	240	43.6571	43.6038	87.2076	2.408
—	—	37.425	1$\bar{5}$0	—	43.7460	87.4920	2.401
7	37.64	37.625	310	44.0009	43.9831	87.9662	2.388
10	38.78	38.78	33$\bar{1}$	45.3533	45.3533	90.7066	2.320
4	39.52	39.515	$\bar{1}$13	46.2322	46.2262	92.4524	2.279
10	41.21	41.20	042	48.2426	48.2307	96.4614	2.189
—	—	41.22	$\bar{2}$42	—	48.2545	96.5090	2.188
20	42.51	42.50	060	49.7922	49.7803	99.5606	2.125
—	—	42.62	13$\bar{3}$	—	49.9235	99.8470	2.119
15	42.63	42.665	151	49.9354	49.9772	99.9544	2.117
5	43.55	43.545	2$\bar{4}$1	51.0340	51.0280	102.0560	2.076
5	44.48	44.47	241	52.1461	52.1341	104.2682	2.035
3	45.29	45.305	202	53.1160	53.1340	106.2680	2.000
10	45.78	45.795	061	53.7033	53.7213	107.4426	1.979
5	47.125	47.145	42$\bar{1}$	55.3179	55.3419	110.6838	1.926

TABLE XXI *(continued)*

I_{Cu}	$2\vartheta_{Cu}$ obs.	$2\vartheta_{Cu}$ calc.	hkl	$2\vartheta_{Co}$ obs.	$2\vartheta_{Co}$ calc.	$4\vartheta_{Co}$ calc.	dÅ
—	—	48.105	$35\bar{1}$	—	56.4966	112.9932	1.890
20	48.115	48.11	222	56.5086	56.5026	113.0052	1.889
8	49.17	49.19	$40\bar{3}$	57.7798	57.8039	115.6078	1.851
10	49.38	49.405	$1\bar{5}2$	58.0331	58.0633	116.1266	1.844
—	—	49.405	$\bar{2}61$	—	58.0633	116.1266	1.843
—	—	49.435	260	—	58.0995	116.1990	1.841
15	49.80	49.82	$2\bar{6}0$	58.5401	58.5642	117.1284	1.829
—	—	49.825	$\bar{2}43$	—	58.5703	117.1406	1.828
65	49.945	49.93	$04\bar{3}$	58.7152	58.6971	117.3942	1.825
—	—	49.98	$35\bar{1}$	—	58.7574	117.5148	1.823
—	—	49.985	$06\bar{2}$	—	58.7635	117.5270	1.823
20	50.54	50.55	113	59.4342	59.4463	118.8926	1.804
30	51.115	51.12	$20\bar{4}$	60.1298	60.1359	120.2718	1.785

[1] The values for Cu radiation have been measured and calculated by J. V. SMITH (1956). Other values were added by the present author. *d*-values calculated from $2\vartheta_{Cu}$ calc.

TABLE XXII[1]

X-RAY POWDER PATTERN OF HEATED AMELIA ALBITE

I_{Cu}	$2\vartheta_{Cu}$ obs.	$2\vartheta_{Cu}$ calc.	hkl	$2\vartheta_{Co}$ obs.	$2\vartheta_{Co}$ calc.	$4\vartheta_{Co}$ calc.	d Å
—	—	13.73	$1\bar{1}0$	16.0097	15.9573	31.9146	6.44
20	13.775	13.79	020	16.0097	16.0272	32.0544	6.42
30	13.93	13.94	001	16.1902	16.2018	32.4036	6.35
3	15.17	15.185	$11\bar{1}$	17.6342	17.6517	35.3034	5.83
3	15.64	15.68	$\bar{1}11$	18.1817	18.2284	36.4568	5.65
2	18.92	18.955	$02\bar{1}$	22.0061	22.0469	44.0938	4.677
60	22.00	21.995	$20\bar{1}$	25.6033	25.5974	51.1948	4.038
40	22.915	22.905	$1\bar{1}1$	26.6732	26.6615	53.3230	3.879
100	23.73	23.715	$1\bar{3}0$	27.6267	27.6091	55.2182	3.749
—	—	23.75	111	—	27.6501	55.3002	3.743
35	24.46	24.47	130	28.4812	28.4929	56.9858	3.635
—	—	24.54	$13\bar{1}$	—	28.5749	57.1498	3.624
5	25.35	—	002β	29.5236	—	—	—
15	25.63	25.635	$11\bar{2}$	29.8517	29.8576	59.7152	3.472
25	26.445	26.46	$\bar{1}12$	30.8071	30.8247	61.6494	3.366
—	—	27.66	$2\bar{2}0$	—	32.2324	64.4648	3.222
160	27.785	27.79	040	32.3791	32.3850	64.7700	3.207
—	—	27.805	$20\bar{2}$	—	32.4026	64.8052	3.206
360	28.095	28.095	002	32.7431	32.7431	65.4862	3.174
40	28.525	28.535	220	33.2480	33.2598	66.5196	3.126
25	29.62	29.62	$1\bar{3}1$	34.5348	34.5348	69.0696	3.013
30	30.295	30.305	$04\bar{1}$	35.3286	35.3403	70.6806	2.947
35	30.54	30.52	$02\bar{2}$	35.6168	35.5934	71.1866	2.926
5?	30.65	30.655	$22\bar{2}$	35.7463	35.7521	71.5042	2.914
35	31.61	31.595	131	36.8764	36.8588	73.7176	2.829

TABLE XXII *(continued)*

I_{Cu}	$2\vartheta_{Cu}$ obs.	$2\vartheta_{Cu}$ calc.	hkl	$2\vartheta_{Co}$ obs.	$2\vartheta_{Co}$ calc.	$4\vartheta_{Co}$ calc.	d Å
12	33.74	33.745	$\bar{1}32$	39.3878	39.3937	78.7874	2.654
—	—	33.78	$31\bar{1}$	—	39.4350	78.8700	2.651
—	—	35.57	$31\bar{2}$	—	41.5499	83.0998	2.522
20	35.62	35.595	$24\bar{1}$	41.6090	41.5794	83.1588	2.520
—	—	35.685	$1\bar{1}2$	—	41.6859	83.3718	2.514
20	35.80	35.78	$\bar{2}41$	41.8219	41.7983	83.5966	2.507
—	—	35.835	$\bar{3}12$	—	41.8633	83.7266	2.497
3	36.655	36.64	112	42.8338	42.8161	85.6322	2.450
—	—	36.645	$1\bar{5}0$	—	42.8220	85.6440	2.450
7	37.94	37.925	240	44.3566	44.3388	88.6776	2.370
5	39.12	39.085	$\bar{3}31$	45.7570	45.7154	91.4308	2.302
4	39.47	39.44	$33\bar{1}$	46.1728	46.1371	92.2742	2.283
5	39.735	39.72	$\bar{1}13$	46.4877	46.4698	92.9396	2.267
3	40.13	40.13	$1\bar{3}2$	46.9573	46.9573	93.9146	2.245
—	40.49	40.485	$\bar{2}42$	47.3855	47.3796	94.7592	2.226
—	—	40.515	$1\bar{5}1$	—	47.4153	94.8306	2.225
2	41.34	41.32	042	48.3974	48.3736	96.7472	2.183
—	—	41.375	$\bar{3}32$	—	48.4391	96.8782	2.180
20	42.19	42.19	060	49.4105	49.4105	98.8210	2.140
—	—	42.535	$31\bar{3}$	—	49.8221	99.6442	2.123
15	42.6	42.665	003	49.8996	49.9772	99.9544	2.117
—	—	42.70	132	—	50.0189	100.0378	2.117
7	43.025	43.025	151	50.4069	50.4069	100.8138	2.100
3?	45.5	45.47	$\bar{1}31$	53.3676	53.3317	106.6634	1.993
5	45.62	45.605	$3\bar{1}1$	53.5115	53.4935	106.9870	1.987
—	—	46.735	$24\bar{3}$	—	54.8493	109.6986	1.942
5	46.77	46.755	$2\bar{2}2$	54.8914	54.8733	109.7466	1.941
3	47.2	47.19	$\bar{4}22$	55.4080	55.3960	110.7920	1.924
15	48.57	48.57	222	57.0566	57.0566	114.1132	1.873
5	49.22	49.175	$40\bar{3}$	57.8401	57.7858	115.5716	1.851
—	—	49.875	$04\bar{3}$	—	58.6306	117.2612	1.827
20	49.89	49.88	$1\bar{1}3$	58.6487	58.6367	117.2734	1.827
—	—	49.88	400	—	58.6367	117.2734	1.826
5	50.1	50.11	260	58.9024	58.9145	117.8290	1.819
35	50.91	50.915	113	59.8817	59.8878	119.7756	1.792
25	51.46	51.455	$20\bar{4}$	60.5476	60.5415	121.0830	1.774

[1] The values for Cu radiation have been measured and calculated by J. V. SMITH (1956). Other values were added by the present author. d-values calculated from $2\vartheta_{Cu}$ calc.

TABLE XXIII[1]

X-RAY POWDER PATTERN OF A SYNTHETIC PLAGIOCLASE ($An_{5.0}$)

$2\vartheta_{Co}$	$4\vartheta_{Co}$	$d\ \text{Å}$	I
16.02	32.04	6.42	m
17.59	35.18	5.83	w
18.25	36.50	5.64	w
21.99	43.98	4.69	vw
25.70	51.40	4.02	s
26.72	53.44	3.866	wm
27.75	55.50	3.732	s
28.61	57.22	3.621	ms
29.96	59.92	3.457	w
30.42	60.84	3.411	f
30.94	61.88	3.354	m
32.48	64.96	3.198	vvs
32.88	65.76	3.160	s
33.38	66.76	3.115	ms
34.66	69.32	3.003	m
35.48	70.96	2.936	ms
35.82	71.64	2.908	m
39.52	79.04	2.646	wm
41.74	83.48	2.510	ms

TABLE XXIV[2]

X-RAY POWDER PATTERN OF A SYNTHETIC PLAGIOCLASE ($An_{10.0}$)

$2\vartheta_{Co}$	$4\vartheta_{Co}$	$d\ \text{Å}$	I
16.00	32.00	6.43	m
17.59	35.18	5.85	w
18.18	36.36	5.66	w
22.04	44.08	4.68	vw
25.70	51.40	4.02	s
26.71	53.42	3.872	wm
27.71	55.42	3.735	s
28.58	57.16	3.623	ms
29.94	59.88	3.463	w
30.32	60.64	3.420	vw
30.90	61.80	3.357	m
31.96	63.92	3.249	vw
32.46	64.92	3.201	vvs
32.86	65.72	3.163	s
33.33	66.66	3.119	ms
34.62	69.24	3.006	m
35.42	70.84	2.941	ms
39.52	79.04	2.646	wm
41.78	83.56	2.508	ms

TABLE XXV[3]

X-RAY POWDER PATTERN OF A SYNTHETIC PLAGIOCLASE ($An_{30.0}$)

$2\vartheta_{Co}$	$4\vartheta_{Co}$	$d \text{ Å}$	I
16.02	32.04	6.42	wm
22.04	44.08	4.68	m
25.74	51.48	4.02	s
26.71	53.42	3.871	wm
27.72	55.44	3.734	s
28.18	56.36	3.673	vw
28.61	57.22	3.620	ms
29.98	59.96	3.458	w
30.46	60.92	3.405	vw
30.96	61.92	3.352	m
31.95	63.90	3.250	vw
32.50	65.00	3.196	vvs
32.86	65.72	3.162	s
33.34	66.68	3.118	ms
34.60	69.20	3.007	m
34.78	69.56	2.993	ms
35.86	71.72	2.905	m
39.48	78.96	2.648	wm
41.74	83.48	2.511	ms

FOOTNOTES

[1] The values in Å units have been measured by GOODYEAR and DUFFIN (1955, table IV, 17). The other values were added by the present author.

[2] The values in Å units have been measured by GOODYEAR and DUFFIN (1955, table IV, 18). The other values were added by the present author.

[3] The values in Å units have been measured by GOODYEAR and DUFFIN (1955, table IV, 19). The other values were added by the present author.

TABLE XXVI[1]

X-RAY POWDER PATTERN OF A SYNTHETIC PLAGIOCLASE ($An_{40.0}$)

$2\vartheta_{Co}$	$4\vartheta_{Co}$	d Å	I
15.89	31.78	6.47	wm
22.08	44.16	4.67	wm
25.74	51.48	4.02	s
26.64	53.28	3.883	wm
27.68	55.36	3.739	ms
28.08	56.16	3.687	w
28.60	57.20	3.621	m
29.98	59.96	3.458	wm
30.42	60.84	3.409	vw
30.88	61.76	3.360	m
31.92	63.84	3.253	m
32.48	64.96	3.199	vvs
32.74	65.48	3.174	vs
33.33	66.66	3.119	ms
34.55	69.10	3.012	m
35.52	71.04	2.932	ms b
39.48	78.96	2.648	wm
41.77	83.54	2.509	ms

TABLE XXVII[2]

X-RAY POWDER PATTERN OF A SYNTHETIC PLAGIOCLASE ($An_{60.0}$)

$2\vartheta_{Co}$	$4\vartheta_{Co}$	d Å	I
15.86	31.72	6.48	wm
22.08	44.16	4.67	wm
25.70	51.40	4.02	s
26.57	53.14	3.892	wm
27.62	55.24	3.746	s
28.15	56.30	3.678	w
28.60	57.20	3.621	ms
29.98	59.96	3.458	wm
30.42	60.84	3.405	vw
30.97	61.94	3.350	m
31.92	63.84	3.250	wm
32.26	64.52	3.220	wm
32.54	65.08	3.192	vvs
32.83	65.66	3.165	s
33.30	66.60	3.121	m
34.50	69.00	3.016	wm
35.48	70.96	2.935	ms b
39.48	78.96	2.648	wm
41.77	83.54	2.509	ms

TABLE XXVIII[3]

X-RAY POWDER PATTERN OF A SYNTHETIC PLAGIOCLASE ($An_{70.0}$)

$2\vartheta_{Co}$	$4\vartheta_{Co}$	d Å	I
15.74	31.48	6.53	w
21.98	43.96	4.69	wm
25.67	51.34	4.03	s
26.57	53.14	3.892	m
27.62	55.24	3.747	s
28.20	56.40	3.672	vw
28.62	57.24	3.618	ms
30.02	60.04	3.454	wm
30.42	60.84	3.405	w
30.96	61.92	3.352	m
32.16	64.32	3.230	ms
32.54	65.08	3.194	vvs
32.82	65.64	3.168	s
33.30	66.60	3.120	ms
34.46	68.92	3.020	m
35.42	70.84	2.941	ms
35.62	71.24	2.924	wm
36.00	72.00	2.894	w
39.54	79.08	2.644	wm
41.82	83.64	2.506	ms

FOOTNOTES

[1] The values in Å units have been measured by GOODYEAR and DUFFIN (1955, table IV, 20). The other values were added by the present author.

[2] The values in Å units have been measured by GOODYEAR and DUFFIN (1955, table IV, 21). The other values were added by the present author.

[3] The values in Å units have been measured by GOODYEAR and DUFFIN (1955, table IV, 22). The other values were added by the present author.

TABLE XXIX[1]

X-RAY POWDER PATTERN OF A SYNTHETIC PLAGIOCLASE ($An_{80.0}$)

$2\vartheta_{Co}$	$4\vartheta_{Co}$	d Å	I
15.81	31.62	6.51	w
21.99	43.98	4.69	wm
25.74	31.48	4.02	s
26.60	33.20	3.888	wm
27.65	35.30	3.743	s
28.10	56.20	3.685	vw
28.73	57.46	3.605	ms
30.10	60.20	3.444	wm
30.54	61.08	3.396	w
31.04	62.08	3.343	m
31.88	63.76	3.257	wm
32.12	64.24	3.233	ms
32.62	65.24	3.185	vvs
32.85	65.70	3.163	vs
33.40	66.80	3.113	s
34.48	68.96	3.018	m
35.50	71.00	2.934	ms
35.71	71.42	2.917	wm
36.08	72.16	2.888	w
39.64	79.28	2.638	wm
41.94	83.88	2.499	ms

TABLE XXX[2]

X-RAY POWDER PATTERN OF A SYNTHETIC PLAGIOCLASE ($An_{90.0}$)

$2\vartheta_{Co}$	$4\vartheta_{Co}$	d Å	I
15.72	31.44	6.54	vw
21.99	43.98	4.69	m
25.64	51.28	4.03	s
26.43	52.86	3.913	wm
27.50	55.00	3.763	s
28.06	56.12	3.690	vw
28.66	57.32	3.614	s
30.02	60.04	3.454	m
30.42	60.84	3.405	w
30.96	61.92	3.354	m
31.92	63.84	3.249	s
32.54	65.08	3.196	vvs
32.70	65.40	3.177	vs
33.30	66.60	3.120	ms
34.30	68.60	3.033	m
35.42	70.84	2.942	s b
36.00	72.00	2.893	vw
39.64	79.28	2.637	wm
41.82	83.64	2.507	ms
42.08	84.16	2.401	ms

TABLE XXXI[3]

X-RAY POWDER PATTERN OF A SYNTHETIC PLAGIOCLASE ($An_{100.0}$)

$2\vartheta_{Co}$	$4\vartheta_{Co}$	$d\ \text{Å}$	I
15.86	31.72	6.48	vw
21.94	43.88	4.70	m
25.59	51.18	4.04	s
26.36	52.72	3.923	wm
27.42	54.84	3.774	s
28.00	56.00	3.698	vw
28.63	57.26	3.617	s
29.98	59.96	3.458	wm
30.45	60.90	3.406	w
30.88	61.76	3.360	m
31.85	63.70	3.260	s
32.42	64.84	3.204	vvs
32.66	65.32	3.181	vs
33.28	66.56	3.124	ms
34.18	68.36	3.044	m
35.35	70.70	2.946	ms b
36.00	72.00	2.894	vw
39.55	79.10	2.645	wm
41.58	83.16	2.520	ms
42.02	84.04	2.495	ms

FOOTNOTES

[1] The values in Å units have been measured by GOODYEAR and DUFFIN (1955, table IV, 23). The other values were added by the present author.

[2] The values in Å units have been measured by GOODYEAR and DUFFIN (1955, table IV, 24). The other values were added by the present author.

[3] The values in Å units have been measured by GOODYEAR and DUFFIN (1955, table IV, 25). The other values were added by the present author.

TABLE XXXII[1]

X-RAY POWDER PATTERN OF OLIGOCLASE ($An_{16.5}$)

$2\vartheta_{Co}$	$4\vartheta_{Co}$	d Å	I
16.14	32.28	6.37	m
17.38	34.76	5.92	f
18.35	36.70	5.61	f
25.72	51.45	4.02	s
26.86	53.72	3.851	wm
27.57	55.14	3.754	ms
28.15	56.30	3.678	m
28.36	46.72	3.651	m
29.78	59.56	3.481	wm
30.92	61.84	3.355	wm
32.48	64.96	3.198	s
32.72	65.44	3.176	vvs
33.08	66.16	3.142	wm
35.00	70.00	2.975	m
35.58	71.16	2.927	ms
36.76	73.52	2.837	m
39.58	79.16	2.642	wm
41.15	82.30	2.545	m
41.74	83.48	2.511	vw
42.55	85.10	2.465	wm

TABLE XXXIII[2]

X-RAY POWDER PATTERN OF ACID ANDESINE ($An_{31.1}$)

$2\vartheta_{Co}$	$4\vartheta_{Co}$	d Å	I
16.06	32.12	6.40	wm
17.56	35.12	5.86	f
18.28	36.56	5.63	f
22.04	44.08	4.68	f
25.68	51.36	4.024	s
26.78	53.56	3.863	wm
27.64	55.28	3.745	ms
27.97	55.84	3.708	ms
28.50	57.00	3.634	ms
29.88	59.76	3.469	wm
30.32	60.64	3.421	vw
30.92	61.84	3.356	m
32.52	65.04	3.195	vvs
32.83	65.66	3.166	s
33.18	66.36	3.132	ms
34.78	69.56	2.993	m
35.56	71.12	2.929	ms b
36.86	73.72	2.829	m
39.52	79.04	2.646	wm
41.42	82.84	2.529	m
41.66	83.32	2.515	vw
42.16	84.32	2.487	wm

TABLE XXXIV[3]

X-RAY POWDER PATTERN OF CALCIC ANDESINE ($An_{38.0}$)

$2\vartheta_{Co}$	$4\vartheta_{Co}$	d Å	I
16.06	32.12	6.40	wm
17.58	35.16	5.85	f
18.22	36.44	5.65	f
22.08	44.16	4.67	f
25.66	51.32	4.03	s
26.72	53.44	3.870	wm
27.58	55.16	3.751	ms
27.86	55.72	3.715	m
28.45	56.90	3.640	ms
29.90	59.80	3.468	wm
30.24	60.48	3.430	vw
30.88	61.76	3.359	m
32.48	64.96	3.199	vvs
32.79	65.58	3.169	vs
33.16	66.32	3.134	ms
34.70	69.40	2.999	m
35.58	71.16	2.928	ms b
36.81	73.62	2.833	m
39.50	79.00	2.647	wm
41.44	82.88	2.528	ms
42.12	84.24	2.489	m

FOOTNOTES

[1] The values in Å units have been measured by GOODYEAR and DUFFIN (1955, table III,2) on a natural low-temperature phase from a granite, Petrick quarry, Llano Co., Texas. The sample has been previously described by EMMONS (1953, no. 4). The other values were added by the present author.

[2] The values in Å units have been measured by GOODYEAR and DUFFIN (1955, table III, 4) on a low-temperature phase from a pegmatite, Corundum Hill mine, Macon Co., N.C., U.S.A. The sample has been previously described by EMMONS (1953, no.28). The other values were added by the present author.

[3] The values in Å units have been measured by GOODYEAR and DUFFIN (1955, table III, 5) on a natural phase from a granodiorite, Crestmore, Calif., U.S.A. The sample has been previously described by EMMONS (1953, no.8). The other values were added by the present author.

TABLE XXXV[1]

X-RAY POWDER PATTERN OF ACID LABRADORITE ($An_{51.6}$)

$2\vartheta_{Co}$	$4\vartheta_{Co}$	d Å	I
15.99	31.98	6.43	w
22.08	44.16	4.67	f
25.67	51.34	4.03	s
26.67	53.34	3.878	wm
27.60	55.20	3.749	ms
27.80	55.60	3.723	ms
28.50	57.00	3.633	ms
29.92	59.84	3.464	wm
30.28	60.56	3.424	vw
30.96	61.92	3.352	m
32.50	65.00	3.197	vvs
32.82	65.64	3.165	vs
33.20	66.40	3.131	ms
34.70	69.40	3.003	m
35.52	71.04	2.933	ms
35.72	71.44	2.916	wm
36.80	73.60	2.834	m
39.48	78.96	2.648	m
41.50	83.00	2.525	ms
42.04	84.08	2.494	m

TABLE XXXVI[2]

X-RAY POWDER PATTERN OF CALCIC LABRADORITE ($An_{64.5}$)

$2\vartheta_{Co}$	$4\vartheta_{Co}$	d Å	I
15.90	31.80	6.47	w
22.08	44.16	4.67	w
25.60	51.20	4.04	s
26.62	53.24	3.885	wm
27.62	55.24	3.747	s
28.52	57.04	3.631	ms
29.94	59.88	3.463	wm
30.30	60.60	3.423	vw
30.88	61.76	3.359	m
31.90	63.80	3.254	wm?
32.24	64.48	3.222	s
32.48	64.96	3.198	vvs
32.78	65.56	3.170	vs
33.20	66.40	3.130	ms
34.54	69.08	3.013	wm
35.42	70.84	2.940	ms b
39.44	78.88	2.651	m
41.54	83.08	2.522	ms
41.81	83.72	2.504	m

TABLE XXXVII[3]

X-RAY POWDER PATTERN OF ACID BYTOWNITE ($An_{71.3}$)

$2\vartheta_{Co}$	$4\vartheta_{Co}$	d Å	I
15.82	31.64	6.50	w
21.98	43.96	4.69	wm
25.68	51.36	4.03	s
26.60	53.20	3.887	wm
27.64	55.28	3.745	s
28.64	57.28	3.615	ms
30.02	60.04	3.454	wm
30.50	61.00	3.401	w
31.00	62.00	3.346	m
32.00	64.00	3.245	wm?
32.24	64.48	3.222	m
32.56	65.12	3.191	vvs
32.88	65.76	3.161	s
33.36	66.72	3.117	ms
34.52	69.04	3.015	wm
35.46	70.92	2.937	ms b
39.58	79.16	2.642	m
41.82	83.64	2.506	s

FOOTNOTES

[1] The values in Å units have been measured by GOODYEAR and DUFFIN (1955, table III, 6) on a natural phase from a hornblende gabbro, Shelby, N.C., U.S.A. The sample has been previously described by EMMONS (1953, no.10). The other values were added by the present author.

[2] The values in Å units have been measured by GOODYEAR and DUFFIN (1955, table III, 7) on a natural phase from an anorthosite, Grand Marais, Minn., U.S.A. The sample has been previously described by EMMONS (1953, no.17). The other values were added by the present author.

[3] The values in Å units have been measured by GOODYEAR and DUFFIN (1955, table III, 9) on a natural phase from an anorthosite, Crystal Bay, Minn., U.S.A. The sample has been previously described by EMMONS (1953, no.25). The other values were added by the present author.

TABLE XXXVIII[1]

X-RAY POWDER PATTERN OF CALCIC BYTOWNITE ($An_{77.0}$)

$2\vartheta_{Co}$	$4\vartheta_{Co}$	d Å	I
15.80	31.60	6.51	w
22.04	44.08	4.68	wm
25.68	51.36	4.02	s
26.66	53.32	3.880	wm
27.68	55.36	3.740	s
28.64	57.28	3.617	ms
30.02	60.04	3.452	wm
30.46	60.92	3.404	w
30.98	61.96	3.350	m
31.94	63.88	3.250	wm?
32.24	64.48	3.222	wm
32.56	65.12	3.190	vvs
32.90	65.80	3.159	s
33.36	66.72	3.116	m
34.56	69.12	3.011	wm
35.44	70.88	2.939	ms b
35.72	71.44	2.916	wm
39.50	79.00	2.647	m
41.74	83.48	2.511	ms

TABLE XXXIX[2]

X-RAY POWDER PATTERN OF CALCIC BYTOWNITE ($An_{81.5}$)

$2\vartheta_{Co}$	$4\vartheta_{Co}$	d Å	I
15.71	31.52	6.52	w
22.04	44.08	4.68	wm
25.70	51.40	4.02	s
26.62	53.24	3.885	wm
27.66	55.32	3.743	s
28.70	57.40	3.609	ms
30.00	60.00	3.456	wm
30.46	60.92	3.404	vw
31.00	62.00	3.347	m
32.14	64.28	3.231	ms
32.56	65.12	3.191	vvs
32.88	65.76	3.160	s
33.38	66.76	3.115	ms
34.50	69.00	3.016	m
35.52	71.04	2.933	ms b
36.10	72.20	2.887	vw
39.42	78.84	2.652	m
41.70	83.40	2.513	ms

TABLE XL[3]

X-RAY POWDER PATTERN OF NATURAL ANORTHITE $(An_{93.0})$

$2\vartheta_{Co}$	$4\vartheta_{Co}$	$d\ \text{Å}$	I
15.70	31.40	6.55	w
21.98	43.96	4.69	m
25.62	51.24	4.03	ms
26.44	52.88	3.911	wm
27.44	54.88	3.770	ms
27.68	55.36	3.740	wm
28.68	57.36	3.611	ms
30.04	60.08	3.452	wm
30.60	61.20	3.390	vw
30.94	61.88	3.354	m
31.96	63.92	3.249	s
32.50	65.00	3.197	vvs
32.84	65.68	3.164	s
33.38	66.76	3.114	ms
34.34	68.68	3.030	m
35.38	70.76	2.944	ms
35.58	71.16	2.927	wm
36.18	72.36	2.880	wm
39.46	78.92	2.649	m
41.60	83.20	2.519	ms
41.98	83.96	2.497	ms

FOOTNOTES

[1] The values in Å units have been measured by GOODYEAR and DUFFIN (1955, table III, 10) on a natural phase from a norite, Rustenburg mines, Transvaal, S. Africa. The sample has been previously described by KRACEK and NEUVONEN (1952, no.4). The other values were added by the present author.

[2] The values in Å units have been measured by GOODYEAR and DUFFIN (1955, table III, 12) on a natural phase from a troctolite, Merril, Wisc., U.S.A. The sample has been previously described by EMMONS (1953, no.27). The other values were added by the present author.

[3] The values in Å units have been measured by GOODYEAR and DUFFIN (1955, table III, 14) on an anorthite from an olivine–norite, Grass valley, Calif., U.S.A. The sample has been previously described by EMMONS (1953, no.1). The other values were added by the present author.

Chapter 11

ON THE IDENTIFICATION OF FELDSPARS IN CLASTIC ROCKS; A CRITICAL DISCUSSION

INTRODUCTION

In the foregoing text the determination of feldspars was discussed in detail without elaborating on its actual application in sedimentology or in soil science. Still, the investigators in these branches of science have used numerous techniques in order to cope with their special problems, and quite often with great success. The identification of the constituents of the light fraction of sediments was begun in the nineteenth century. It is not our aim to give a review of the development of this special aspect of petrography. As an illustration, however, we may recall the work of RETGERS (1891).

Retgers was the first geologist to give a quantitative mineralogical composition of a quartz-rich dune sand from Scheveningen, a sea-side resort in The Netherlands. He used various liquids with differing specific gravities in order to obtain a number of fractions. These contained one or a few minerals in large quantities, thus enabling a more efficient determination in grain mounts.

In his paper we can find the statement that only a suitable concentration technique allows for an efficient determination method, because "in the dune sands of The Netherlands the greatest difficulties are encountered due to the small percentage of the extraordinary minerals. These minerals are quantitatively negligible in comparison with the large amount of quartz grains". Moreover, he writes: "The main principle of the investigation is the isolation of the large quantity of quartz particles by applying two liquids, one slightly lighter than quartz, one slightly heavier. In this way the extraordinary minerals are from the beginning separated into two main groups." For the group of minerals with a specific gravity higher than quartz it was necessary to divide it again into groups with limiting specific gravities in order to come to quantitative results.

Although Retgers' work is not of a recent date it is still worth while to read it. A rather large part of the know how of the study of heavy and light minerals is laid down in these 48 pages. Sedimentologists as well as soil scientists may be astonished to learn that Retgers was quite aware of the significance of grain morphology and of inclusions in detrital minerals, especially in quartz and feldspar. In short, this paper (written in Dutch) would still be found highly interesting if it had been written in 1965.

Although Retgers' paper contains the basic principles of the mineralogical analysis of sediments and soils, we may not end this chapter here. A schematical treatment of the expected problems and the different procedures used or advocated is still wanting. Such a systematical discussion can be presented in at least two ways. We may choose the various properties of groups of sediments as a criterium. On the other hand, the various types of questions sedimentologists and soil scientists want to solve by a study of detrital feldspars can be used for such a schematical presentation.

We can divide the various sediments into two groups according to the state of consolidation. The chemical composition of such sediments, whether they are rich in silicon, in alumina, in calcium carbonate or in dolomite, also gives a useful basis for a subdivision. The more so, because this chemical composition is an important indication for the type of pretreatment of the sample.

The type of information wanted determines the combination of useful procedures to a large extent. In a number of cases a thin section or a stained sand sample provides the qualitative or semi-quantitative data satisfactorily. If the investigator is interested in the quantification of details a great deal of work is involved. Others are perhaps less interested in the composition of the feldspar fraction. They are eager to get information on the genesis of the rock or on the type of source rock of a sediment. Still others want a stratigrafic criterium that is not to be found in the fossils or in the heavy mineral fraction. It may also be hidden among the minerals of the heavy fraction in such a way that it can only be brought about by a tedious counting of heavy minerals in narrow size ranges.

Apart from the questions formulated by sedimentologists we want to concentrate on the different problems raised by soil scientists. They are not only interested in provenance, genesis or composition of a soil; the question of soil fertility is also closely related with the mineralogical composition. They may not be interested in the potassium or the calcium stored in feldspars, but only in the amount of trace elements. It has been shown in Chapter 2 that feldspars are rich in trace elements.

In order to illustrate how feldspars can be concentrated and identified, the following sections and paragraphs treat the study of detrital feldspars schematically according to rock type. The results of such a study are sketched as far as possible from examples taken from the abundance of available literature. The selection does not indicate any preference for these papers above others not listed. The examples suit the purpose perfectly and the author felt no need to search for better ones, if they exist.

Considering the aspects of identification and quantification of detrital feldspars of a sediment sample, it turns out that the discussion of a quantitative feldspar analysis has to precede the treatment of qualitative methods. But above all, let us decide what is meant by a quantitative feldspar analysis. Such an analysis contains at least the following data: (1) the amount of feldspars in the sample, either in weight percentages or in number percentages; (2) the composition of the feldspar fraction in terms of alkali feldspars, albite, acid plagioclases, intermediate plagioclases and calcic plagioclases; (3) the distribution of the various classes over the size fractions.

Moreover, additional information is usually sought for. One may be interested in the composition of the alkali-feldspar fraction in terms of ordered or disordered phases and in terms of homogeneous fragments or perthites. For others, data on the twinning patterns in plagioclases are of great importance.

Contrary to such a rather complete quantitative analysis, the nature of a qualitative analysis is often rather fragmentary. We prefer to stick to the literal meaning of the term qualitative. Consequently, information on the nature of the feldspars is judged a qualitative datum; any indication on the importance of the feldspar fraction is considered of quantitative nature.

ASPECTS OF A QUANTITATIVE DETRITAL FELDSPAR ANALYSIS

Before entering upon the details of a quantitative feldspar analysis we must realize that in quite a number of cases the complete quantitative analysis of the feldspar fraction of a sediment or a soil is an unworkable task. Especially the identification of the minute feldspar fragments present in the clay fraction is met with unsurmountable difficulties with our present knowledge. In most cases we must be content with a fair estimate of the total amount of feldspar in this fraction. Sometimes it may be possible to distinguish between plagioclase and alkali feldspar. This, however, seems to be the most one can expect. On the other hand, the results obtained from the coarser fractions are rather encouraging.

We shall adopt the main principle of mineral identification in the light fraction formulated by RETGERS (1891). For an efficient study of the feldspars of any sediment a feldspar concentrate is necessary. The amount of feldspars in sediments is generally rather small. For all practical purposes we may fix this somewhere between 2 and 20 weight %, for sandstones and sands or sandy soils. The feldspar content of argillaceous or carbonate sediments is generally much lower and often less than 1 weight %. Such a concentration technique is also useful for sediments with about 20 or more weight % of feldspars if one wants to study the structural state of alkali feldspars or the composition of the plagioclase fraction. In a thin section too many fragments may have an orientation unfit for a proper identification. This is especially true for samples with a pronounced anisotropic fabric.

In recognizing the truth of Retgers' maxim, a rock must be treated in such a way that a feldspar concentrate remains. The pretreatment, therefore, aims at a sample of incoherent feldspar fragments with the smallest possible admixture of fragments from other minerals. It will be seen later that the separation of quartz and feldspar is one of the most difficult tasks. As soon as a residual fraction containing exclusively quartz and feldspars has been prepared, the treatment of this fraction is the same for all samples regardless of the original rock type. Consequently, the preparation of such quartz-feldspar fractions will be considered first. Afterwards the procedures for handling such fractions will be discussed.

In most cases it is possible to arrive at a quantitative mineralogical analysis of a sediment by other methods. A number of excellent papers prove this beyond any doubt. Numerous investigators arrived at such results by studying thin sections only. Such studies, however, are in some cases highly inefficient even though the results are the same. If we advocate the concentration technique as a first requisite, this is done for reasons of efficiency. It certainly does not mean that the ultimate result will be any better. Therefore, mention will be made in the following paragraphs of other approaches that have been successful. Whether or not they have been less efficient is left to the reader's judgment.

In the next sections the sediments will be divided into four groups: a group of sediments rich in silicon dioxide; a group of rocks relatively rich in aluminium, due to abundant phyllosilicates; a group of rocks of sedimentary origin rich in carbonates; and a miscellaneous group composed of such sediments as bauxites, gypsum-rich, ferruginous or carbonaceous sediments.

Quartz- and feldspar-rich arenaceous sediments and soils

These sediments may consist of rock fragments or mineral fragments or both. They may contain varying amounts of very fine particles. In other words, they may contain some clayey material. The majority of the samples in this group is of clastic origin, in the sense of the A.G.I. GLOSSARY. This nomenclator defines a clastic rock as being composed of detritus transported mechanically into its place of deposition.

The fragments may not adhere as in sands or soils. They can show some adherence due to a slight induration as observed in friable sandstones. The rocks can also be well consolidated. Such a state is observed in sandstones cemented by silica which has grown in optical continuity around each fragment. These solid sandstones are quite often called "quartzites" according to the proposal found in HOLMES' nomenclator (1928).

The majority of soil samples lands in this group. Even if organic material forms the bulk of a sample, we will find the sample in this section for its mineralogical composition. An exception is formed by such soils with a high amount of organic material, rich in clay.

Consolidated or indurated quartz- and feldspar-rich arenaceous sediments
Examples. For a study of the mineralogical composition of sandstones and graywackes one is used to rely almost entirely on thin section studies. As an example of such an investigation we may ask again attention for the paper of J. MICHOT

(1963), who studied the detrital feldspars of the Devonian and Carboniferous sediments of Belgium. These rocks, covering an area of approximately 20,000 km², are stratigrafically divided into a number of Devonian units and a few units of the lower Carboniferous. Lithologically they belong to various rock types, such as sandstones, graywackes, calcareous sandstones and limestones.

The author of this study devoted himself to the observation of numerous thin sections. For a quantification an unknown counting method has been used. Information on the reliability of the reported results is lacking. The following classes have been distinguished: untwinned alkali feldspars, microcline, micro-perthitic microcline, and acid plagioclase. On the basis of information about the contents of these feldspars, important conclusions have been drawn about the type of source rocks and the geological history of the regions of provenance. Especially the relations between the source regions and the Variscian geosyncline during the latter part of the Paleozoicum received his special interest. It was established that the rocks of the Famennian have an outstanding origin. They are rich in feldspars contrary to all the other rocks. Alkali feldspars are more important than plagio-clases or albite. Moreover, these rocks contain mesoperthites or hair perthites. The latter feature led the author to some tentative suggestions about the region of provenance. Mesoperthites have been described so far from granulites. Such rocks are known to occur in a limited number of regions in Europe, e.g., in Scandinavia, Saxony and northern Spain. It is only logical that Michot favoured Scandinavia as the possible region of provenance.

From a sedimentological point of view it is interesting that Michot leaves no doubt as to the fact that such detailed information on the history of his sedi-ments could not have been ascertained by a study of the heavy minerals alone. The extraordinary position of the Famennian rocks, clearly indicated by their outstanding feldspar fraction, goes practically undetected if only heavy minerals are studied.

As an example of the study of slightly indurated sediments we would like to point to the work of LÜTHY et al. (1963). These authors studied the sediments of an artificial outcrop near Neubrügg, north of Bern, Switzerland. The outcrop consists of Lower Fresh Water Molasse and unconsolidated younger sediments. The sediments of the Molasse are sandstones and marlaceous slates. All the samples were pretreated in order to arrive at a set of incoherent minerals and rock fragments. This implies that the sandstones had to be crushed and disaggregated, which is a rather easy task because the rocks have a small carbonate content and are only slightly indurated. Lüthy and co-workers obviously preferred the analysis of grain mounts above a thin section study. The authors counted the light fraction in an index liquid. They distinguished between quartz, fresh feldspar, altered feldspar and rock fragments. The reported results suggest the usage of one or another concentration method. It is established that only a combination of numerical observations on both the heavy and the light fraction allows for a distinction between Molasse sandstones and the younger sands. The authors point to the fact that the assemblage of heavy minerals is apparently rather constant because of the extremely high epidote content. This high epidote content obscures the variation of the contents of other heavy minerals.

Thin section study. We will refrain from a discussion of other papers for illustrative purposes. The reader can easily find numerous examples in recent literature. From these examples it follows that consolidated sediments of the composition under consideration can be studied in different ways. If the sample is comparatively rich in feldspars one may still prefer the study of a thin section. In order to reach reliable numerical results about the volume percentages of the alkali feldspar and the plagioclase fractions, the following method is advocated.

Prepare a thin section of the sample. Do not cover. Polish the surface of this section and stain with hemateine as given on p.52. Determine the amount of feldspar with the ordinary microscope in incident light by point counting. Clean the section with a 2 N HCl to which a few drops of 30°/₀ H_2O_2 per milliliter are added. Another method for cleaning is slightly grinding the surface and repolishing. Stain yellow after slightly repolishing. Determine the volume percentage of alkali feldspar in the same way. Clean again and cover the section. Determine the nature of the plagioclases and the alkali feldspars in the normal way with a petrographic microscope. For an inventory of the frequency of specific twinning laws in plagioclases we advocate the use of the universal stage as described on p.156 et seq. The paper of MITZUTANI (1959) illustrates the results to be expected from a twin inventory. This paper is discussed in some detail on p.274.

If the sample is poor in feldspars, numerous thin sections must be studied in the way described in order to arrive at reliable numerical results. Therefore, one may prefer to cut a slab of such a sample. After polishing, the slab can be stained in much the same way as a thin section (cf. p.51). Counting can be performed with a stereomicroscope with incident light. For such a counting procedure an integration ocular is rather efficient. After an analysis of the numerical values of the total feldspar and the alkali-feldspar fraction, more information is frequently needed. Such additional information can be obtained from thin sections. Again large numbers of sections are needed. It is clear that in these cases a concentration method may be successfully tried.

Disintegration of the sample. If we want to concentrate feldspars of consolidated silica-rich sediments, the samples have to be crushed or disaggregated in another way. For samples with a slight carbonate content we may proceed as follows.

Break the sample into small fragments of about $^1/_2$ cm³. Treat these pieces with cold diluted HCl. The concentration of the liquid must depend on the toughness of the sample and the nature of the carbonates. On p.247, a consideration of HCl-treatments is given in detail. As a rule it is felt that even in case of feldspars over aggressive acids must be avoided. Moreover, basic plagioclases are attacked by strong acids. Wash the fragments after the solution of all carbonates, collect the sand and small rock fragments and rub these with a tough-rubber pestle in a mortar of not too hard material. Do not crush severely. Repeat the acid treatment and rub again.
    If the sample resists the acid treatment one may use alternatively an acid treatment and an H_2O_2 procedure on a waterbath (cf. p.256). Good results may especially be reached with the H_2O_2

treatment if the sample contains some mica or clay material. If the sample resists these treatments also, one may either try an alkali digestion or an alternate boiling with strong HCl and HNO_3. This treatment, however, is certainly damaging for some minerals and will cause the vanishing of others entirely, especially if they are of a not too large grain size.

If our sample does not contain mica or carbonate and the induration is rather strong, one may choose simple crushing. There is always the risk of breaking the initial minerals by a crushing method. This can, however, be avoided to some extent by not using a mill. Jaw crushers, lined with ceramic material, give good results. Sieve the crushed material in order to remove the particles that are already fine enough and crush the coarse fraction carefully again. Crushing may also be done by hand in a cast iron mortar with a steel or a ceramic pestle. Do not take too much material at a time. Good results have been reached with a sliced rock sample. Slice the sample with a diamond saw and crush the thin slices afterwards in a mortar.

Slightly indurated samples can be disaggregated by rubbing. Some sandstones fall apart by rubbing with the fingers or with a massive rubber ball or pestle. Such balls as are used as dogs' toys render useful service. One can also rub two flat pieces of sandstone against each other.

Needless to say, the above treatments have their disadvantages. The nature of these disadvantages may, however, be unknown. Therefore we will discuss them briefly. Firstly, it is known that every chemical treatment attacks the surface of any mineral, even the most inert ones. Secondly, both chemical and mechanical treatments artificially produce some fine material that cannot be easily studied. Because of the pronounced cleavage planes of feldspars these minerals are more susceptible to such pulverization than quartz. Consequently the fine artificially produced powder is expected to contain more feldspars than the original sample. Mutatis mutandis, the coarser fractions used for the study of the light mineral fraction contain more quartz than the original sample. It goes without saying that for these reasons the fine fractions may not be discarded. They must be retained for an X-ray analysis. This analysis enables the investigator to correct the results obtained from the other fractions. For all practical purposes we must assume that microclines do not pulverize more easily than oligoclase or vice versa. On the basis of this assumption only the total feldspar content is corrected. It is quite obvious that errors made in this way are not too great. Some investigators will therefore refrain from corrections and discard the artificially produced fine fractions. We will not discuss this attitude towards the fine fraction, except for one remark. Whether or not the fines are discarded, they must first be weighed carefully.

It goes without saying that the results of a simple crushing are unfit for a granulometric analysis. The results of an acid treatment and of rubbing may be used in a sieve analysis. The grain-size frequency distribution of these disaggregated samples may be assumed to be comparable to the real distribution. Much has been said about the granulometric analysis of solid sediments. A common opinion on this aspect of sedimentology does not yet exist. The controversial subject has been treated by several authors and especially by Griffiths, Friedman, Folk and others. The present author also ventured to make some general remarks on the subject in a paper from 1962.

The quartz–feldspar residue that interests us after concentration is made of the incoherent mineral particles and rock fragments that have been prepared in the way described above. This material, however, has another unpleasant property. The loose sample may contain fragments consisting of more than one mineral. The original sediment may have contained these fragments. They may, on the other hand, be the result of an incomplete fragmentation. The sample may also show the presence of a few small feldspar fragments, constituting parts of one single detrital grain in the original rock.

If point counting or weighing is used as a means to arrive at numerical results, this is not a serious drawback. If, however, line counting or ribbon counting methods are used, serious errors are expected to occur. The reasons for this type of error are discussed by VAN DER PLAS (1962).

Coarse-grained samples. The evaluation of the feldspar content of conglomerates, coarse-grained graywackes and indurated glacial drift material poses a special problem. Although this is not an aspect of detrital feldspar analysis, we may philosophize a bit about it. Much information on the study of such rocks is not available. After finishing this text, MATTER's thesis (1964) came out, treating such sediments.

It seems practical to divide the rocks under discussion into two groups, one group containing the pebbles, cobbles and boulders much larger than a thin section, and another group containing fragments of such a size that a fair number of such fragments can be studied in one thin section. The coarse group must be studied in the outcrop and in rock slabs. Specimens of the various fragments, as well as of the matrix, can be studied in one thin section.

If one is interested in detrital feldspars of coarse sediments, the feldspars present in the granite or basalt pebbles and cobbles are of less interest than those of the matrix. The interest in the feldspars of sediment fragments is also questionable. The feldspars of the matrix can be isolated by one of the given techniques. If a distinction has to be made between the feldspars of the various components, each of these components has to be treated as a separate sample according to the schemes set out in this text. If one is interested in the relationships between the feldspars of the matrix and those in the large fragments, the course of the investigation is only too obvious.

Conclusive remarks. The aspects of the study of detrital feldspars in consolidated sediments are not finished with here. But as soon as the feldspar containing loose material is produced, the type of sediment is irrelevant for the selection of further methods. For this reason we will first treat other sediments and the concentration of their feldspars. A further procedure for the loose material starts on p.255. In summarizing this section it is clear that the study of feldspars of consolidated sediments has several contradictory aspects. If one fears, for instance, the disadvantage of a disaggregation, the drawbacks of a thin section or rock slab study must be put up with. On the other hand, those who prefer not to study thin sections must acquiesce in the disadvantages of concentration methods. The results of either of both studies are highly awarding. Especially because the feldspars of a sediment store much information on various aspects of genesis, provenance and history of the source area. In Fig.62, the previous methods are schematically represented.

Friable arenaceous quartz- and feldspar-rich sediments and sandy soils
For a study of the mineralogical composition of friable arenaceous sediments, sands and sandy soils one is used to relying on grain mounts. Examples of such investigations are so abundant that it is hardly necessary to give an example. Still, for completeness sake we may mention two papers, one on sediments and one on soils, reporting the results of a study of the mineralogical composition of such samples.

Examples. Beginning with sediments, we choose the paper of NOTA and BAKKER (1960). Although the title of this paper suggests that it is all about soils, the samples discussed are sediments. The paper has been written in order to introduce a refined method for the accurate mineralogical investigation of the light fraction of sands. It discusses a combination of heavy mineral analysis and the study of the light fraction separated in several parts by means of heavy liquids and an additional study of these separates in grain slides with immersion liquids. The authors introduced also a representation of the results that gives the total mineralogical composition as a square diagram. Such squares taken from the paper under discussion are given here as Fig.63. They illustrate clearly what can be reached with this type of investigation.

   KHADR (1960) used exactly the same methods as those described by Nota and Bakker (loc. cit). A number of Egyptian soils are the subject of investigation. The total mineralogical composition of the investigated samples is given, because Khadr combined X-ray work on the fine fractions with specific-gravity separation, and optical investigation of the coarse fractions. Moreover, he describes the pretreatment used in this type of analysis. His analytical results are also represented in the square diagrams introduced by Nota and Bakker.

   As a result of this work, a number of interesting conclusions could be drawn. It became apparent that attrition during river transport plays a rather subordinate role. Secondly, he established the fact that these Egyptian soils are rather rich in feldspars, in alkali feldspars as well as in intermediate plagioclases.

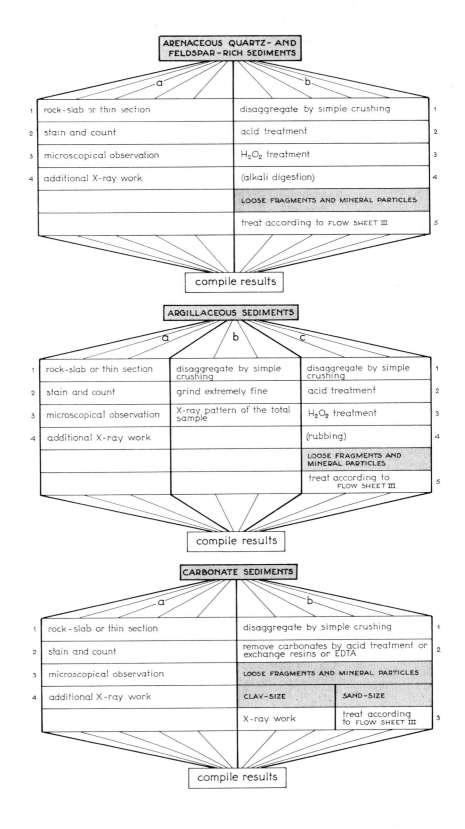

ARENACEOUS QUARTZ- AND FELDSPAR-RICH SEDIMENTS

	a	b	
1	rock-slab or thin section	disaggregate by simple crushing	1
2	stain and count	acid treatment	2
3	microscopical observation	H_2O_2 treatment	3
4	additional X-ray work	(alkali digestion)	4
		LOOSE FRAGMENTS AND MINERAL PARTICLES	
		treat according to FLOW SHEET III	5

compile results

ARGILLACEOUS SEDIMENTS

	a	b	c	
1	rock-slab or thin section	disaggregate by simple crushing	disaggregate by simple crushing	1
2	stain and count	grind extremely fine	acid treatment	2
3	microscopical observation	X-ray pattern of the total sample	H_2O_2 treatment	3
4	additional X-ray work		(rubbing)	4
			LOOSE FRAGMENTS AND MINERAL PARTICLES	
			treat according to FLOW SHEET III	5

compile results

CARBONATE SEDIMENTS

	a	b		
1	rock-slab or thin section	disaggregate by simple crushing		1
2	stain and count	remove carbonates by acid treatment or exchange resins or EDTA		2
3	microscopical observation	LOOSE FRAGMENTS AND MINERAL PARTICLES		
4	additional X-ray work	CLAY-SIZE	SAND-SIZE	
		X-ray work	treat according to FLOW SHEET III	3

compile results

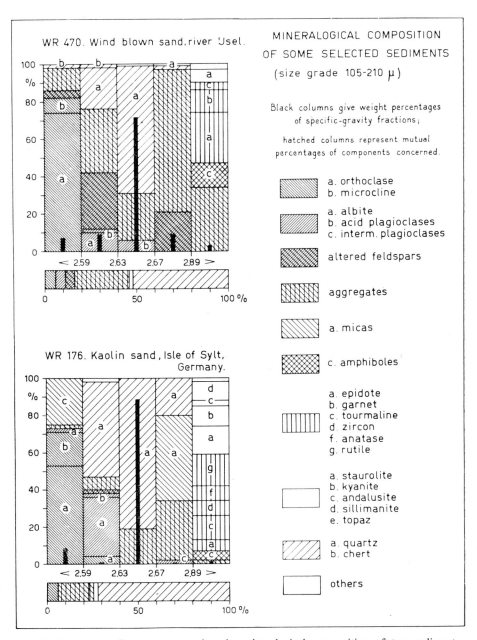

Fig.63. The square diagram representing the mineralogical composition of two sediments. (After NOTA and BAKKER, 1960.)

Fig.62. FLOW SHEET I. Flow sheets for the concentration and identification of detrital feldspars in several types of rock.

Finally, this high feldspar content is linked up with soil fertility. Some Egyptian soils are rather fertile and were able to withstand intensive cultivation practised for ages with good results.

Thin section study. Sand samples are mostly studied in grain slides and they are separated in size fractions with sieves. Still some investigators prefer a study of thin sections even of such samples. One of these is MOORE (1963). In a paper reporting investigations on bottom sediments of Buzzard Bay, U.S.A., this author states that he used thin sections and X-ray powder patterns. Consequently, he has impregnated his sands with some or other resin before cutting slabs that were made into thin sections. From the numerous photographs in this paper it can be inferred that here is a truly interesting subject for a study of detrital feldspars.

VOGEL (1965) also prefers the study of thin sections. Before we begin discussing his arguments, let us consider his preparation method in some detail.

After removal of the heavy fraction with bromoform, thin sections are prepared from the total sand fraction 50–500 μ. Lakeside thermoplastic cement is preferred above other cements because of its index of refraction. The cement is melted in glass tubes with a flat bottom and a diameter of about 1 inch. After melting the grains are added. Afterwards the gas bubbles are removed by tapping the tube with a metal rod. In this way the grains are also more densely packed, leading to a much easier grinding afterwards. After this the tube is placed on a hot plate for 24 h. The temperature of the plate is between 90° and 100° C. After cooling the flat bottom of the tube is ground away, the tube is broken and the disk holding the sample is removed. Thin sections are prepared in the normal way. The remaining part of the disk can be used for a second section if necessary.

Vogel lists the following advantages of thin section studies on the study of grain mounts. The birefringence of the minerals can be used as a distinction mark because all the fragments are equally thick. The thickness of the slide can be measured as described on p.137. If the highest birefringence of quartz is faintly yellow, that of oligoclase and andesine is still first-order-gray. Such properties as undular extinction, authigenic rims, kataclastic phenomena, twinning patterns, saussuritization, myrmekite and others can be studied easily in thin sections but not in grain mounts. Preferred orientation of plagioclase fragments is avoided with this technique. As one of the advantages, we may mention that (010) twins in plagioclases are easier to observe. The index of refraction of the cement provides an easy distinction between alkali feldspars and plagioclases. Questionable minerals can be marked and afterwards studied with a universal stage. Subdivision in the category of rock fragments is possible. The relatively tight packing of the grains allows for an easy counting of 500 particles in each slide without running the risk that one of them is counted twice. Vogel (personal communication, 1960) used a point counting method with these sections in a study of recent Rhine sediments.

As a disadvantage he lists only the fact that the preparation of the slide takes about 2 h. The counting of 500 grains takes again 2 h. Furthermore, small particles of the abrasive tend to settle in the cement, due to the softness of lakeside.

A detailed abstract of Vogel's paper has been given because the advantages of thin section study have never been treated with the penetrating enthusiasm found in this paper. A critical consideration of the argument shows that Vogel is right in many instances. If, however, the investigator is only interested in the total feldspar content, without further information, staining techniques are more efficient. The same holds true for an analysis of both the plagioclase and the alkali-feldspar content.

Vogel is able to distinguish between alkali feldspars and plagioclases. In the case of alkali feldspars he can distinguish between visibly twinned and non-twinned fragments and between perthites and non-perthites as far as they can be seen. These categories, though important as qualitative information, are not mutually exclusive. A microcline with an unfortunate orientation lands in the group of untwinned alkali feldspars. Its axial angle is perhaps visible and this may put the same mineral into the category of untwinned microcline. In general, untwinned microcline, adularia and sanidine land in the same group. Crypto-perthites go undetected in a number of cases, X-ray perthites always go undetected. In the group of plagioclases the observation will not lead to a number of categories unless the universal stage is used. It may be possible to determine the chemical composition of a number of grains with a favourable orientation. Such information is from a quantitative point of view more fragmentary than counting grain mounts in a set of index liquids. Only if the universal stage is used may Vogel rightly stress the supremacy of his method over a combined analysis of stained heavy liquid separates with index liquids. In this case, however, the question about the efficiency of the method remains.

The above remarks are not directed against Vogel's argument. They are by no means given as derogatory to the merits of his paper. On the contrary, the present author was only too pleased to have the opportunity to read this paper in manuscript. In this discussion we meant to make clear the true advantages of a thin section study. This will qualify Vogel's approach, among the other available techniques, in such a way that the reader is able to choose the method best adapted to his problem and to his personal preference.

SWINEFORD and FRYE (1951) used both grain mounts and thin sections for their study of the Peora loess in Kansas. The feldspars constitute about one fourth of the quartz content in these samples. With this combined technique they could distinguish between "orthoclase", microcline and plagioclase.

Before finishing the description of the study of detrital feldspars in sands and soils, we must point to the increasing influence of soil micromorphology. The investigators study, among others, thin sections of soil monoliths, impregnated with Vestopal[1]. Such thin sections not only give information on clay accumulation in cracks and vugs and biopores, on the distribution and decay of organic material

---

[1] Vestopal H is a solution of unsaturated reactive polyester in monostyrene, produced by Chemische Werke Hüls A.G., Marl, Germany.

and on coatings and iron accumulations, they also contain *minerals*. Especially if these thin sections are of a modest size (some micromorphologists have a peculiar preference for rather large thin sections) they can be studied with a normal petrographic microscope and even on a universal stage.

Conclusive remarks. We may finish this paragraph here. The remaining procedures, including the pre-treatment, is given on p.255. In conclusion we may state that with rather primitive means an interesting amount of information can still be obtained. Both with thin section studies as well as with specific-gravity separates and index liquids good results have been obtained. If the limitations of these methods are well understood they may lead to interesting results on the detrital feldspars in a sample. Fig.62 schematically illustrates the previous methods.

Argillaceous sediments and clay-rich soils

The terms in the heading of this section attempt to include all those rocks rich in clay or mica. Such sediments are relatively rich in aluminium because clays consisting of hydrous micas and kaolinite contain large percentages of Al_2O_3. In the Niggli nomenclature such sediments are named alumo-silicate rocks. This term does not seem to have become current in the English language. Therefore, the term argillaceous has been chosen here, although it seems to pertain more to clay-rich rocks than to mica-rich sediments.

   The fragments in these rocks may not adhere as in recent river clays. They can show some adherence as in clay-stones. They can be consolidated or rather lithified as in shales. In some cases the name slate is used for these sediments. The author prefers to reserve the term slate for slightly altered or rather metamorphosed argillaceous rocks. For a proper definition of the concept shale as used here, the reader may consult the A.G.I. Glossary.

   The aspects of a detrital feldspar analysis of these rocks will again be discussed in two sections, one dealing exclusively with the indurated or consolidated samples, the other treating their unconsolidated counterparts.

Consolidated or indurated argillaceous sediments

A study of the feldspar fraction of these sediments is rather difficult because of the small particle size of the minerals. It is quite often impossible to find feldspars in thin sections of such rocks. A study of the X-ray powder pattern of the total sample will at the same time show the presence of feldspars. Here we must be rather careful with the interpretation. In some cases the X-ray powder pattern shows an abundance of albite, while the thin section of the same sample does not show albite particles great enough for an unambiguous determination. The submicroscopical albite may be the result of an alteration of the sediment in many cases. In the present context it is not unimportant to consider this "alteration" of the sediment with regard to the correct usage of such names as diagenesis, induration, metamorphosis or one of the rich set of terms for this process. The study of such a sample in the hand specimen may lead to the conclusion that it is rather lithified. The microscopical study will often show that apparently little has changed. X-ray powder patterns, finally, may reveal the presence of well-preserved hydrous micas next to newly-formed albite or adularia or certain zeolites.

On the other hand, we know of argillaceous sediments exhibiting particles of sand or silt size not too densely sown in a clay matrix. A study of the sand fraction of such samples in thin sections may produce results. Needless to say, this study is time consuming because more than one thin section has to be analysed. The feldspar content can also be estimated in stained sections or with stained rock slabs. The latter are more difficult to make and even more difficult to stain, because the dye tends to be absorbed in the mica-rich material. Careful polishing and even more careful staining is necessary.

Disaggregation of the sample. Sediments of the type under discussion are easy to disaggregate. Moreover, the fragments do not suffer much damage from mechanical treatment. One may either use a kind of liquid promoting the swelling of the still-present clay minerals in order to perform a detachment of the coherent particles. One may also rely on mechanical crushing. Carefully crushing in a mortar or with a jaw crusher will lead to good results. Other samples lead to a set of non-coherent particles if treated carefully in an ultrasonic cleaner. Some investigators use pressure chambers on wetted fragments. The mica still adhering to quartz or feldspar particles can be removed by gentle rubbing on a rubber surface with a pestle. A comparable method is used by investigators in the field of age determination, who want to detach zircons and apatite from mica flakes. The author observed the application of a comparable method for the first time in the Petrographical Laboratory of Bern University, Bern, Switzerland. He is not aware of a publication giving details.

Another useful technique has been developed by WICK (1947). The manual on sediment-petrographical methods of MÜLLER (1964), which became available just before this text was finished, also gives a method derived from the one developed by Wick.

The sample is crushed. The fragments after crushing have a size of about 1 cm³. Cover the crushed sample with a 15% H_2O_2 solution in a large glass beaker. The pulp begins to effervesce. If effervescence has not begun after 15 min, the beaker may be placed over a water bath in a well ventilated hood. Müller also advocates the addition of a tiny amount of KOH solution to start the process[1]. If the first treatment is not sufficient, the procedure can be repeated a few times. It has been noted

---

[1] See also the remark on p.257 for the influence of K ions on the structure of clay minerals. The amount of KOH should therefore be restricted to a minimum if clay minerals are also to be involved in the further study.

that clay minerals do not suffer structurally from this treatment. It is unknown if the grain-size distribution of the clay minerals changes, but this can be expected.

X-ray methods. X-ray powder methods are known to be most powerful in studying clay-rich sediments. Still, the reader must be on guard in using powder methods on indurated or lithified clays. If the total sample is powdered and analysed, unexpected minerals may turn up. If the sample has a red colour, pointing to the presence of hematite or goethite, copper radiation cannot be used with cameras. Either the samples have to be deironed or the use of another type of tube is necessary. This may constitute a reason for using cobalt tubes.

If the total rock is analysed the X-ray diffractometer can be used, but the operator must be willing to scan a rather large portion of the entire $90°$.

Experience with hydrothermal experiments beginning with natural clays carried out by Winkler and Von Platen over a couple of years, has taught that the identification of the reaction products is efficiently done with a Guinier-De Wolff camera. Another complication encountered in the study of the samples under consideration is the occasional presence of zeolites such as phillipsite and heulandite or minerals of the leucite group such as analcime.

Conclusive remarks. In closing this section we may conclude that shales are not rich in feldspars. The study of the feldspar fraction can be done with conventional methods as long as these feldspars occur in the fraction of the larger particles. The feldspars in the finer fractions can only be estimated with X-ray powder methods. The occasional occurrence of authigenic feldspars as well as zeolites must be expected. The various steps outlined in the foregoing text have been schematically illustrated by the flow sheet in Fig.62.

Unconsolidated argillaceous sediments and clay-rich soils

The terms in the heading of this paragraph are meant to include all those clays, loams, silty clays and clay-rich soils having a grain-size distribution with a large amount of fine material, i.e., material with a particle size smaller than $2~\mu$. This fraction consists for a large part of hydrous micas and minerals of the montmorillonite kaolinite and chlorite group. Furthermore, quartz is nearly always present in this fraction and feldspars are encountered in fair amounts in some cases.

X-ray methods. The study of such sediments is a problem of quantitative X-ray analysis of the clay fraction. This problem, though severely attacked from all sides, has not yet been solved satisfactorily. Some progress has been made by BRINDLEY and KURTOSSY (1961) for the quantitative determination of minerals of the kaolinite group.

If quartz and feldspar have to be quantitatively identified, the problem is somewhat easier. These minerals give less cause to orientation effects. Moreover, such properties as lattice defects, incomplete or degraded structures often encountered in clay minerals, are virtually absent in feldspar or quartz. For an estimation of the amount of quartz and feldspars in clay samples we may start from standard samples with a known admixture of these minerals of a carefully prepared grain-size range.

It seems that both in the range below 1 μ and in the range between 1 and 2 μ, quartz and feldspar may occur. The standard samples must account for this occurrence. The estimation of the quantities of these minerals in clays must be done with a preparation of random orientation. The following considerations will show why samples with a preferred orientation may lead to unreliable results. Oriented samples of clays are made with a technique whereby the clay particles are allowed to settle slowly onto a glass slide from a liquid. The smallest particles will arrive at the slide surface after all the coarser particles have settled down, thus covering these coarse particles with a thin film of well-oriented small flakes. In this way they may interfere with the intensity of the reflections of quartz and feldspars.

For these reasons we advocate the method of BRINDLEY and KURTOSSY (1961), or any other similar technique if a diffractometer is used. It consists of a stirring of the sample in liquid Canada balsam or any other resin. The mixture is left to become hard and brittle. Afterwards it is ground and the powder thus obtained is filled in the sample holder.

With a quadruple Guinier-De Wolff camera the problems are less difficult to solve. The primary X-ray beam runs perpendicular through a flat preparation. Preferred orientation can be disturbed by scratching the sample with a needle in order to produce a kind of grating. This method was developed by PORRENGA (1958).

Examples. In order to demonstrate what has been reached in a study of detrital feldspars from clay-rich samples we give two examples from recent papers. Let us first turn to the work of PETERSON and GOLDBERG. (1962) These investigators noticed that from a group of samples from the Pacific Ocean the following minerals had been studied before: quartz, montmorillonite, extremely old terrestrial illite and kaolinite. Feldspars, however, had "escaped" systematic investigation (and not only in South Pacific pelagic sediments). This caused the above-mentioned investigators to begin a systematic analysis, the results of which were reported in 1962.

The samples, the upper 20 cm of bottom sediments, were separated into two size-fractions in order to segregate the local contribution of feldspars and to contrast them with a more regional background contribution, perhaps eolian in origin. The fraction above 32 μ was assumed to represent the local contribution. A fine fraction between 4 and 8 μ, separated by settling techniques, is assumed to contain material transported over long distances by either atmospheric or oceanic circulations, along with some locally derived material. The minerals calcite, phillipsite, montmorillonite, apatite, and ferro-manganese minerals were chemically removed. The remainder was studied with X-rays on a powder diffractometer. The authors relied on the techniques suggested by J. V. SMITH (1956) and J. V. SMITH and GAY (1958). For the identification of plagioclases they used the separation of 131 and 1$\bar{3}$1 (see also p.199). For the alkali feldspars they used the $\bar{2}$01 spacing, advocated by Bowen and Tuttle (see also p.180). Quartz was identified with its 3.34 Å spacing. A discussion of these methods has been given in Chapter 10.

The authors could distinguish between sanidine, anorthoclase, oligoclase-andesine and andesine-labradorite. Sanidine occurred in a few samples. Anortho-clase was more frequently found, but in minor quantities, and especially the plagio-clases in the range between oligoclase and andesine were widespread and important constituents. The authors could establish the absence of microcline in the samples. Especially this led them to conclude that even the fine material was derived from the area producing the coarse feldspars by way of volcanic activity, largely of a submarine nature. The way in which these authors represent their numerical results is worth mentioning. They plot the quotient of the total intensity of the alkali feldspars and the plagioclase diffraction lines along the ordinate and the localities along the abscis. In the same manner is the ratio quartz/plagioclase shown.

The geological conclusions of this study demonstrate what can be decided from a study of detrital feldspar distribution. First of all, the authors could delineate sediment-petrographical provinces in this large area. Furthermore, they found feldspars present in every sample they studied. This find has an important bearing on the thermodynamical stability of feldspars in a marine environment at a depth between 3 and 5 km. The sediment-petrographical provinces are charac-terized by feldspar assemblages. One is of basic volcanism, roughly coinciding with linear arrays of large volcanoes. A province of acidic volcanism is associated with the East Pacific Rise south of Easter Island. The sediment-petrographical provinces found near the coast of South America and in the vicinity of the island arcs northeast of Australia, have a more heterogeneous feldspar assemblage than the other suites found in the provinces already mentioned. In the region about the Equator north-northwest of Easter Island a quite smooth area devoid of feldspars has been found to exist.

A paper by D. E. HILL and TEDROW (1961) treats the weathering and soil forma-tion in arctic environments. The clay fractions of these soils found in northern Alaska are rich in feldspars if the source rock and the parent material contain these minerals in certain amounts. The paper gives an ample discussion of the aspects of weathering, the particle size of such soils and its mineralogical composition, and also considers the development of the insight into soil formation in arctic regions from about 1932 onwards. The four Arctic Brown soil profiles discussed are without exception rich in fine particles. From the description it follows that all these samples contain an important amount of loam. The largest size fraction is found in the silt range from 50 to 2 μ. The clay fraction ($< 2\mu$) still consists of about 10 weight percentages on the average. In this fraction hydrous mica is the dominant mineral. Furthermore, kaolinite, quartz feldspar and goethite are found.

The coarse fractions contain relatively fresh feldspars. Alkali feldspars as well as plagioclases have been distinguished. Optical methods help to identify the nature of these feldspars more accurately in the coarse fractions. In the clay fraction no distinction has been made between plagioclase and alkali feldspar. Some remarks concerning the pretreatment can also be found in the paper by Hill and Tedrow.

Conclusive remarks. In conclusion it can be said that the identification of feldspars in clay fractions is sometimes successfully done with X-ray methods. Further information on this aspect can be found in Chapter 10. The methods treated in this paragraph have been schematically given in the flow sheet of Fig.62.

Carbonate sediments and soils

In this section carbonate rocks and soils rich in carbonates are meant in the first place to comprise those sediments which consist entirely or mainly of carbonates. As important carbonates we may list the carbonates of calcium, magnesium and to a lesser degree those of iron and manganese. Such rocks may contain in addition clay and sand. The additional material may in some cases exist of volcanic debris. Moreover, the presence of carbonates in moderate amounts is often enough to determine the main characteristics of a rock. Therefore, next to the pure and impure limestones and dolomites we will deal with those sediments named calcareous. For instance, marls, in the sense of calcareous clays or silts, calcareous sandstones and even shell deposits, whether they contain silt or sand, are treated as described in the following paragraphs.

The group of sediments under discussion is largely made up of rocks in the literal sense of the word. Even today we can witness the genesis of real limestones. Furthermore, unconsolidated carbonate sediments tend towards compaction and subsequent cementation by the specific properties of carbonates. With these sediments the process of becoming a coherent aggregate of minerals is more rapid than with sands or clays. On the other hand, they are more susceptible to weathering and disaggregation under the influence of soil-forming processes and solution by rain water. The susceptibility is a consequence of the same properties of carbonates. This implies that if, in the following paragraphs, one paragraph treats coherent rocks and the other loose samples, recent sediments are to be found in both groups; this is quite contrary to the solid rocks of arenaceous or argillaceous composition treated in the former sections.

In the paragraphs following this introduction some rocks are discussed that have properties comparable with those treated previously, except for the presence of carbonates. Further treatment after the removal of carbonates is therefore rather similar too. Consequently, it is unavoidable that the reader will find some of the procedures again in the following lines. This repetition is not avoided, because in this way each section can be read independently.

Solid carbonate sediments

Thin section studies are currently used to study dolomites and limestones. For the identification of the non-carbonate minerals other methods have been used. The choice of a particular method for the study of these samples is highly dependent on the amount of non-carbonate minerals as well as on the type of carbonate. For instance, if we deal with calcareous sandstones there is often no reason at all for not trying a thin section study.

Thin section study. In the majority of cases thin sections give sufficient information on impure limestones, impure dolomites and calcareous sandstones or shales[1]. The information one may expect from thin sections in these cases is similar to that obtained from shales or sandstones. As soon as the carbonate content increases and the crystals show a configuration that is unfavourable for the study of quartz or feldspar, other methods may have their advantages. This is the case if every single quartz or feldspar grain is surrounded by carbonates. The possibilities of determining optical properties of these grains is then rather restricted. Especially the estimation of the indices of refraction is difficult.

    In other cases the amount of calcite or dolomite is so large that only a few fragments of other minerals are seen in a thin section. The study of these other minerals with thin sections becomes a rather inefficient procedure. If this type of rock has to be studied we may decide that the removal of carbonates is necessary.

Removal of carbonates. Several methods have been developed for the removal of all types of carbonates. The diversity of the methods is not only a matter of personal preference but also due to the fact that acid treatments are known to attack some minerals severely, while others completely vanish. Especially clay minerals suffer from acid treatments. This implies that investigators interested in both feldspars and clay must be rather careful. Methods for this dual purpose exist. In general feldspars will not suffer from any one of these more gentle techniques.

    It is often wise to study the sample with a thin section in all the available cases. It may help to decide about the type of pretreatment. For instance, some limestones are so poor in other minerals that a treatment of more than 1,000 g of sample is necessary to produce only 1 g of residue or even less. A preliminary thin section study can tell us if we have brought a sufficient amount of sample

---

[1] For a study of limestones, carbonatites, etc., etching techniques have several advantages in combination with vertical incident light, cf., VAN DER VEEN (1963).

home from our fieldwork. It happens that such investigations simply have to wait until after the next field trip. If enough sample is available, a thin section study will reveal something about the nature and the grain size of the residual minerals. In this way we get a first impression of the type of pretreatment.

The nature of the carbonates can be studied with simple methods. Calcite is soluble in cold 0.1 N HCl, with effervescence; dolomite is only slowly soluble in cold 0.1 N HCl; magnesite is not soluble in cold concentrated HCl but soluble in hot concentrated HCl; siderite is slowly soluble in concentrated cold HCl. Other techniques exist for such a determination. The indices of refraction of siderite and magnesite are determinative. Moreover, staining techniques can be applied. These have been reviewed by FRIEDMAN (1959).

Procedures. It is necessary before any treatment to fragmentate the sample by simple crushing. The rock fragments must be of about 0.5 cm in size. With smaller fragments one runs the risk of breaking the non-carbonate mineral fragments. After fragmentation the particles are put in large glass beakers or in large Erlenmeyer flasks. Afterwards the samples are treated with acid. It must be mentioned that the author is against the use of boiling acid or concentrated acid as long as this can be avoided[1]. This attitude is based on the experience that the surface of any mineral is attacked by such acids. In the rest of the study of these minerals such surfaces may interfere with staining methods, the study of surface properties, etc.

Before doing anything else we may calculate the amount of acid of a specific concentration that is necessary for the digestion of the amount of calcite or dolomite in the sample. The advice has a psychological effect. The investigator who knows how much acid he needs to treat his sample properly, will not get impatient. Impatience has spoiled quite a number of promising experiments.

Although we do not doubt that every reader of this book is quite able to perform such a calculation, an example will be given here to save the time needed for looking up the necessary constants in a compendium. Starting from:

$$CaCO_3 + 2\ HCl \rightarrow CaCl_2 + CO_2 + H_2O$$

the equation says that 2 gmol of HCl is necessary for the digestion of 1 gmol of $CaCO_3$. It is known that a 1 N solution of HCl contains exactly 1 gmol/l. The molecular weight of $CaCO_3$ is about 100. Consequently, 2 l of a 1 N HCl decomposes 100 g of $CaCO_3$. Dealing with dolomite, formula MgCa $(CO_3)_2$, we need 2.18 l of 1 N HCl for the digestion of 100 g of dolomite. The molecular weight of dolomite is about 184. Needless to say, we need a good pail of diluted acid for the treatment of a sample of about 1 kg.

We must not fill in the calculated amount of acid at once in performing such a treatment. This has three disadvantages. Firstly, we need extremely large vessels for such experiments; secondly, the acidity of the solution is rather low at the end of the experiment; thirdly, the minerals that have been freed from the rock fragments in the first phase of the experiment are for the remainder of it exposed to the influences of this acid environment.

It is advised to add small amounts of liquid at a time. Stir well or agitate until the effervescence stops. Decant the suspension and collect the non-carbonate mineral fragments from this suspension. Try to remove the non-carbonate minerals of larger size also. Rinse the minerals with 0.5 N HCl and afterwards with distilled water. The rock fragments in the container are treated repeatedly in this way, until all the carbonates are dissolved. This procedure renders a sample of minerals of larger size and unaltered clay minerals.

Other methods exist for the removal of carbonates. They are either based on the use of exchange resins or on the properties of EDTA. W. E. HILL and GOEBEL (1963), for instance, studied

---

[1] A practical method using cold 2 N HCl has been described by BASSET (1953).

the rates of solution of limestones in EDTA solutions. They reached the conclusion that the amount of calcite going into solution during 24 h at room temperature in an EDTA solution of optimum concentration is about equal to the amount of calcite going into solution during 8 h in a 0.5 N HCl solution at room temperature. On p.256 more will be said about these methods.

Examples. The study of the residual minerals obtained from limestones and dolomites has been carried out by numerous authors. Only one of these reports will be briefly considered, others will be mentioned by title only.

SCHÖNER (1960) discussed the non-carbonate minerals present in calcareous sediments from the surroundings of Hannover in Germany. The samples derived from two large quarries providing raw material for the production of Portland cement. The samples studied weighed between 300 and 500 g. The removal of carbonates was carried out by an acid treatment in much the same way as described earlier. Schöner was interested in the clay minerals also; therefore, a solution of 0.5 N HCl at room temperature was used. Even authigenic heulandite crystals have been found among the detrital minerals because of this gentle preparation technique.

Among the investigations carried out on the non-soluble minerals we may mention an analysis of the grain-size distribution; a qualitative and a semi-quantitative analysis of the clay fraction; an analysis of the quartz fraction and an investigation of the origin of both the detrital and the authigenic quartz; an analysis of the composition of the detrital and the authigenic opaque minerals fraction; an analysis of the heavy fraction, among others authigenic tourmaline; an analysis of the micro fossils. We are only interested in the feldspar fraction, consisting of both detrital and authigenic feldspars. In addition to quantitative mineralogical analyses, Schöner prepared a number of chemical analyses of fractions of the residue. The chemical composition of the samples was compared with the mineralogical composition. In this way a useful control of the quantitative mineralogical analysis was achieved. Especially this aspect renders Schöner's report an intrinsic value that is often lacking in other papers.

Feldspars have been found in every grain-size fraction. The amount of feldspars in the coarse fractions is larger than that in the fines. The feldspars constitute less than 1 % of the total residue, on the average. Both detrital and authigenic feldspars have been found among the alkali feldspars and the plagioclases. Authigenic feldspars are rare and constitute less than one thousandth of the total residue. Detrital feldspars are generally present as monoclinic phases, characterized by the presence of an axial angle of about 43°. This statement is based on universal stage measurements of 20 fragments. In addition, microcline and microcline perthites have been found in small amounts. Microcline is determined by the presence of cross-hatched twinning. The fraction larger than 60 μ yielded three authigenic feldspar crystals with idiomorphic outlines showing Carlsbad twins. Detrital feldspars never show authigenic rims.

Detrital plagioclases are present as albite and oligoclase. Again the grains are free of authigenic rims. Some fragments show the characteristic multiple twins. In the fraction larger than 60 μ authigenic albites have been found. The morphology of these crystals is rather typical. Similar crystals have been found elsewhere and were already described in the 19th century as Roc-Tourné quadruplets. FÜCHT-BAUER (1956) studied similar feldspars from comparable rocks. Schöner devoted much of his work to a description and discussion of these authigenic albites.

In order to arrive at quantitative data on the mineralogical composition of the residue, grain mounts were used. Counts were made in liquids of 1.548 and 1.527 index of refraction. Smaller than 1.527, alkali feldspars and heulandite; inbetween 1.527 and 1.548, quartz and this total feldspar fraction; larger than 1.548, all the other minerals such as mica, heavy minerals, etc. Both the fractions larger than 60 μ and those in between 20 and 60 μ were counted in this way. In some preparations the number of counts is about 700. Schöner reports the use of phase-contrast microscopy with good results in both fractions.

After this detailed analysis of residual minerals from a limestone, it is felt that a consideration of other examples is hardly worth while. The various aspects of the procedure have been touched upon. Other authors have reached comparable results with rather similar techniques and other samples. For instance, TOPKAYA (1950) reports the results of a study of the authigenic minerals of Swiss limestones and calcareous sediments. Feldspar as well as tourmaline received his special attention. Moreover, he gives a fairly complete list of the available papers on this subject.

FÜCHTBAUER (1956) reports results on limestones from nearby Göttingen. The clay fraction of these rocks consists exclusively of illite, coarser fractions contain authigenic quartz, alkali feldspar and albite.

Conclusive remarks. In this section we considered various analytical methods for the study of the non-soluble residues of calcareous sediments. Other combinations of methods have been applied with great success. Some of these are the same for solid rocks and for arenaceous material. Therefore, the reader may turn now to p.255 for a discussion of these aspects.

In general, much can be expected from a study of the detrital minerals present in these rocks. The methods are fairly easy and the results are rewarding. The flow sheet of Fig.62 illustrates schematically the various steps of the investigation.

Carbonate-bearing unconsolidated sediments and carbonate-rich soils
The study of the group of sediments and soils described in the heading of this paragraph needs no special treatment. If the sample is to be treated as a sand or a clay the carbonates must be removed. If the total sample is studied it is simply treated as a comparable sample without carbonates. Although it is off the subject, we may warn against the erroneous interpretation of sieve results of such samples with as well as without the carbonates.

If we concentrate for a moment on the true sediments in this group, we must be prepared to deal frequently with recent marine sediments or with recent erosion products of limestone cliffs, whether along the coast or in other regions. Unconsolidated calciferous sediments and soils are often found in arid regions because a profusion of rain will have leached such products in a short time, leaving a non-calcareous residual cover on the surface.

With regard to soils, it is common experience that the top soil found on limestone parent material is frequently free or almost free of calcium carbonate in moderate climates. Both the influence of the vegetation as well as the percolating rain water have leached this part almost entirely. As an example we may point to the decalcification of the upper part of a number of loesses, among others, in the southern part of The Netherlands. Soils found in subtropical regions with an arid climate may still contain carbonates in the top soil. Such soils can be studied with the same methods as the ones described for solid limestones.

Since the work of Kuguchkov, and others, we know of soils suffering from carbonate salinization. Such soils are, among others, found in the Zeravshan Valley, U.S.S.R. UZAKOV (1961) reports some data about these soils. Calcite and magnesite form hardpans in these soils. Both minerals found constitute about 10% of the total mineral matter of the top soil. A study of such soils is difficult because of the presence of magnesite. Treatment with stronger acids seems necessary. As long as the acid is added in small amounts and as long as the residual minerals of the suspension are shortly afterwards thoroughly rinsed with distilled water, one may expect to arrive at a residue in which the alteration of clay minerals is restricted to a workable minimum. On the other hand, the use of exchange resins or chelating compounds is expected to give more reliable results.

As soon as the samples are free of carbonates the following procedures are the same for all samples. A consideration of various useful procedures can again be found on p.255. For completeness sake, a schematical illustration of the treatment of the samples under consideration has been given in the flow sheet of Fig.62.

Miscellaneous sediments and soils

After the preceding treatment of the more common types of sediments and soils every reader will point to the existence of such rocks as ferruginous sandstones, laterites, kaolinite deposits, soils containing gypsum, etc. Some readers may also perhaps want me to treat the analysis of these sediments and soils in detail. The reason is simple. These groups of sediments and soils are known to cause serious difficulties in routine procedures, and sometimes even unsurmountable difficulties. An investigator who has tried to remove the abundant amount of gypsum from his sample in order to study the clay minerals more efficiently, knows exactly what difficulties are in store for him. Others may have tried the mechanical analysis of samples containing gibbsite. Such samples are notorious for their refusal to peptize well.

If we note now down that a treatment of these miscellaneous samples is beyond the scope of a text on the identification of detrital feldspars, this may still be judged as an easy way out. Therefore, some remarks must be made on the pretreatment of such samples. The reader must be informed, however, of the fact that the present author has only a rather limited experience with such samples. A study of the available literature gives one the impression that the pretreatment of these samples remains difficult even if a detailed enumeration is given of possibly everything that has been tried on them. Therefore, we will refrain from completeness and assume that some indications as to the possible ways of approach are sufficient. For further information both the sedimentologist and the soil scientist are advised to consult such standard works as the texts by BLANCK (1929), KRUMBEIN and PETTIJOHN (1938), GORBUNOV (1950, 1960), STRAKHOV (1958), MILNER (1962), MÜLLER (1964), and others.

Ferruginous samples

It seems to be common practice, at least among sedimentologists, to treat lavishly the samples with concentrated HCl and concentrated HNO_3. And as if this is not enough, they sometimes even prefer to boil their minerals for some time in this cocktail. This "method" will *not* be treated here.

Ferruginous samples can be successfully treated with sodium-dithionite. De-ironing of samples with "dithionite" has a number of advantages. First of all, such minerals as glauconite, chlorite, apatite and a few others are left rather unimpaired. Secondly, clay minerals resist the influence of a dithionite treatment much better than any other method for the removal of iron and manganese. The majority of the iron minerals such as goethite, hematite and various iron–manganese compounds are removed by this method. A description of the procedure is given on p.259.

If one dithionite treatment fails we may try a repetition; such a repetition may be combined with mechanical crushing.

An intelligent combination of magnetic separation and a repetition of a dithionite treatment will produce good results in some cases. In other cases an attrition of coatings by a mutual abrasion method has been used. Such a technique does not leave the grain surfaces unattacked. Finally, if all these techniques have failed the investigator may judge it necessary to try the boiling HCl–HNO_3 cocktail in order to remove the iron compounds.

Gypsum- and anhydrite-bearing samples

According to numerous manuals on laboratory techniques, gypsum and anhydrite are removed with an acid treatment. Either HCl or acetic acid are prescribed. The disadvantages of an acid treatment have been discussed previously. Moreover,

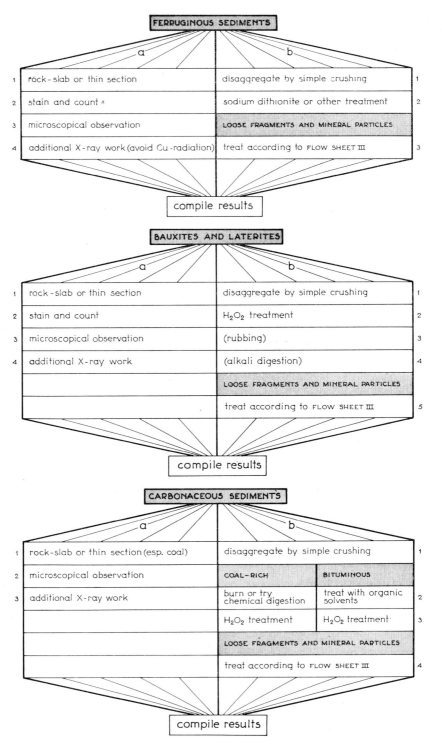

Fig.64. FLOW SHEET II. Flow sheets for the concentration and identification of detrital feldspars in several types of rock.

the two minerals under discussion are only moderately soluble in acids. On the other hand, literature on this subject lists a few other methods that are less destructive for clay minerals. These methods are also time-consuming but this is hardly an objection.

The other techniques are based on a stimulation of the solution of gypsum in addition to a removal of the ions from the solution. BOLT and FRISSEL (1960) advocate the use of exchange resins for the removal of sulphates, chlorides, nitrates and carbonates from soils. The specifications of the procedures are given on p.258 and 259. J. Ch. L. Favejee (personal communication, 1963) finds it more satisfactory to use a detour instead of a straightforward solution of the gypsum crystals; he is experimenting with a method that changes gypsum into a carbonate. Afterwards the sulphate ions are removed and the residue containing carbonates is treated in the normal way. Procedures using chelating properties of several chemical compounds for the removal of gypsum have not yet come to the author's attention. Still, one can expect good results from such an approach.

Bauxites and laterites

It seems that there is not yet a satisfactory procedure for the removal of gibbsite, boehmite, and other aluminium hydroxides from samples. As far as can be inferred from available information, alkaline digestion will sometimes give fair results. This is especially the case if opaline silica cement is present also. In general it seems impossible to isolate the heavy and light minerals from such sediments without damaging some of them. In such cases, however, it is often a matter of choice. Either no concentration at all of specific minerals or a concentrate of partially damaged minerals. The problem at hand will help to decide in favour of one of the two alternatives.

Carbonaceous sediments

Sediments containing coal or bituminous material have been studied intensively because of their economic value. If the quantitative mineralogical composition has to be evaluated, rather cumbersome methods must be applied.

Bituminous sediments. The mineralogical analysis of these samples has been carried out in two different ways. Either thin sections have been made, or the bituminous material has been removed prior to a study of the minerals. The bituminous material can be extracted with one of the many organic solvents in a large soxhlet extractor. In some cases this is not even necessary and the sample can be treated in a glass beaker, washing the bituminous material away with an organic solvent and removing the supernatant liquid afterwards. In other cases the sample, crushed into small fragments, can be treated in an ultrasonic cleaner with a mixture of aethanol and benzene (N.B. the procedure may be dangerous). For details see MÜLLER (1964, p.42).

Coal and coal-bearing sediments. One of the simplest methods for the isolation of silicates from coal is simple burning. If burning is done carefully and extreme temperatures are avoided, this method renders useful samples for the study of a number of heavy minerals and feldspars. Feldspars suffer from heat treatments with temperatures over 700 °C. If the structure of this mineral is not of interest to the investigator, this burning can still be used because they remain feldspars. Heavy liquid separation, staining methods as well as counting in index liquids is possible with such mineral fragments. If the clay minerals present in the sample are also to be studied, burning must be avoided because most clay minerals suffer from temperatures even less than 120 °C.

Other methods for the extraction of silicates from coal and coal-bearing sediments are based on gentle pulverization and a digestion of the carbon. A disaggregation of the particles can be brought about afterwards by a chemical treatment. The following chemical compounds have been used to this effect: pyridine, phenol, chloroform, sodium hypochlorite or a solution of KOH. Some of these chemicals are known to attack at least clay minerals to a high degree. But here again, we have to choose between two evils: either no information at all, or partial information on partly-damaged minerals.

Conclusive remarks. The pretreatment of the samples which fall in one of the last categories is difficult, cumbersome, time consuming and not entirely satisfactory. But these samples do occur from time to time in an investigation. The investigator may regard them as a nuisance, because they disturb the well settled routine and the general flow sheet of the laboratory. Others, however, may welcome these samples as a real adventure amidst the boring daily routine. They may stimulate this worker to search for the most efficient procedure and the most intelligent solution. Moreover, these samples produce a rewarding amount of new information, at least on laboratory methods.

For this reason I may point out that the attitude more than the skill of the investigator determines to a much higher degree the results with such samples. And even after a number of unsuccessful attempts the stubborn samples can be made into a number of thin sections. In this way we may turn to the methods used in a preliminary start as a reliable last resource.

A FLOW SHEET FOR THE STUDY OF DETRITAL FELDSPARS

Introduction

In the foregoing section a variety of quantitative methods have been considered. These methods were different for different types of sediment. Moreover, it has been argued that the production of an incoherent mineral aggregate has certain advantages over other methods of study. The reader will be more fully informed about the procedure after the production of the aggregate, in a later paragraph.

Before entering in a discussion of the further aspects of a detrital feldspar analysis, we must warn against too great expectations. It is principally impossible to develop one method only that can adequately cover all the possible problems. Much depends on the investigator's skill and on his talent for improvisation. Much depends also on the laboratory equipment and on the nature of the samples.

In the following we begin with the assumption that the sample has been made into a collection of incoherent minerals of various sizes. The aggregate may still contain carbonates, sulphates, iron or manganese compounds and coated grains. The procedure for the removal of these substances will be given in a set of formulas in the text. They are referred to with such terms as acid treatment, removal of gypsum or de-ironing in other parts, together with the associated page number. Furthermore, it is assumed that the reader is familiar with such procedures as sieving and heavy mineral separation. If this is not the case, he may turn to such manuals as the ones by KRUMBEIN and PETTIJOHN (1938) or MÜLLER (1964). Formulas for staining and flotation, as well as procedures for X-ray powder analyses, optical methods and twin recognition, are given in the preceding chapters. In the following these methods will be mentioned and referred to, but will not receive further discussion.

The sample

The sample under investigation is reduced to a collection of large and small mineral fragments. Feldspars are expected to occur in both the large and in the small size fraction. It has been previously argued that the methods for studying these minerals in the various fractions differ considerably. Moreover, we are here concerned with feldspars and not with grain-size distributions of the natural samples. Consequently, the normal objections against the removal of coatings and the isolation of the mineral particles from cemented fragments are not valid in this case. For this research the feldspar fragments have to be available in the state in which they were deposited or in the state they were in before cementation began.

Consequently, the sample must be treated in such a way that the feldspar grains are freed of coatings and cement. Only then can the sample be divided by sieving into fractions containing feldspar fragments of different sizes; the fine fraction can be divided into a clay fraction and a silt fraction.

If the investigator began with a solid rock, a limestone or a quartzite, the procedure for disaggregating the sample often provides for a large number of the just listed conditions. One or a few of the steps described in the following may therefore be omitted; it is left to the reader to decide which ones.

The pre-treatment

The sample used for a study of detrital feldspars must be free of organic material, iron and manganese coatings, carbonates and sulphates. The following sequence of procedures is advocated.

The sample of incoherent fragments, whether a soil or a sediment or an artificial product containing organic material is treated with peroxide as described below.

Oxidation of organic compounds

Reagents
H_2O_2 solution, 30%; H_2O_2 solution, 10%.

Procedure
Put the sample in a glass beaker, which fits a water bath. The beaker should be large enough, because froth is produced by the escaping CO_2. Add 10% H_2O_2 solution. A sample of about 50 g should be covered with about 50 ml of liquid. Smaller samples are also covered with this amount of peroxide of hydrogen. Place over a boiling water bath. During the digestion of the organic material, such as humus, a froth is formed. Add so much 30% H_2O_2 solution from time to time, that the remaining liquid is always as strong as 10% H_2O_2. Continue until the formation of bubbles has slowed down and the organic compounds are entirely decomposed. Keep over the water bath until the excess H_2O_2 has vanished. Allow to cool. If the sample is rich in clay material leave it in the beaker overnight. The next day the clean supernatant liquid can be siphoned off for a large part.

After oxidation, the carbonates are removed as completely as possible by one of the several techniques described now. The acid digestion with diluted cold HCl will be used in the majority of cases.

Removal of carbonates

Acid digestion
Reagents. Solution of HCl, 1 N; solution of HCl, 6 N.

Procedure. Put the sample, free of organic compounds in a glass beaker, or leave it there after the H_2O_2 treatment. Add so much cold 1 N HCl solution and/or H_2O, that the liquid just covering the sample is approximately 0.2 N HCl. Agitate the sample, if possible with a magnetic stirrer. Add small amounts of the 1 N HCl solution in order to keep the liquid covering the sample at about 0.2 N.

Samples extremely rich in carbonates consume the HCl so rapidly that by adding small amounts of a 1 N solution the acidity drops too rapidly. In this case we may add small amounts of cold 6 N HCl. Take care not to use strong acids too lavishly.

If effervescence stops, and all the carbonates are decomposed, the sample must be rinsed with H_2O. Clay-rich samples are efficiently washed in a centrifuge. Bring the content quantitatively in a centrifuge tube and spin the minerals down. Siphon the supernatant liquid off. Add H_2O, and stir the clay cake with this water until a homogeneous suspension has been formed. Stirring is most efficiently done in the centrifuge tube with a small electric stirring device. Repeat this until the clay starts to peptize. If peptization is not wanted at this stage because of further treatment, this can be undone by simply adding a small drop of 1 N HCl.

EDTA treatment
Reagents. Sodium, potassium or ammonium-substituted salts of EDTA or ethylenediaminetetraacetic acid, commercially known as Versene, Komplexon or Idranal in solutions of a pH of about 8.

Procedure. The sample is put in a glass beaker and treated with a solution of an EDTA salt over a water bath until all calcite has been removed. It must be mentioned that iron as well as barium, strontium and to a lesser degree magnesium are also caught by the EDTA ion. The anion has a certain selectivity dependent on the pH of the liquid. Iron is preferentially refused at pH values of about 8 and higher.

It is difficult to give a cut-and-dried technique here. First of all, the method depends on the EDTA salt used or available. W. E. HILL and GOEBEL (1963) came to the conclusion that the potassium and the ammonium salts were most effective. These were not, as far as these authors knew, commercially available. Therefore, they prepared EDTA acid from the commercially available tetra-sodium EDTA by treating the solution of the salt with reagent-grade HCl in small increments until a pH of 1 was attained. According to their text, "the solution and precipitation of tetra-hydrogen EDTA were carried out in 20-quart polyethylene wastebaskets placed on a magnetic stirrer". In this way they converted 3–5 kg of EDTA at the same time. The precipitate was washed with 10% HCl and vacuum-filtered. The filter cakes were afterwards dissolved in solutions of KOH and NH_4OH in order to produce the solutions wanted according to the formula

$$4 (M)OH + H_4(EDTA) \rightarrow (M)_4(EDTA) + 4H_2O$$

where M is a monovalent cation.

Hill and Goebel describe easy methods for recovering used EDTA. If clay minerals are to be studied also, the potassium and ammonium salts must be avoided because these cations are strongly fixed in the hydrous micas, changing their properties.

The use of EDTA has also been described by MÜLLER (1964). This author treats exclusively the use of sodium salts.

Solutions of EDTA salts can also be used in removing dolomite or other carbonates. But especially the "absorption" of magnesium ions is rather slow in comparison to calcium ions. This property has been used by WEISSMANN and DIEHL (1954) for the determination of the calcite/dolomite ratio in carbonate rocks.

Exchange resins

Reagents. Cationic exchange resins, commercially known under a large variety of names.

Procedure. The sample consisting of mineral particles is put in a glass beaker and covered with distilled water. A sufficient amount of an H-resin is added and the sample is stirred until the carbonates are removed. Both MÜLLER (1964) and BOLT and FRISSEL (1960) advocate this method. Müller, in describing the method as used by Lloyd, uses an exchange column of 1 m long and 5 cm wide filled with resin particles larger than 0.5 mm. Bolt uses a beaker with a suspension of mineral particles and resin particles for coarse-sized samples, and columns for clay.

In order to remove the mineral particles from the resin particles the sample with the resin is washed a few times with distilled water after the removal of the carbonates. Afterwards so much NaCl is added to the liquid that the resin particles begin to float. The floating particles are removed in a separation funnel and the mineral particles are washed free of NaCl. The resin is collected and reactivated by percolating with NaCl.

In most cases the acid digestion is both rapid and reliable and the investigator is not interested in other minerals. If, however, other minerals have to be studied the reader is advised to try one of the other techniques, which have certain advantages over acid procedures. First of all, they can be carried out outside a laboratory hood. Secondly, in routine methods time is not such a crucial factor because of the large numbers of samples having to pass this link in the total chain of procedures. If time is not too important, the aspect of leaving the other minerals rigorously unimpaired may be attractive.

If gypsum is present it is advisable to remove this sulphate directly afterwards, or simultaneously with the carbonates. For the removal of gypsum several methods are given below.

Removal of gypsum

Introduction
Numerous manuals on laboratory techniques advocate the use of HCl for gypsum removal. Although this method works, it is found to be both slow and damaging for the other minerals. Gypsum is not rapidly dissolved in acid environments, and therefore the HCl treatment is not very efficient. Some investigators have tried to develop other procedures starting out from quite another angle, and have tried the use of EDTA or exchange resins.

Acid digestion, I
Reagents. Solution of HCl, 1 N; solution of HCl, 6 N.

Procedure. The sample is treated in the same way as described on p.256 for the digestion of calcite with HCl. It is advisable for the removal of gypsum to work at slightly elevated temperatures, if slight damage to clay minerals and glauconite is not important.

   The damage to the clay can be restricted to a minimum even with warm HCl (approximately 40°C), by removing the suspension from time to time. This suspension can be brought onto a filter or in a centrifuge tube, and the clay minerals can be rinsed or washed with distilled water in the normal way.

Acid digestion, II
Reagents. Solution of cold HNO_3, 1 N.

Procedure. Much the same as the acid treatment of carbonates. The HNO_3 is added in small amounts and the sample is agitated. The feldspars are known to remain unimpaired as long as the concentration of the acid is not too high. Other minerals, such as clay minerals, pyrite etc. suffer from this treatment.

EDTA treatment
Although the present author was unable to find sufficient information on the removal of gypsum with one of the various salts of EDTA, it seems only logical that this is a promising method. Still, research along this line of approach is wanting, and the reader does well to do some experimenting in this field of pre-treatment.

Exchange resins
Reagents. Anionic exchange resins, commercially known under a large variety of names.

Procedure. BOLT and FRISSEL (1960) carried out some experiments with exchange resins on the removal of gypsum. They used an anionic resin with chloride ions available for exchange with SO_4 ions. Gypsum is thus changed into $CaCl_2$. The sample, free of carbonate, is put in a glass beaker. The anionic resin is added to the distilled water covering the sample. The mixture is stirred until all gypsum is removed. From the paper of Bolt and Frissel it can be inferred, that the time necessary for the entire removal of gypsum may be rather long (14 days for the removal of $2^1/_2\%$ gypsum from an illite).

   After the gypsum has been removed, the mixture of minerals and resin pellets is washed free of Ca ions. Afterwards so much NaCl is added that the specific gravity of the solution causes the resin pellets to float. The minerals are separated from the resin in a separation funnel and they are washed free of NaCl. By adding NaCl, the resin is brought once again into its initial state, because the SO_4 ions are thus removed in favour of Cl.

Favejee's treatment
Recently J. Ch. L. Favejee (personal communication, 1964) conducted experiments with the removal of gypsum with a sodium carbonate solution. The reaction was:

$$CaSO_4 \cdot 2H_2O + Na_2CO_3 \rightarrow CaCO_3 + Na_2SO_4 + 2H_2O$$

NaCl is added in order to increase the solubility of gypsum.

Reagents. A solution of 10 g NaCl and 2 g Na_2CO_3 on 100 ml distilled water.

Procedure. Add the solution to 20 g of sample. Take care that the amount of gypsum in this 20 g is not more than can be easily decomposed by 2 g Na_2CO_3. Heat the sample in a beaker for about 2 h at 40°C. Wash carefully with distilled water. Treat afterwards according to one of the procedures for the removal of $CaCO_3$ described on p.256. Repeat this treatment if necessary until all the gypsum is removed. The method is rapid and reliable in comparison to other techniques previously discussed.

The sample now free of organic material, carbonates and sulphates must be freed of iron compounds and coatings of iron and manganese minerals. In this book a sodium dithionite procedure is advocated for the removal of such materials. Again, a variety of methods has been described by numerous authors, and they all have some advantages and some disadvantages. The performance of the sodium dithionite method as modified in the Wageningen Mineralogical Laboratory will be given below. Moreover, another variant of this method developed by MEHRA and JACKSON (1959) will be given. The sodium dithionite method has been re-introduced by DEB (1950), the first mention of it was made by Galabutskaya and Govorova in 1934.

Removal of iron oxide

According to MEHRA and JACKSON (1959)
Reagents. Sodium citrate solution, 0.3 M; $NaHCO_3$ solution, 1 M; solid sodium dithionite ($Na_2S_2O_4$); saturated NaCl solution; acetone.

Procedure. A suitable amount of sample, containing about 0.5 g of extractable Fe_2O_3 or less, is placed in a 100 ml centrifuge tube. Add 40 ml of the sodium citrate solution and 5 ml of the $NaHCO_3$ solution. Heat over a water bath to 80°C. Add 1 g of solid sodium dithionite and stir constantly for 1 min, and occasionally for the following 15 min. Add 10 ml of the NaCl solution and 10 ml of acetone. Mix and warm in a water bath. Spin the minerals down with a centrifuge and decant the supernatant liquid. A final washing is made with the sodium citrate solution (with some NaCl solution and acetone, if necessary to promote flocculation). The sample is now kept in water and is ready for further investigations. If necessary, the procedure can be repeated a few times. The supernatant liquid can be collected and used for the determination of Fe, Al and Si content.

According to the formula of the Wageningen Laboratory
Reagents. A sodium dithionite solution, 20 g in 100 ml H_2O (the solution is unstable, prepare anew each time; old reagents cause the production of free sulfur in the liquid); a 0.02 N HCl solution; a 0.1 N HCl solution; a 0.5 N HCl solution.

Procedure. Put the sample in a glass beaker. It must be free of $CaCO_3$, gypsum and organic material. The beaker should not be too large (250 ml). If the sample is clay-rich add the 0.02 N HCl solution until the sample is just covered. HCl is added in order to promote flocculation. Allow to rest for some time. The supernatant liquid is siphoned off. Add a 20% sodium dithionite solution. The total amount of liquid on the sample should have about 10% of sodium dithionite. If the sample is of sand-size, addition of HCl is superfluous. A 10% sodium dithionite solution can be used immediately. Agitate the beaker and keep agitating while putting it over a water bath for 15 min. Allow to cool. Rinse with H_2O, rinse twice with 0.1 N HCl and afterwards with 0.5 N HCl. Wash thoroughly with distilled water immediately afterwards. If sand samples are treated, the entire procedure can be performed in the glass beaker. Clay samples are treated in centrifuge tubes and washed in the centrifuge tube in the normal way.

The treatment can be repeated if iron coatings or iron compounds are still present.

The nascent hydrogen method

Reagents. Solid oxalic acid; a cilinder of aluminium or magnesium ribbon.

Procedure. Add distilled water (300 ml) to the sample (20 g) in a glass beaker (500 ml). Add 15 g of oxalic acid. Put the aluminium cylinder or the magnesium in the beaker. The metal should be above the level of the liquid. Boil gently for 20 min. Remove the metal, decant the supernatant liquid and wash with distilled water.

The details of this method have been found in the work of MÜLLER (1964, p.45) and MEHRA and JACKSON (1959, p.318).

After these treatments the sample is free of all the disturbing compounds, and only silicates remain. The sample can be stored in distilled water, or in 0.005 N NaOH or in a very weak HCl solution (0.005 N). Drying the sample has some disadvantages over which more will be said below.

Sieving and the preparation of size fractions

After the proper pretreatment the sample must be divided into a number of size fractions. The fraction boundaries are not of fundamental importance as long as they are more or less close to the boundaries given here. It will be shown that fractions below 2 μ, from 2 to about 8 μ, from about 8 to 32 μ and the fraction between approximately 32 μ and 64 μ must be treated differently. Fractions of more than 64 μ are treated more or less in similar ways.

An efficient way of preparing these fractions is given below. Sieve the total sample in aqueous suspension or in a 0.005 N NaOH solution over a 32 μ, a 50 μ or a 64 μ sieve. The fine fraction may be washed, dried and weighed afterwards. Some investigators prefer to sieve the fraction larger than, e.g., 64 μ again through the 64 μ sieve in a dry state for better quantitative results. Weigh the coarse fraction also.

After this first separation both the fine and the coarse fraction go different ways. This is schematically given in the flow sheet of Fig.65.

The fine fraction

Bring the fine fraction again in a 0.005 N NaOH solution. Prepare the fractions smaller than 2 μ, 2–8 μ, 8–16 μ, etc., in the normal way, by settling velocity techniques. For quantitative results these separations have to be repeated at least seven times. If clay minerals are also of interest, the clay fraction may be treated with the classical calcium-acetate or with calcium resins in order to saturate the clay minerals with calcium ions.

Because we are not mainly concerned with clay minerals here, they will not be considered any further.

After having been rinsed and dried the fractions thus obtained are stored in glass tubes for further investigation. Rinse thoroughly if the calcium acetate method is used for the saturation of clay minerals; otherwise lines of calcium acetate appear on the X-ray diffractograms.

The coarse fraction

The coarse fraction, free of fines, is separated in a number of size fractions. Whatever boundaries are chosen, they may not be too far apart. In the following we will consider the sieve fractions 64–105 μ, 105–210 μ and 210–420 μ. The rest may also be separated in fractions, and they will be treated together as the fraction larger than 420 μ. After weighing, store them in glass tubes or in a liquid containing 0.01 N HCl, depending on the rest of the procedure. If flotation is used they should be stored in the acid liquid.

If we deal with samples obtained by a disaggregation of a solid rock or with mica-rich samples, the abundant micas have to be removed prior to other treatments. If the investigator is interested in the grain-size distribution, the micas must be removed after being sieved. They may otherwise be gotten rid of before this procedure. Micas may be partly removed by magnetic separation with a Frantz isodynamic separator. The sample containing the non-magnetic minerals generally contains pure muscovite, quartz, feldspars, zircon, sillimanite, staurolite and kyanite. Amphibole, pyroxene, epidote, garnet, chlorite, biotite and magnetite are present in the magnetic fraction.

Magnetic separation produces a non-magnetic fraction that is rather easily handled. Moreover, a well-adjusted magnetic separator works rather without supervision, leaving time for other things. The heavy minerals of the non-magnetic fraction can be separated from the rest with bromoform, the non-magnetic muscovite remains in the float. A choice from the available variants depends on the program of the investigator.

The separation of heavy and light minerals

In dealing with heavy and light mineral separation, the fine and the coarse fractions must be considered separately.

The fine fraction

Feldspars of the fraction below 16 μ are usually studied with X-ray methods. For this reason a removal of heavy minerals is not necessary. Cases in which the X-ray powder patterns of these fractions show the presence of heavy minerals, such as amphiboles or pyroxenes, are exceptional.

Feldspars of the fractions larger than 8 μ will sometimes be studied with a microscope. In this case the removal of heavy minerals is also unnecessary. If these fractions (usually over 32 μ) are stained it may be possible that a few heavy minerals catch a stain meant for feldspars. If the heavy mineral content is low, this hardly influences the counting results.

In cases where the amount of heavy minerals is exceptionally high, or in case one wants to study these minerals separately, separating techniques can be found in the well-known textbooks. In most cases centrifuging is the only possible method.

The coarse fraction

The coarse fraction will be subjected to a heavy mineral separation in most cases, for two reasons. First, the investigator wants to study the heavy minerals for various reasons and he may intend to combine these results with the study of the light fraction. Secondly, the samples will be separated again with liquids into an alkali feldspar and a plagioclase fraction. If flotation is applied, the heavy minerals may disturb the process. Therefore, the heavy minerals must be removed in a number of cases; so must the micas.

We will not consider the large arsenal of possible methods for the separation and the study of heavy minerals. The textbooks again carry abundant information on this subject.

The specific-gravity separation of feldspars is limited to fractions larger than approximately 105 μ, if funnels are used. With a centrifuge smaller fragments can be separated. For an efficient use of the Favejee funnel, described in Chapter 5, fractions of more than 105 μ are necessary. It seems superfluous to dwell upon the necessity of weighing the fractions carefully.

Flotation of the light fraction

A preliminary study of the sample may have shown that a further concentration of the feldspars is necessary before identification can efficiently be performed. In this case the reader may consider a flotation of his sample as described in Chapter 5. Some additional remarks can be made here. Flotation of fractions with a size below approximately 75 μ did not lead to satisfactory results in the author's preliminary experiments. This does not mean to say that such fractions can not be floated successfully. It only means to state that the proper experimental details have not yet been found for laboratory use. The best results are obtained from samples well over 75 μ.

The flotation of samples with narrow size ranges is more successful than a flotation of the whole sample. Prior to flotation the fines must be removed thoroughly. Heavy minerals have to be removed to a large extent, but a quantitative removal is not necessary. This implies that purification with a magnetic separator is sufficient. Mica is also a nuisance and the mica flakes must therefore be removed prior to flotation. In Chapter 5 the removal of micas is considered in some detail.

It goes without saying that the tailing of a flotation must be studied also.

Staining techniques render useful service in this case. If none of the minerals of the tailing catches a hemateine stain, the tailing is clean of feldspars.

If only a subordinate amount of the tailing consists of feldspars, it is advisable to isolate some of these fragments with a needle for further study in a grain mount. In studying these fragments concentrate on the difference between the feldspars of the tailing and of the float; it may be that flotation is selective in some cases. Finally determine the total feldspar content of the tailing in order to use this as a correction of the numerical results obtained from the float.

Staining of feldspars

Staining of feldspars is limited to fragments well over 64 μ, if reliable results and efficient procedures are aimed at. A careful performance of the procedures described in Chapter 4 will lead to well-stained samples. The fact that some flint fragments sometimes catch a stain has been discussed already. It was felt that this did not constitute a difficulty.

Stained feldspar fragments of the coarse fractions can be easily separated with a needle for further inspection. In this way it is for instance possible to study a few of the alkali feldspars from a specific fraction more carefully and in more detail. One may also try to remove some feldspars that are of the same "appearance". It has been experienced that feldspars belonging to one group, for instance the group of sanidines, are rather alike in appearance. Other alkali feldspars simply look "different". By establishing the true nature of these appearances, we are given a method for establishing more mutually exclusive classes in the counting result.

Staining of feldspars is a versatile method. It may be used as a final identification mark. It may be used to spot the feldspars for further identification. It may be used for an efficient study of the performance of a separation method (for the tailing of a flotation experiment as well as for the tailing of a heavy liquid separation). It may, finally, be used as a preliminary method of inspection for determining how a sample must be studied in more detail. As a result, the staining method will be seen more than once in the flow sheet of Fig.65.

Some remarks about counting methods

Remarks on counting methods are judged beyond the scope of this text on detrital feldspars and their identification. Still, some remarks simply must be made, because the available literature on this subject is not always easy to read and some techniques are of a questionable nature. Moreover, the present author holds some unconventional views on counting methods.

As soon as the investigation of the total sample has been performed we are faced with the problem of how to compile these numerical results. Information on the fine fraction obtained with X-ray methods is usually expressed in weight percentages. Information on floats and heavy mineral and light mineral separates is given in weight fractions also. Information on the feldspar content of these fractions is given in other units, depending on the counting method applied.

The numerical results of point counting methods are assumed to represent volume fractions. The results of ribbon counting methods are given in number fractions and the results of a line counting procedure are given in indefinable units.

As a result we advocate the use of point counting on thin sections and rock slabs. The numerical results thus obtained are assumed to represent volume percentages and can be recalculated into weight percentages, making use of the specific gravity of the minerals involved. In grain slides and grain mounts of a large-size range, ribbon counting or point counting should be applied, which give number percentages or volume percentages respectively. Counts on grain mounts or grain slides with a narrow-size range (for instance the fraction between 105 and 210 μ) can be performed with a line counting method. The result may be assumed to represent volume percentages that can easily be transformed into weight percentages.

The reader interested in the fundamental aspects of counting techniques may read, among others, CHAYES (1956), and VAN DER PLAS (1959, 1962b). Especially the effect of fragment size as influencing the counting result if the distance between the lines or points is not adequately chosen, is stressed by these authors.

The reliability of counting results

This is once again a subject that might be considered outside this text. Still, we stress the application of proper reliabilities if the reader has gone through all the tedious separation and counting. It is simply a loss of information if this aspect is overlooked. Instead of going into the background of statistics, we refer to the consultation of such standard works as DIXON and MASSEY (1957) and SIEGEL (1956). These can be used to the advantage of every investigator. In order to get an insight into problems of reliability, reproducibility and accuracy, the reader is advised to read MORONEY (1957).

For a rapid estimate of the reliability of a counting result VAN DER PLAS and TOBI (1965) have developed a rather crude but easy method. The basis of the method is a chart giving the reliability of a count in terms of a 95% confidence interval of a given length. The chart stresses the poor reliability of measurements on small fractions. The paper discusses briefly the correlation effect between grain-size and distance between the observations.

Finally, we must caution against the use of the so-called probable error recently reintroduced in German literature (see for instance MÜLLER, 1964, p.160). From a theoretical point of view no objections can be made as long as it is clearly stated that this reliability "is as likely to be exceeded as not" (cf., MORONEY, 1957, p.114). Moroney writes that the term, "a poor one", is now very obsolete. It has been said that "it is neither an error nor probable". There is another objection.

It is thought unfair to use the "probable error" as soon as one expects some of his readers to be unfamiliar with statistics. In that case it may suggest a reliability that is not present. The "probable error" describes the reliability of even a poor estimate in terms of neat small numbers. As an example let us assume a count of 100 points, 10 on feldspar. The "probable error" of this measurement is 2. In other words, the sample contains between 8 and 12% feldspar. A statistician will add here: "in one out of every two measurements". In every second measurement the result may be farther from the true value. If we are interested in the result of this count in 95 out of every 100 times we find it, the "error" is 6%. In other words, we may assume that such a counting result indicates in general that the value of the feldspar content is between 4 and 16%. This is quite a difference.

The measure of reliability of the second example may for shortness sake be termed the "95% reliability" of the count. In the denounced passage of the papers we have in mind while writing these lines the German term is given as "Absoluter Fehler". The translations into English and French are worse than the original English term "probable error". They are given respectively as "Absolute error" and "Erreur absolue". Readers accustomed to the Zeiss-Nomogramm G40-195 may arrive at a 95% reliability of the count by taking three times the values found with this nomogram. The Zeiss-Nomogramm is based on the concept of the probable error.

A discussion of the flow sheet of Fig.65

The flow sheet of Fig.65 begins with a sample divided into size fractions containing light minerals exclusively. Let us consider the fine fractions in the left part of the sheet first. The treatment of the fractions with a size below 16 μ is given in the sheet and discussed on p.261. X-ray work and some additional counting with a petrographic microscope, with or without the help of a phase contrast equipment, is all that can be done. The treatments of the other fractions are more complex. They will be considered below.

Fractions between 16 and 64 μ

The best method so far has been found to be counting in index liquids. NOTA and BAKKER (1960) preferred a liquid with $N = 1.528$ for a distinction between alkali feldspars and plagioclases in fractions > 105 μ. Plagioclases can be subdivided into three groups with the liquids $N = 1.54$ and $N = 1.56$. The distinction that can be made in such counts is:

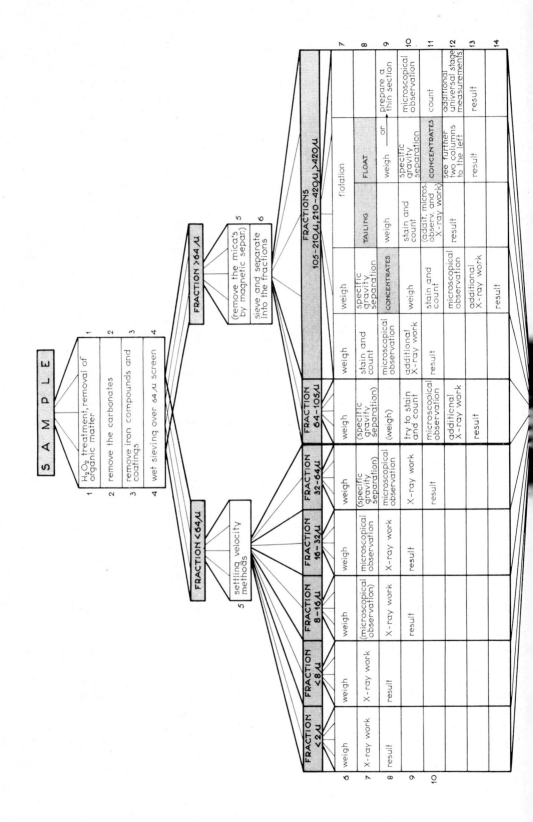

	SAMPLE	
1	H₂O₂ treatment, removal of organic matter
2	remove the carbonates
3	remove iron compounds and coatings
4	wet sieving over 64 μ screen

FRACTION <64μ
5 settling velocity methods

FRACTION >64μ
5 (remove the mica's by magnetic separ.)
6 sieve and separate into the fractions

FRACTIONS
105–210μ, 210–420μ, >420μ

	FRACTION <2μ	FRACTION <8μ	FRACTION 8–16μ	FRACTION 16–32μ	FRACTION 32–64μ	FRACTION 64–105μ				
6	weigh	weigh	weigh	weigh	weigh	weigh	weigh	weigh	weigh	
7	X-ray work	X-ray work	(microscopical observation)	microscopical observation	(specific gravity separation)	(specific gravity separation)	stain and count	specific gravity separation	TAILING	flotation
8	result	result	X-ray work	X-ray work	microscopical observation	(weigh)	microscopical observation	CONCENTRATES	weigh	FLOAT
9			result	result	X-ray work	try to stain and count	additional X-ray work	weigh	stain and count	weigh
10					result	microscopical observation	result	stain and count	(addit. micros. observ. and X-ray work)	specific gravity separation
11						additional X-ray work		microscopical observation	CONCENTRATES	count
12						result		additional X-ray work	result	additional universal stage measurements
13								result		result
14										

FLOAT — or — prepare a thin section
microscopical observation
count
additional universal stage measurements
result

see further two columns to the left

alkali feldspar   albite   oligoclasel–abradorite   labradorite–anorthite

The presence of microcline can be ascertained by the observation of crosshatched twinning. A quantitative evaluation of the amount of microcline cannot be made optically! An X-ray powder pattern of the alkali-feldspar fraction, isolated with a specific-gravity method, must be used for such a quantitative statement. The same holds for perthites; they can be qualitatively observed with optical methods. X-ray work is necessary for quantitative information.

Consequently, a combined optical and X-ray investigation can give additional information on the alkali-feldspar fraction:

monoclinic phases   triclinic phases   perthites

Fractions between 64 and 105 μ

It has been experienced that both heavy liquid separation and staining can be performed on the fragments in this size range. The use of a centrifuge gives the best results for heavy liquid separation as far as one can conclude from the available literature and the experience of colleagues in this field. It is our experience that staining can be successfully performed as has been described in the paper by DOEGLAS et al. (1965). With stained samples we can distinguish between the categories feldspar and alkali feldspar. Subtraction gives the amount of plagioclases. Consequently the following distinction is possible:

alkali feldspars   plagioclases

In counting results the investigator must avoid the following trap. Counts on samples stained with hemateine lead to higher percentages than those on cobaltinitrite stained samples. The nature of the reliability of counts will lead to two different counts with different reliabilities if the same number of counts is made in both preparations. This must be avoided. Therefore, count as much points in the sample with the cobaltinitrite stain as are necessary for reaching a comparable reliability as obtained in the sample stained blue. With the graph of VAN DER PLAS and TOBI (1965) this is easily worked out.

For a distinction between sodic and calcic plagioclase the sample can be counted in index liquids. One may also perform a specific-gravity separation on the sample. The float and the tailing are afterwards only stained and counted. For additional information on the alkali-feldspar fraction, this fraction must be separated and the separate can be subjected to X-ray analysis. If large amounts of sample are used (which is possible with most modern centrifuges) the float and

Fig.65. FLOW SHEET III. Flow sheet for the concentration and identification of detrital feldspars in soils, incoherent sediments, or quartz–feldspar concentrates.

the concentrates can be made into thin sections. These thin sections can be stained prior to finishing with a cover glass.

Fractions between 105 and 420 μ

With these fractions every possible technique can be successfully used. They can be stained, separated with heavy liquids, used in a flotation cell, isolated with a needle, made into powder for X-ray analysis, etc. In the following the complete flow sheet will be described in its most efficient order. It is self-evident that the reader can select the steps he thinks worth while.

A first step in the analysis of this fraction is a concentration of feldspars by means of flotation. The tailing as well as the float are inspected for efficiency. Feldspars of the tailing are qualitatively investigated in order to ascertain the aselectivity of the procedure.

The float is divided into an alkali-feldspar fraction, an albite fraction, a quartz–oligoclase fraction and a calcic plagioclase fraction by specific-gravity separation as described in Chapter 5.

The alkali-feldspar fraction, s.g. < 2.59

This fraction containing alkali feldspars and perthites exclusively is stained and counted. Some flint fragments are also stained, but these are recognized with incident light. Suspicious fragments are isolated with a needle and inspected with a petrographic microscope and perhaps even with X-ray techniques, using HIEMSTRA's method (1956).

Partly stained fragments occur frequently, because the grain size in this size-range allows for the presence of both small rock fragments and perthites. Partly stained particles cause difficulties in counting procedures. Some of these may consist of albite and alkali feldspar, others of quartz and alkali feldspar. Either isolation and further inspection, or an isolation followed by staining with hemateine must solve such problems.

The above procedure allows for a distinction between the following categories:

alkali feldspars   perthites   rock fragments   quartz   flint fragments

An additional optical inspection of the cleaned sample with a petrographic microscope will furnish information on the presence of microcline (crosshatched twins and a large axial angle) and monoclinic feldspars (small axial angle). For a quantitative evaluation of the various phases in the alkali-feldspar fraction, an X-ray powder pattern of the total sample in addition to X-ray powder patterns of selected fragments is necessary. Optical inspection alone can not give this information, as has already been stated in this text. On the other hand, much detailed information can be obtained from a thin section of the flotation concentrate. This is especially true if such thin sections are studied with a universal stage. Still, some information is not obtained in this way. As an example, we may point to the presence of optically undetectable crypto-perthites and submicroscopically twinned alkali feldspar.

The albite fraction, s.g. 2.59–2.63
This fraction, containing quartz and alkali feldspars next to albites, must be stained with hemateine and afterwards with cobaltinitrite. The blue stain enables the evaluation of the total feldspar content, the yellow particles give information on the importance of alkali feldspars. In this fraction one must expect the presence of perthites. Problems are again solved by the isolation of grains and an additional inspection with the petrographic microscope. A felicitous combination of X-ray methods with optical work will lead to rather detailed results.

The quartz–plagioclase fraction, s.g. 2.63–2.67
This fraction will contain the majority of the quartz fragments of the total sample. Even if the sample has been subjected to flotation, the present fraction will show all the remaining quartz. For these reasons the investigator must be prepared to expect rather low feldspar figures. It may be advantageous to prepare a flotation preparation of this fraction only, if the sample is poor in feldspars. For such flotation procedures, about 0.5 g of sample suffices.

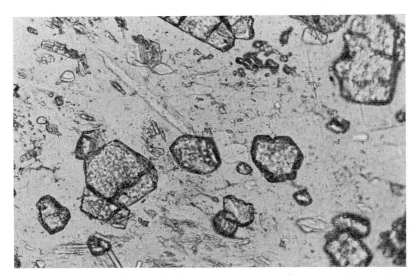

Fig.66. An albite crystal studded with small garnets, amphiboles and epidotes. The rock is an amphibole-bearing albite schist produced by greenschist facies metamorphism. Thin section no. LP 46a, sample no. LP 46a, Locality Peil in the village Vals Platz, Graubünden, Switzerland. (For further information see VAN DER PLAS, 1959.) Ocular 8×, objective 10×, plane polarized light.

The total feldspar content of the fraction is measured by counting a stained sample. Staining with hemateine is sufficient, as alkali feldspars are assumed to be rigorously absent. Furthermore a number of blue grains is isolated and cleaned for microscopical inspection. This is necessary, because some plagioclases may be rather crowded with inclusions of heavy minerals. Albites and plagioclases of some metamorphic rocks are particularly rich in such inclusions, as can be seen in Fig.66, showing albites from greenschist metamorphic rocks. Such albites can have the specific gravity of andesines! The isolated grains are identified in an index of refraction liquid, for a check on the specific-gravity results.

If the plagioclase under study is assumed to have derived from volcanic rocks, an X-ray investigation of the isolated particles, combined with a measurement of the refractive indices will reveal the structural state. Such a result can also be obtained with the universal stage, but this method is expensive in man-hours. X-ray powder patterns can be made by analysts, and counts in stained samples and measurements of refractive indices can also be performed by analysts, whereas a group of about 20 measurements on the universal stage requires a specialized investigator and time.

The calcic plagioclase fraction, s.g. 2.67–2.89

The treatment of fractions in this density range is much the same as the treatment described in the former paragraph. Here too a control measurement on indices of refraction will reveal the presence of plagioclases with numerous inclusions. Moreover, the plagioclases in this group are to a large extent of high-temperature origin. Consequently, an investigation on the nature of the structure as described earlier is advisable. Unfortunately the optical properties of both high- and low-temperature phases in this compositional range are rather similar. Therefore, optical methods are in most cases of no avail.

Some remarks on the X-ray analysis of these minerals must be made here. In Chapter 10, it was shown that the methods developed by J.V.SMITH and GAY (1958) are most suitable for calcic plagioclases. The method has been worked out for copper radiation. Curves for iron or cobalt radiation are still wanting.

Compiling the results

After this discussion of the flow sheet of Fig.65, let us consider the remark at the bottom of this sheet. It reads "compile the results". It is a cumbersome task to arrive at the quantitative composition of the feldspar fraction of a sediment from the many results obtained from size fractions and specific-gravity fractions within size fractions. Above everything else we must be aware of the true nature of each result. The nature of numerical data depends on the type of measurement. Data on size fractions are often present in weight percentages. Data on the mineralogical composition of the fine fractions are also given as weight percentages in most cases. The other results are obtained by counting methods.

Compilation of data must be based on a few assumptions and numerous calculations and transformations. Volume percentages obtained by point counting are assumed to be transformed into weight percentages by multiplication with the specific gravity of the specific mineral type. Line counting results in narrow size fractions are assumed to produce numerical results expressed in volume percentages. Number percentages obtained from ribbon counting methods can be transformed into weight percentages by calculations on the basis of assumptions about the average grain size and the specific gravity of the type of mineral. A much larger number of difficulties can be envisaged. However, as this book is not a text on counting techniques and the inherent calculations, it is left to the reader to develop his own calculation scheme.

ASPECTS OF A QUALITATIVE DETRITAL FELDSPAR ANALYSIS

Before entering upon the details of a variety of analytical techniques we must be clear about the use of the term qualitative. In this section the identification of properties of individual feldspars is considered. As an example, the reader may find here indications for the determination of twinning laws, structural state, morphology, etc. The acquirement of numerical data related to the amount of feldspars or twins or high-temperature phases is of secondary importance in this section.

It is self-evident that weighing and counting is not stressed in this part. On the other hand, the investigations on a small number of isolated fragments are emphasized. Notwithstanding the importance of other techniques, the procedures already described in the foregoing pages are successfully applied in this field of study. Especially staining as a means of marking feldspars in a grain sample renders useful service.

In order to arrive at a conveniently arranged text, the same sequence of objects as well as the same criteria for subdivision will be used as in the previous sections.

Quartz- and feldspar-rich arenaceous sediments and soils

The properties of these rocks, dealt with on p.230, will not be repeated here. For the aspects of consolidation, induration and friability the reader may also consult the previous sections. The disaggregation of these samples has been the subject of p.232 et seq. These subjects are exactly similar for the investigations at hand.

If the nature of the feldspars is only of interest, the following questions must be considered (*1*) how to study the chemical composition of individual grains; (*2*) how to study the structural state of individual grains; and (*3*) how to study the morphology of individual grains. Other questions concern the twinning patterns and exsolution phenomena.

The aspects enumerated have been the subject of the various previous chapters. If they are going to be dealt with here again, this section must function as a sign-post.

Qualitative investigations on detrital feldspars have been performed in a number of cases. Authigenic feldspars have been studied rather widely, twinning patterns are the subject of only a limited number of papers and the structural state is rarely identified. The above argument prescribes the description of the subjects. They are discussed in as many small paragraphs together with some of the available examples.

The chemical composition

The chemical composition of detrital feldspar fragments cannot successfully be studied optically if alkali feldspars are concerned. As a result X-ray powder methods have to be applied. But it is rather difficult to isolate a sufficient number of similar particles from a sand, not to speak of a sandstone or a quartzite. Only if the particle size of the sample is fairly large, say larger than 200 μ, the method of Hiemstra, cf. p.177, will give a useful powder pattern of one single grain.

One may also try to collect a number of coarse feldspar particles that "look similar", and have similar optical properties. Such a collection can best be made from a sample containing a large number of feldspars, e.g., from a "float". An X-ray analysis of such a collection of fragments may reveal that it consists of particles with about the same chemical composition or not. Interesting results can be obtained with such trial and error techniques.

The chemical composition of plagioclases can be measured rather accurately with a variety of optical methods. Both grain mounts and thin sections are successfully used. Grain mounts are efficiently studied with immersion methods, cf. p.75. Thin sections should preferably be mounted on a universal stage, cf. p.115.

The structural state

The structural state of alkali feldspars has to be measured with X-ray methods. These patterns must have a high resolution of the diffraction lines. In this type of research the Guinier-De Wolff camera is successfully used. The patterns must be made from a number of fragments, selected by handpicking. As a result again a trial and error technique for the selection of the proper fragments must be applied. Fortunately the camera just mentioned has four sample holders, therefore four such collections can be tried at once. A pattern of the total feldspar fraction in addition gives ample information on the type of phase that is present in considerable amounts. The aspects of such an analysis have been treated on p.202.

With a universal stage some information on the structural state can be obtained in thin sections. Particles with an axial angle larger than 45° are triclinic in all probability. The others are on the average monoclinic. The presence of microcline can be ascertained by the visible twinning. Still one must bear in mind that untwinned fragments may well be either microcline or sanidine.

The structural state of plagioclases can be measured from axial angles and extinction angles, cf. p.96 and 106. For such investigations thin sections are necessary. The axial-angle method is not valid for plagioclases of high calcium contents, as described on pp.96. An identification of the structural state with X-ray methods alone is difficult, if possible, in all cases.

The morphology of detrital feldspars

Grain shape, typical inclusions, type of alteration and other such properties are useful identification marks. In a detrital feldspar assemblage the individuals derived from one source often exhibit the same morphological properties. Such properties are useful if a collection of fragments of the same properties has to be made by handpicking. They can also be of importance in questions of provenance or lithological criteria.

Zoned plagioclases, an example. Let us consider the work of PITTMAN (1963) as an illustration of the importance of morphological criteria. In this work the argument is brought that the various types of zoning (a result of the gradual growth of a plagioclase in an environment with a varying chemical composition during the time of growth) are characteristic for specific rock types. An investigation of the frequency of the two types of zoning in a large series of samples showed a correlation between type of zoning and type of rock. The presence of zoning, regardless of type, is strongly indicative of a derivation from igneous rocks. Oscillatory zoning is often seen in volcanic rocks. Metamorphic rocks are characterized by plagioclases without zoning or with progressive zoning. The latter, however, are rare.

Pittman applied this insight to a group of sandstones. He counted the plagioclases according to zoning type. As a result, the origin of these plagioclases is guessed at with the above criteria. The presence of other minerals or even of fragments of volcanic rocks strongly corroborate these guesses, and a correlation between zoning type and type of source rock is definitively established.

Morphology of authigenic feldspars. Sandstones and sands are on the average not rich in authigenic feldspars. From the literature on authigenic feldspars in these rocks it can be inferred that such feldspars have rather particular forms. Whether or not the preference for a specific form has some bearing on the type of genesis is not quite evident as yet.

Twinning patterns

The twinning pattern of the assemblage of detrital feldspars seems to be an important property. For a discussion of twinning see Chapter 9. Twinning in

alkali feldspars is assumed to be of less importance for sedimentological investigations, because the twins in alkali feldspars are mostly simple twins. This implies
that they have large domains, and their appearance in sediments is a matter of
chance. In general, the size of the particles is such that the probability of finding
an alkali feldspar twin is highly reduced.

With plagioclases, rich in multiple twins, the situation is quite different.
We may expect to find a rather good record of the twinning patterns of the source
rock in the sediment, provided the particles are not too small. The work of
MITZUTANI (1959) illustrates better than general descriptions what may be expected from an investigation on twinning patterns in plagioclases from sedimentary
rocks.

The study has been carried out in a greywacke-sandstone formation of
Permian age intercalated with lavas and tuff. A study of the twinning patterns in
the sandstones (albite–Ala-B and albite law) and in the volcanics (Carlsbad,
albite–Carlsbad and albite laws) made it indeed plausible that the plagioclases of
the sandstones derived from other sources to a large extent. The source is presum-
ably a metamorphic terrain. This conclusion is corroborated by a study of the
average chemical composition of plagioclases in sandstones and volcanics. The
study made with thin sections has been carried out on a universal stage. In this
way the chemical composition and the twinning type could be studied simultaneously. In each section 7–8 fragments were measured on the average. In some
cases measurements were performed on as many as 40 fragments.

Perthites

A study of perthites in sediments and soils has not frequently been made. The
reason may well be that among the investigators the significance as well as the
ubiquity of perthites is not fully understood. For a discussion of perthites we
refer to Chapter 3. In one instance the presence of a specific type of perthite
leads to important sedimentological conclusions. The example has been mentioned
twice, both in Chapter 1 and in this chapter. The presence of mesoperthites in
Devonian sandstones led J. MICHOT (1963) to the tentative conclusion that some of
the material of these rocks derived from Norway.

Argillaceous sediments and clay-rich soils

On p.240 these rocks got a detailed treatment. Because of their particular nature,
the study of the nature of the inherent feldspars is thought to be rather difficult,
if not impossible. The small particle size hampers the application of concentration
methods. Some remarks are made in the following paragraphs.

The chemical composition

The determination of feldspars in the clay or silt fraction has to be made with

X-ray methods in most cases. In some instances the use of a phase-contrast outfit on the petrographic microscope may be of some help. In both cases high accuracy as well as high reliability of the numerical results may certainly not be expected. Especially Correns and Kalk have pioneered in the use of phase-contrast methods on fine fractions. Kalk, for instance, gave a lecture on the results quite recently at the 2nd International Working Meeting on Soil Micromorphology at Arnhem (The Netherlands) in the fall of 1964. It must be made clear that the results of such analyses are only tolerable as long as the particle sizes are not less than 8 μ.

The structural state
Without probing very far into speculative possibilities, it must be clear that only if the clay or silt fraction is rather rich in feldspars can something be said about the structural state of alkali feldspars. Information on the structural state of plagioclases is only obtainable in exceptional cases.

The morphology
Studying fractions of small grain size with high power optics may lead to interesting results in some cases. Again, a petrographic microscope equipped with phase contrast seems to give the best results. With phase contrast it is possible to locate the feldspar fragments. Inspection with the normal optical arrangement will show characteristic morphological features. Especially the presence of authigenic minerals will draw the attention of the investigator.

Twinning patterns
From the particle size of the fragments it follows that only microcline twins have a fair chance of being observed. The presence of plagioclase twins in such small particles is thought to be rather exceptional.

Perthites
In some cases the presence of perthites can be seen on microscopical inspection. In X-ray powder patterns the presence of perthites goes undetected as long as the total sample is used. The preparation, even in a centrifuge, of alkali-feldspar concentrates is met with serious difficulties. The particles tend to clot together. Vibration of the centrifuge tube, containing the sample in a specific-gravity liquid, in an ultrasonic cleaner prior to centrifuging will often improve on the results.

Carbonate sediments and soils

The nature of these sediments prescribes a pretreatment in most cases. The aspects of such a pretreatment have been considered at length in the previous sections. After the removal of carbonates, the sample is comparable either to that of a sand or to that of a clay. We may therefore conclude by referring to p.235 and 242.

If thin sections of these rocks are studied, the techniques to be applied have also been considered previously. Staining techniques are successfully used in the case of thin sections as well as on rock slabs. Sedimentologists may find it tempting to combine the staining methods for the various carbonates (cf. FRIEDMAN, 1959) with those for feldspars. The same methods have also been given by MÜLLER (1964), but in the German language. This book on methods for sediment investigation may be called one of the most up-to-date and handy manuals available.

Carbonate sediments are rather rich in authigenic minerals. Both alkali feldspars and albites are frequently present. A qualitative study of these crystalline phases has attracted numerous investigators. We will not repeat the list of reports given elsewhere in this text. The reader is therefore referred to p.31.

Final remarks

The last section of this book could list only the various aspects of a qualitative feldspar study. Although an impressive number of investigators have dealt with this subject, it is felt that still more can be achieved. The group of workers interested in detrital feldspars is not too large but is growing steadily. The reasons for this are obvious. The subject is thought to be difficult and suitable only for specialists. The reader who still has such an attitude after trying a few pages of this text for reading matter is asked to try a few of the experiments described in this last chapter. As his interest grows he will experience that he can easily master the necessary background for further progress.

REFERENCES

ADAMSON, O. J., 1944. The petrology of the Norra Kärr district. *Geol. Fören. Stockholm Förh.*, 66: 113–255.

AGAFONOVA, T. N., 1953. The influence of heating on the shiller of labradorites from Novyj Bobrik. *Dokl. Akad. Nauk S.S.S.R.*, 89: 933–936. (In Russian.)

A. G. I. GLOSSARY, see Glossary.

ANONYMOUS, 1961. Faciesprobleme der metamorphen Gesteine. *Neues Jahrb. Mineral., Abhandl.*, 96: 125–320.

ANSILEWSKI, J., 1959. The problem of classification of the alkali feldspars. *Arch. Mineral.*, 23: 5–59.

ARMOUR INDUSTRIAL CHEMICAL CY., 1955. *Mineral Flotation with Armour Cationic Chemicals.* Armour Industrial Chemical Cy., Chicago, Ill., 19 pp.

AZZINI, F., 1933. Adularia e albite di Val Devero, Ossola. *Atti Acad. Sci. Veneto–Trentino–Istriana*, 23: 45. See also *Mineral. Abstr.*, 5: 366.

BAILEY, E. H. and STEVENS, R. E., 1960. Selective staining of K-feldspar and plagioclase on rock slabs and thin sections. *Am. Mineralogist*, 45: 1020–1026.

BAILEY, S. W. and TAYLOR, W. H., 1955. The structure of a triclinic potassium feldspar. *Acta Cryst.*, 8: 621–632.

BALASANYAN, S. I., 1963. Optical determinations of plagioclases. *Dokl. Akad. Nauk Arm. S.S.R.*, 36: 289–292. (In Russian.)

BAMBAUER, H. U. und LAVES, F., 1960. Zum Adularproblem. 1. Adular vom Val Casatcha: Mimetischer Lamellenbau, Variation von Optik und Gitterkonstanten und ihre genetische Deutung. *Schweiz. Mineral. Petrog. Mitt.*, 40: 177–205.

BARABANOW, W. F., 1958. The genesis of feldspars on the quartz–wolframite-veins in Transbajkaly. *Dokl. Akad. Nauk S.S.S.R.*, 121: 538–540. (In Russian.)

BARBER, C. T., 1936. The effects of heat on the optical orientation of plagioclase feldspars. *Mineral. Mag.*, 24: 343–352.

BARBIER, P. et PROUST, A., 1908. Sur l'existence d'un feldspath sodique monoclinique isomorphe de l'orthose. *Bull. Soc. Chim. France*, 3: 894–899.

BARKER, D. S., 1962. Ammonium in alkali feldspars. *Geol. Soc. Am., Progr., Ann. Meeting*, 1962: 9A.

BARKER, D. S., 1964. Ammonium in alkali feldspars. *Am. Mineralogist*, 49: 851–859.

BARTH, T. F. W., 1929. Ueber den monoklinen Natronfeldspat. *Z. Krist.*, 69: 476–481.

BARTH, T. F. W., 1931. Permanent changes in the optical orientation of feldspars, exposed to heat. *Brøgger Volume—Norsk Geol. Tidsskr.*, 12: 7–72.

BARTH, T. F. W., 1934. Polymorphic phenomena and crystal structure. *Am. J. Sci.*, 27: 273–286.

BARTH, T. F. W., 1961. The feldspar lattices as solvents of foreign ions. *Cursillos Conf. Inst. "Lucas Mallada"*, 8: 3–7.

BASKIN, Y., 1956. Observations on heat treated authigenic microcline and albite crystals. *J. Geol.*, 64: 219–224.

BASSET, H., 1953. The isolation of the insoluble constituents of impure limestone. *Records Geol. Surv. Tanganyika*, 18: 86–92.

BEAR, E., 1955. Chemistry of the soil. *Am. Chem. Soc., Monograph.*, 126: 1–373.

BELYANKINA, E. D., 1953. Chemical–mineralogical study of potassium-sodium feldspars of Caucasus and Transcaucasia. *Trans. Inst. Geol. Sci. Acad. Sci. U.S.S.R., Petrograph. Ser.*, 147: 185. See also *Mineral. Abstr.*, 12: 417.

BEREK, M., 1924. *Mikroskopische Mineralbestimmung mit Hilfe der Universaldrehtischmethoden.* Borntraeger, Berlin, 168 pp.

BEREK, M., 1930. Ein zum Gebrauch am Polarisationsmikroskop geeigneter elliptischer Kompensator. *Zentr. Mineral. Petrol., Abt. A*, p.508.

BERG, R. R., 1952. Feldspathized sandstones. *J. Sediment. Petrol.*, 22: 221–223.

BITTER, J. H., 1963. De slikverwerking. *Geol. Mijnbouw*, 42: 81–85.

BLANCK, E., 1929. *Handbuch der Bodenlehre.* Springer, Berlin, 2: 314 pp.

BOLT, G. H. and FRISSEL, M. J., 1960. The preparation of clay suspensions with specific ionic composition by means of exchange resins. *Soil Sci. Soc. Am. Proc.*, 24: 172–177.

BOWEN, N. L., 1913. The melting phenomena of the plagioclase feldspars. *Am. J. Sci.*, 35: 577–599.

BOWEN, N. L. and TUTTLE, O. F., 1950. The system $NaAlSi_3O_8$–$KAlSi_3O_8$–H_2O. *J. Geol.*, 58: 489–511.

BOWN, M. G. and GAY, P., 1958. The reciprocal lattice geometry of the plagioclase feldspar structures. *Z. Krist.*, 111: 1–14.

BRADLEY, J. E. S. and BRADLEY, O., 1956. A first attempt at a determination of feldspars by activation analysis. *Mineral. Mag.*, 31: 164–172.

BREITHAUPT, A., 1860. Regelmässige Verwachsung von je zwei verschiedene Spezies des Genus der Felsite. *Berg-Hüttenmänn. Z.*, 20: 123. *Neues Jahrb. Mineral. Geognosie Geol. Petrefaktenkunde*, 1860 (IV): 445.

BRETT, R., 1963. Experimental data from the system Cu–Fe–S and their bearing on exsolution textures in ores. *Geol. Soc. Am., Progr., Ann. Meeting*, 1963: 21A.

BRINDLEY, G. W. and KURTOSSY, S. S., 1961. Quantitative determination of kaolinite by X-ray diffraction. *Am. Mineralogist*, 46: 1205–1216.

BROWN, W. L., 1960a. Lattice changes in heat-treated plagioclases. The existence of monalbite at room temperature. *Z. Krist.*, 113 (Laue Festschrift): 297–330.

BROWN, W. L., 1960b. The crystallographic and petrologic significance of peristerite unmixing in the acid plagioclases. *Z. Krist.*, 113 (Laue Festschrift): 330–344.

BROWN, W. L., 1962. Peristerite unmixing in the plagioclases and metamorphic facies series. *Norsk Geol. Tidsskr.*, 42 (Feldspar Volume): 354–383.

BRUN, E., HARTMANN, P., STAUB, H. H., HAFNER, ST. und LAVES, F., 1960. Magnetische Kernresonanz zur Beobachtung des Al Si-Ordnungs/Unordnungsgrades in einigen Feldspäten. *Z. Krist.*, 113: 65–76.

BUCKENHAM, M. H. and ROGERS, J., 1954. Flotation of quartz and feldspar by dodecylamine. *Bull. Inst. Mining Met.*, 575: 11–30.

BUERGER, M. J., 1945. The genesis of twin crystals. *Am. Mineralogist*, 30: 469–482.

BURRI, C., 1953. Zur Theorie und Praxis der Drehkompensatoren nach Berek und Ehringhaus. *Z. Angew. Math. Phys.*, 4: 6.

BURRI, C., 1956. Charakterisierung der Plagioklasoptik durch drei Winkel und Neuentwurf des Stereograms der optischen Orientierung für konstante Anorthit-Intervalle. *Schweiz. Mineral. Petrog. Mitt.*, 36: 540–592.

BURRI, C., 1962a. Gustav Eduard Kayser (geb. 1803) und die Zwillingsgesetze der Plagioklasen. *Schweiz. Mineral. Petrog. Mitt.*, 42: 25–36.

BURRI, C., 1962b. A survey of feldspar twinning. *Norsk Geol. Tidsskr.*, 42 (Feldspar Volume): 193–206.

BURRI, C. und NIGGLI, P., 1945. Die jungen Eruptivgesteine des mediterranen Orogens. Anhang F.V., Alphabetische Liste der Basismolekule und Aequivalentnorm-Mineralien. *Vulkaninst. Immanuel Friedländer, Publ.*, 3: 620–624.

BURRI, C., PARKER, R. L. and WENK, E., 1961. Project of a new general catalogue of data for the determination of plagioclases by the universal stage method. *Cursillos Conf. Inst. "Lucas Mallada"*, 8: 1.

BURRI, C., PARKER, R. L. and WENK, E., 1962. The optical orientation of the plagioclases. *Norsk Geol. Tidsskr.*, 42 (Feldspar Volume): 207–214.

CARL, J. D., 1962. An investigation of minor element content of potash feldspar from pegmatites, haystack range, Wyoming. *Econ. Geol.*, 57: 1095–1115.

CHAISSON, U., 1950. The optics of triclinic adularia. *J. Geol.*, 58: 537–547.

CHANDRASEKHAR, S., FLEET, S. G. and MEGAW, H. D., 1961. The structure of "body-centred" anorthite. *Cursillos Conf. Inst. "Lucas Mallada"*, 8: 141.

CHAO, S. H. and TAYLOR, W. H., 1940. Isomorphous replacement and super-lattice structures in the plagioclase feldspars. *Proc. Roy. Soc. (London), Ser. A*, 176: 76–87. See also *Mineral. Abstr.*, 8: 13.

CHAYES, F., 1950. On the relation between anorthite content and X-index of natural plagioclase. *J. Geol.*, 58: 593–595.

CHAYES, F., 1952a. Notes on the staining of potash feldspar with sodium cobaltinitrite in thin section. *Am. Mineralogist*, 37: 337–340.

CHAYES, F., 1952b. Relations between composition and indices of refraction in natural plagioclase. *Bowen Volume—Am. J. Sci.*, 1: 85–107.

CHAYES, F., 1956. *Petrographic Modal Analysis*. Chapmann and Hall, London, 113 pp.

COLE, W. F., SÖRUM, H. and KENNARD, O., 1949. The crystal structures of orthoclase and sanidinized orthoclase. *Acta Cryst.*, 2: 280–287.

COLE, W. F., SÖRUM, H. and TAYLOR, W. H., 1951. The structures of plagioclase feldspars. 1. *Acta Cryst.*, 4: 20–29.

CORRENS, C. W., 1961. The experimental chemical weathering of silicates. *Clay Minerals Bull.*, 4: 249–266.

CORRENS, C. W., 1962. Über die chemische Verwitterung von Feldspaten. *Norsk Geol. Tidsskr.*, 42 (Feldspar Volume): 272–282.

DAVIS, G. L. and TUTTLE, O. F., 1952. Two new crystalline phases of the anorthite composition $CaO.Al_2O_3.2SiO_2$. *Bowen Volume—Am. J. Sci.*, 1: 107–114.

DAVIS, T. E. and SLEMMONS, D. B., 1962. Observations on order–disorder relations of natural plagioclase. III. Highly ordered plagioclases from the Sudbury intrusive, Ontario, Canada. *Norsk Geol. Tidsskr.*, 42 (Feldspar Volume): 567–578.

DEB, B. C., 1950. The estimations of free iron oxide and their removal. *J. Soil Sci.*, 1: 212–220.

DEER, W. A., HOWIE, R. A. and ZUSSMANN, J., 1963. *Rock-forming Minerals. 4. Framework Silicates*. Longmans, London, 435 pp.

DE JONG, W. F., 1959. *General Crystallography, a Brief Compendium*. Freeman, San Francisco, Calif., 281 pp.

DES CLOIZEAUX, A., 1861. Note sur les modifications temporaires et sur une modification permanente que l'action de la chaleur apporte à quelques propriétés optiques du feldspath orthose. *Compt. Rend.*, 53: 64–68.

DE WOLFF, P. M., 1948. Multiple focussing camera. *Acta Cryst.*, 1: 207–211.

DE WOLFF, P. M., 1950. An adjustable curved crystal monochromator for X-ray diffraction analysis. *Appl. Sci. Res., Sect. B*, 1: 119–126.

DIETRICH, R. V., 1962. K-feldspar structural states as petrogenetic indicators. *Norsk Geol. Tidsskr.*, 42 (Feldspar Volume): 394–415.

DIXON, W. J. and MASSEY, F. J., 1957. *Introduction to Statistical Analysis*. MacGraw-Hill, New York, N.Y., 488 pp.

DOEGLAS, D. J., 1940. A reliable and rapid method for distinguishing quartz and untwinned feldspar with the universal stage. *Am. Mineralogist*, 25: 287–296.

DOEGLAS, D. J., FAVEJEE, J. CH. L., NOTA, D. J. G. and VAN DER PLAS, L., 1965. On the identification of feldspars in soils. *Mededel. Landbouwhogeschool Wageningen*, 65(9): 14 pp.

DOLAR MANTUANI, L., 1952. The feldspar in the intrusive rocks near Beaverdell, B.C. *Am. Mineralogist*, 37: 492–530.

DOMAN, R. CH., 1961. *Causes of Optical Scatter in Plagioclase Feldspar*. Thesis, Univ. Wisconsin, Madison, Wisc., 95 pp. (Order No. Mic. 61-1527.)

DONNAY, G. and DONNAY, J. H. D., 1952. The symmetry change in the high-temperature alkali feldspar series. *Bowen Volume—Am. J. Sci.*, 1: 115–133.

DONNAY, J. H. D., 1940. Width of albite-twinning lamellae. *Am. Mineralogist*, 25: 578–586.

DUPARC, L. et REINHARD, M., 1923. Les méthodes de Fédorof et leur application à la détermination des plagioclases. *Schweiz. Mineral. Petrog. Mitt.*, 3: 1–74.

EBERT, H., 1932. Die Bestimmung der saueren Plagioklasen mit Hilfe der Zonenmethode. *Mineral. Petrog. Mitt.*, 42: 8–26.

EHRINGHAUS, A., 1931. Drehbare Kompensatoren aus Kombinationsplatten doppelbrechender Kristalle. *Z. Krist.*, 76: 315–321.

EHRINGHAUS, A., 1938. Ein Drehkompensator aus Quartz mit grossem Messbereich bei hoher Messgenauigkeit. *Z. Krist.*, 98: 394–406.

EHRINGHAUS, A., 1939. Drehkompensatoren mit besonders grossem Messbereich. *Z. Krist.*, 102: 85–111.

EISINGER, V. J., SWINDERMAN, J. N. and SLEMMONS, D. B., 1962. Observations on order–disorder relations of natural plagioclase. II. Order-disorder relations in metavolcanic and plutonic rocks of the Prison Hill Area, Carson City, Nevada. *Norsk Geol. Tidsskr.*, 42 (Feldspar Volume): 555–566.

EMERSON, D. O., 1959. Correlation between X-ray emission and flame photometer determination of the K_2O content of potash feldspars. *Am. Mineralogist*, 44: 661–663.

EMMONS, R. C., 1943. The universal stage (with five axes of rotation). *Geol. Soc. Am., Mem.*, 8: 204 pp.

EMMONS, R. C. (Editor), 1953. Selected petrogenetic relationships of plagioclases. *Geol. Soc. Am., Mem.*, 52: 142 pp.

EMMONS, R. C. and GATES, R. M., 1943. Plagioclase twinning. *Bull. Geol. Soc. Am.*, 54: 287–304.

EMMONS, R. C. and GATES, R. M., 1948. The use of Becke line colors in the refractive index determination. *Am. Mineralogist*, 33: 612–618.

EMMONS, R. C., CRUMP, R. M. and KETNER, K. B., 1960. High- and low-temperature plagioclase. *Bull. Geol. Soc. Am.*, 71: 1417–1420.

ERD, R. C., WHITE, D. E., FAHEY, J. J. and LEE, D. E., 1964. Buddingtonite, an ammonium feldspar with zeolitic water. *Am. Mineralogist*, 49: 831–851.

ESKOLA, P., 1952. On the granulites of Lapland. *Bowen Volume—Am. J. Sci.*, 1: 133–171.

FAIRBAIRN, H. W., 1949. *Structural Petrology of Deformed Rocks*. Addison-Wesley, Cambridge, Mass., 344 pp.

FAVEJEE, J. CH. L., 1939. Zur Methodik der Röntgenographischen Bodenforschung. *Z. Krist.*, 100: 425–436.

FEDOROV, E., 1898. Universalmethode und Feldspathstudien. III. Die Feldspäthe des Bogoslowsk'-schen Bergreviers. *Z. Krist.*, 29: 604–658.

FERGUSON, R. B., 1960. The low-temperature phases of the alkali feldspars and their origin. *Can. Mineralogist*, 6: 415–437.

FINNEY, J. J. and BAILEY, S. W., 1964. Crystal structure of an authigenic microcline. *Z. Krist.*, 119: 437–453.

FISHER, D. J., 1956. Calibration of Guinier-de Wolff camera. *Z. Krist.*, 109: 73–80.

FOSTER, W. R., 1955. Simple method for the determination of the plagioclase feldspars. *Am. Mineralogist*, 40: 179–186.

FOUQUÉ, F., 1894. Contribution à l'étude des feldspaths des roches volcaniques. *Bull. Soc. Mineral. France*, 17: 283–611.

FRANCO, R. R. and SCHAIRER, J. F., 1951. Liquidus temperature in mixtures of feldspars of soda, potash and lime. *J. Geol.*, 59: 259–267.

FRIEDMAN, G. M., 1959. Identification of carbonate minerals by staining methods. *J. Sediment. Petrol.*, 29: 87–97.

FÜCHTBAUER, H., 1948. Einige Beobachtungen an authigenen Albiten. *Schweiz. Mineral. Petrog. Mitt.*, 28: 709–716.

FÜCHTBAUER, H., 1956. Zur Entstehung und Optik authigener Feldspäte. *Neues Jahrb. Mineral., Monatsh.*, 1956: 9–23.

FUERSTENAU, D. W., METZGER, P. H. and SEELE, G. D., 1957. How to use this modified Hallimond tube for better flotation testing. *Eng. Mining J.*, 153: 93–95.

FYFE, W. S., TURNER, F. J. and VERHOOGEN, J., 1958. Metamorphic reactions and metamorphic facies. *Geol. Soc. Am., Mem.*, 73: 259 pp.

GABRIEL, A. and COX, P., 1929. A staining method for the quantitative determination of certain rock minerals. *Am. Mineralogist*, 14: 290–292.

GAME, P. M., 1949. Plagioclase from Sultan Hamed, Kenya. *Mineral. Mag.*, 28: 682–687.

GAUDIN, A. M., 1957. *Flotation*. McGraw-Hill, New York, N.Y., 513 pp.

GAY, P., 1953. The structures of the plagioclase feldspars. III. An X-ray study of anorthites and bytownites. *Mineral. Mag.*, 30: 169–177.

GAY, P., 1954. The structures of the plagioclase feldspars. V. The heat-treatment of lime-rich plagioclases. *Mineral. Mag.*, 30: 428–438.

GAY, P., 1956. The structure of intermediate plagioclase feldspars. VI. Natural intermediate plagioclases. *Mineral. Mag.*, 31: 21–40.

GAY, P. and BOWN, M. G., 1956. The structures of the plagioclase feldspars. VII. The heat treatment of intermediate plagioclases. *Mineral. Mag.*, 31: 306–313.

GAY, P. and TAYLOR, W. H., 1953. The structures of the plagioclase feldspars. IV. *Acta Cryst.*, 6: 647–650.

GERHARD, D., 1861. Über lamellare Verwachsung zweier Feldspath-Species. *Z. Deut. Geol. Ges.*, 14: 151–159.

Glossary of Geology and related Sciences. 1957. Am. Geol. Inst., Washington, D.C., 325 pp.

GOLDICH, S. S., 1934. Authigenic feldspars in sandstones of southeastern Minnesota. *J. Sediment. Petrol.*, 4: 89–95.

GOLDSMITH, J. R., 1950. Gallium and germanium substitutions in synthetic feldspars. *J. Geol.*, 58: 518–536.

GOLDSMITH, J. R. and LAVES, F., 1954a. The microcline-sanidine stability relations. *Geochim. Cosmochim. Acta*, 5: 1–19.

GOLDSMITH, J. R. and LAVES, F., 1954b. Potassium feldspar structurally intermediate between microcline and sanidine. *Geochim. Cosmochim. Acta*, 6: 100–118.

GOLDSMITH, J. R. and LAVES, F., 1961. The sodium content of microclines and the microcline–albite series. *Cursillos Conf. Inst. "Lucas Mallada"*, 8: 81–96.

GOODYEAR, J. and DUFFIN, W. J., 1955. The identification and determination of plagioclase feldspars by the X-ray powder method. *Mineral. Mag.*, 30: 306–326.

GOODYEAR, J. and DUFFIN, W. J., 1957. Harmonic reflexions with a camera of the Guinier type. *Acta Cryst.*, 10: 597–598.

GORAI, M., 1950a. Method of distinguishing C-twins and A-twins of plagioclase under ordinary polarisation microscope. *Chishit sugaku Zasshi*, 56 (1950): 414–443. (In Japanese with English summary.)

GORAI, M., 1950b. The features of plagioclase twinning in various granitic rocks. *Chishit Sugaku Zasshi*, 56 (1950): 515–518. (In Japanese.)

GORAI, M., 1951. Petrological studies on plagioclase twins. *Am. Mineralogist*, 36: 884–901.

GORBUNOV, N. I., 1950. Method of separating soil and clay into fractions for X-ray and thermal study. *Pochvovedenie*, 1950 (7): 431–435. (In Russian.)

GORBUNOV, N. I., 1960. Method of preparing soil, soil material, river suspension and marine sediments for mineralogical analysis. *Pochvovedenie*, 1961: 79–85. *Soviet Soil Sci.* (*English Transl.*), 1960: 1212–1218.

GOTTARDI, G., 1961. Zum Studium der Temperatur-Formen der Plagioklase in Graniten und Granodioriten. *Compt. Rend. Soc. Mineral. Italiano*, 27: 628–635.

GRADWELL, R., 1958. A simple fusion method for determination of plagioclase feldspars from thin sections. *Am. Mineralogist*, 43: 368–370.

GYSIN, M., 1948. Les feldspaths potassiques des granites de Gastern et de quelques granites de l'Aar. *Schweiz. Mineral. Petrog. Mitt.*, 28: 230–245.

HAFNER, ST. und LAVES, F., 1956. Ordnung/Unordnung und Ultrarotabsorption. I. (Al, Si)-Verteilung in Feldspäten. *Z. Krist.*, 108: 52–63.

HAFNER, ST. und LAVES, F., 1957. Ordnung/Unordnung und Ultrarotabsorption. II. Variation der Lage und Intensität einiger absorptionen von Feldspäten. Zur Struktur von Orthoklas und Adular. *Z. Krist.*, 109: 204–225.

HAFNER, ST. und LAVES, F., 1963. Magnetische Kernresonanz von Al[27] in einigen Orthoklasen. *Schweiz. Mineral. Petrog. Mitt.*, 43: 66–69.

HARTMAN, P., 1956. On the morphology of growth twins. *Z. Krist.*, 107: 225–237.

HAY, R. L., 1960. Diagenetic K-feldspar in the John Day formation in north central Oregon. *Geol. Soc. Am., Progr., Ann. Meeting*, 1960: 116–117.

HAY, R. L. and MOIOLA, R. J., 1962. Authigenic silicate minerals in Pleistocene sediments of Searles Lake, California. *Geol. Soc. Am., Progr. Ann. Meeting*, 1962: 68A.

HAYES, J. R. and KLUGMAN, M. A., 1959. Feldspar staining methods. *J. Sediment. Petrol.*, 29: 227–232.

HEALD, M. T., 1950. Thermal study of potash-soda feldspars. *Am. Mineralogist*, 35: 77–89.

HEIER, K. S., 1960. Petrology and geochemistry of high-grade metamorphic and igneous rocks on Langnöy, northern Norway. *Norg. Geol. Undersøk*, 207: 246 pp.

HEIER, K. S., 1962. Trace elements in feldspars, a review. *Norsk Geol. Tidsskr.*, 42 (Feldspar Volume): 415–455.

HEIER, K. S. and TAYLOR, S. R., 1959a. Distribution of Ca, Sr and Ba in southern Norwegian Precambrian alkali feldspars. *Geochim. Cosmochim. Acta*, 14: 286–304.

HEIER, K. S. and TAYLOR, S. R., 1959b. Distribution of Li, Na, K, Rb, Cs, Pb and Tl in southern Norwegian Precambrian alkali feldspars. *Geochim. Cosmochim. Acta*, 15: 284–304.

HIEMSTRA, S. A., 1959. An easy method to obtain X-ray diffraction patterns of small amounts of material. *Am. Mineralogist*, 41: 519–521.

HILL, D. E. and TEDROW, J. C. F., 1961. Weathering and soil formation in the arctic environment. *Am. J. Sci.*, 259: 84–101.

HILL, W. E. and GOEBEL, E. D., 1963. Rates of solution of limestone using chelating properties of versene (E.D.T.A.) compounds. *Geol. Surv. Kansas, Bull.*, 165: 7–15.

HOLMES, A., 1928. *The Nomenclature of Petrology, with References to Selected Literature*. Murby, London, 2: 284 pp.

HOOGENDAM, I. en VAN DIJK, M. C., 1963. Therapie na contact van de huid met fluorwaterstof. *Ned. Tijdschr. Geneesk.*, 107: 781–783. (Engl. summary).

HOWIE, R. A., 1955. The geochemistry of the charnockite series of Madras, India. *Trans. Roy. Soc. Edinburgh*, 62: 725–768.

HUANG, C. K., 1953. Adularia from Kukutzu, Taiwan. *Sci. Rept. Natl. Taiwan Univ., First Ser., Acta Geol. Taiwan*, 5: 27–34.

HUANG, C. K., 1961. Peculiar optical properties of adularia from Kukutzu, Taiwan. *Sci. Rept. Natl. Taiwan Univ., First Ser., Acta Geol. Taiwan*, 9: 1–5.

INGERSON, E., 1952. Twinning frequency in feldspar phenocrysts from a quartz latite sill at Sierra Blanca, Texas. *Bowen Volume—Am. J. Sci.*, 1: 189–202.

JEFFRIES, C. D., 1937. The mineralogical composition of the very fine sands of some Pennsylvanian soils. *Soil Sci.*, 43: 357–366.

JEFFRIES, C. D. and JACKSON, M. L., 1949. Mineralogical analysis of soils. *Soil Sci.*, 68: 57–73.

JONES, J. B. and TAYLOR, W. H., 1961a. The structure of orthoclase. *Cursillos Conf. Inst. "Lucas Mallada"*, 8: 33–36.

JONES, J. B. and TAYLOR, W. H., 1961b. The structure of orthoclase. *Acta Cryst.*, 14: 443–445.

KALK, E. und MEYER, B., 1964. Verwitterungs-Morphologie der Mineral Spezies in mitteleuropäischen Holozän-Böden aus Pleistozänen und Holozänen Lockersedimenten. In: A. JONGERIUS (Editor), *Soil Micromorphology*. Elsevier, Amsterdam, pp. 109–129.

KANO, H., 1955. High-temperature optics of natural sodic plagioclases. *Mineral. J. (Tokyo)*, 1: 255–277.

KARL, F., 1954. Über Hoch- und Tieftemperaturoptik von Plagioklasen und deren petrographische und geologische Auswertung am Beispiel einiger alpiner Ergussgesteine. (Die Existenz von Uebergangslagen). *Festband Bruno Sander—Mineral. Petrog. Mitt.*, 3, 4: 320–328.

KAYSER, G. E., 1834. *De Cyclo quodam Legum Duodecim Secundum quas Crystalli Generum Feldspathi Familiae Singulariorum Geminatim Conjunctim Inveniuntur*. Thesis, Berlin, Berolini, Typis Nauckianis.

KAYSER, G. E., 1835. Ueber einen Cyclus von zwölf Zwillingsgesetzen, nach welchen die ein- und eingliedrigen Feldspathgattungen verwachsen. *Ann. Physik*, 34: 109–129, 301–319.

KELLEY, K. K., TODD, S. S., ORR, R. L., KING, E. G. and BONNICKSON, K. R., 1953. Thermodynamic properties of sodium–aluminium and potassium–aluminium silicates. *U.S., Bur. Mines, Rept. Invest.*, 4955: 21 pp.

KEMPSTER, C. J. E., MEGAW, H. D. and RADOSLOVICH, E. W., 1962. The structure of anorthite, $CaAl_2Si_2O_8$. I. Structure analysis. *Acta Cryst.*, 15: 1005–1017.

KHADR, M., 1960. An examination of the light fraction of some Egyptian soils. *Mededel. Landbouwhogeschool Wageningen*, 60: 1–12.

KIMIZUKA, K., 1932. A study of potash-anorthoclase from Taiji, Kii province, Japan. *Japan. J. Geol. Geograph., Trans.*, 9: 213–242.

KING, E. G., 1957. Low-temperature heat capacities and entropies at 298.15°K of some crystalline silicates containing calcium. *J. Am. Chem. Soc.*, 79: 5437.

KING, E. G. and WELLER, W. W., 1961. Low-temperature heat capacities and entropies at 298.15°K of some sodium- and calcium-aluminium silicates. *U.S., Bur. Mines, Rept. Invest.*, 5855: 8 pp.

KIRCHBERG, H., 1955. Feldspataufbereitung. *Montan Rundschau*, 3: 290–293.

KLOCKMANN, F., 1900. *Lehrbuch der Mineralogie*. Enke, Stuttgart, 2: 672 pp.

KÖHLER, A., 1923. Zur Bestimmung der Plagioklase in Doppelzwillingen nach dem Albit- und Karlsbader Gesetz. *Mineral. Petrog. Mitt.*, 36: 42–64.

KÖHLER, A., 1942a. Die Abhängigkeit der Plagioklasoptik vom vorangegangenen Wärmeverhalten. (Die Existenz einer Hoch- und Tieftemperaturoptik). *Mineral. Petrog. Mitt.*, 53: 24–49.

KÖHLER, A., 1942b. Drehtischmessungen an Plagioklaszwillingen von Tief- und Hochtemperaturoptik. *Mineral. Petrog. Mitt.*, 53: 159–179.

KÖHLER, A., 1948. Erscheinungen an Feldspaten in ihrer Bedeutung für die Klärung der Gesteinsgenesis. *Mineral. Petrog. Mitt.*, 1: 51–68.

KRACEK, F. C. and NEUVONEN, K. J., 1952. Thermochemistry of plagioclase and alkali feldspars. *Bowen Volume—Am. J. Sci.*, 1: 293–318.

KRUMBEIN, W. C. and PETTIJOHN, F. J., 1938. *Manual of Sedimentary Petrography*. Appleton-Century, New York, N.Y., 549 pp.

KUELLMER, F. J., 1959. X-ray intensity measurements on perthitic materials. I. Theoretical considerations. *J. Geol.*, 67: 648–660.

KUELLMER, F. J., 1960. X-ray intensity measurements on perthitic materials. II. Data from natural alkali feldspars. *J. Geol.*, 68: 307–323.

KUELLMER, F. J., 1961. Alkali-feldspars from some intrusive porphyries of south western United States. *Cursillos Conf. Inst. "Lucas Mallada"*, 8: 111–125.

LARSSON, W., 1940. Petrology of interglacial volcanics from the Andes of northern Patagonia. *Bull. Geol. Inst. Univ. Upsala*, 28 (1941): 191–405.

LAVES, F., 1952a. Phase relations of the alkali feldspars. I. Introductionary remarks. *J. Geol.*, 60: 436–450.

LAVES, F., 1952b. Mechanische Zwillingsbildung in Feldspäten in Abhängigkeit von Ordnung–Unordnung der Si/Al-Verteilung innerhalb des (Si, Al)$_4$O$_8$-Gerüstes. *Naturwissenschaften*, 39: 546–547.

LAVES, F., 1954. The coexistence of two plagioclases in the oligoclase compositional range. *J. Geol.*, 62: 409–411.

LAVES, F., 1960. Al/Si-Verteilungen, Phasen-Transformationen und Namen der Alkalifeldspäte. *Z. Krist.*, 113: 265–296.

LAVES, F. and GOLDSMITH, J. R., 1961. Polymorphism, order, disorder, diffusion and confusion in the feldspars. *Cursillos Conf. Inst. "Lucas Mallada"*, 8: 71–80.

LAVES, F. und SCHNEIDER, T., 1956. Ueber den rhombischen Schnitt in sauren Plagioklasen. *Schweiz. Mineral. Petrog. Mitt.*, 36: 622–623.

LAZARENKO, A. A., 1961. Degrees of weathering of feldspars in Dniepr sediments and its causes. *Dokl. Akad. Nauk S.S.S.R.*, 114: 193–196.

LEAVITT, F. G. and SLEMMONS, D. B., 1962. Observations on order–disorder relations of natural plagioclase. IV. Order–disorder relations in plagioclase of the White Mountain and New Hampshire Magma series. *Norsk Geol. Tidsskr.*, 42 (Feldspar Volume): 578–598.

LEBEDSINSKIJ, W. T. and TSCHU, ZSJA-SJANG, 1958. Anorthoclase in alkali basalts of the southern border of the mongolian plateau. *Zap. Vses. Mineralog. Obshchestva*, 87: 14–22. See also *Zentr. Mineral., Tl. I*, 59: 83.

LEDENT, D., PATTERSON, C. and TILTON, G. R., 1963. Ages of zircon, and feldspar concentrates from North American beach and river sands. *J. Geol.*, 72: 112–122.

LEWIS, C. C. and EISENMENGER, W. S., 1948. Relationships of plant development to the capacity to utilize potassium in orthoclase feldspar. *Soil Sci.*, 65: 495–500.

LUNDEGÅRDH, P. H., 1941. Bytownit aus Anorthosit von Bönskär im nördlichen Teil der Stockholmer Schären und seine Beziehungen zu verschiedenen Feldspatsbestimmungskurven. *Bull. Geol. Inst. Univ. Upsala*, 28 (12): 415–430.

LÜTHY, H., MATTER, A. und NABHOLZ, W. K., 1963. Sedimentologische Untersuchung eines temporären Quartäraufschlusses bei der Neubrügg nördlich Bern. *Eclogae Geol. Helv.*, 56: 119–145.

LUTJEN, G. P., 1953. Kona plant features flexibility. *Eng. Mining. J.*, 154: 92–95.

LYON, R. J. P., TUDDENHAM, W. M. and THOMPSON, C. S., 1959. Quantitative mineralogy in 30 minutes. *Econ. Geol.*, 54: 1047–1055.

MACKENZIE, W. S., 1952. The effect of temperature on the symmetry of high temperature soda-rich feldspars. *Bowen Volume—Am. J. Sci.*, 2: 319–343.

MACKENZIE, W. S., 1954. The orthoclase–microcline inversion. *Mineral. Mag.*, 30: 354–366.

MACKENZIE, W. S. and SMITH, J. V., 1955. The alkali feldspars. I. Orthoclase microperthites. *Am. Mineralogist*, 40: 707–732.

MACKENZIE, W. S. and SMITH, J. V., 1955. The alkali feldspars. IIA. Simple X-ray technique for the study of alkali feldspars. *Am. Mineralogist*, 40: 733–747.

MACKENZIE, W. S. and SMITH, J. V., 1962. Single crystal X-ray studies of crypto- and micro-perthites. *Norsk Geol. Tidsskr.*, 42 (Feldspar Volume): 72–104.

MALLARD, F., 1876. Explications des phénomènes optiques anomaux, qui presentent un grand nombre de substances cristallisées. *Ann. Mines, Mém., Sér. 7*, 10: 187–240.

MARFUNIN, A., 1958. A new diagram of optical orientation of acid and intermediate plagioclases. *Dokl. Akad. Nauk S.S.S.R.*, 118: 1183–1186. (In Russian.)

MARFUNIN, A., 1961. The relation between structure and optical orientation in potash-soda feldspars. *Cursillos Conf. Inst. "Lucas Mallada"*, 8: 111–124.

MARFUNIN, A., 1962a. Phase relations, optical properties and geological distribution of feldspars. *Tr. Inst. Geol. Nauk, Akad. Nauk S.S.S.R., Geol. Ser.*, 78: 276. (In Russian.)

MARFUNIN, A., 1962b. Some petrological aspects of order-disorder in feldspars. *Mineral. Mag.*, 33: 298–314.

MARSHALL, C. E., 1962. Reactions of feldspars and micas with aqeous solutions. *Econ. Geol.*, 57: 1219–1228.

MARSHALL, C. E. and JEFFRIES, C. D., 1945. Mineralogical methods in soil research. I. The correlation of soil types and parent materials with supplementary information on weathering processes. *Proc. Soil Soc. Am.*, 10: 397–405.

MATTER, A., 1964. Sedimentologische Untersuchungen im östlichen Napfgebiet. *Eclogae Geol. Helv.*, 57: 315–428.

MAXWELL, J. A., 1963. The laser as a tool in mineral identification. *Can. Mineralogist*, 7: 727–737.

MCANDREW, J., 1963. Relationship of optical axial angle with the three principal refractive indices. *Am. Mineralogist*, 48: 1277–1285.

MEGAW, H. D., 1959. Order and disorder in the feldspars. *Mineral. Mag.*, 32: 226–241.

MEGAW, H. D., 1961a. The structure of the intermediate plagioclase feldspars. *Cursillos Conf. Inst. "Lucas Mallada"*, 8: 143–147.

MEGAW, H. D., 1961b. Bibliography of papers dealing with structure analyses of feldspars. *Cursillos Conf. Inst. "Lucas Mallada"*, 8: 167.

MEGAW, H. D., KEMPSTER, C. J. E. and RADOSLOVICH, E. W., 1962. The structure of anorthite, $CaAl_2Si_2O_8$. II. Description and discussion. *Acta Cryst.*, 15: 1017–1035.

MEHRA, O. P. and JACKSON, M. L., 1959. Iron oxide removal from soils and clays by a dithionite-citrate system buffered with sodium bicarbonate. *Clays Clay Minerals, Proc. Natl. Conf. Clays Clay Minerals*, 5 (1959): 317–328.

MELLOR, J. W., 1955. *Higher Mathematics*. Dover, New York, N.Y., 641 pp.

MERWIN, H. E., 1911. The temperature stability ranges, density, chemical composition and optical and crystallographic properties of the alkali feldspars. *J. Wash. Acad. Sci.*, 1: 59.

MESSNER, W. E., 1955. Scrubbing solves sand flotation problem. *Mining Engr.*, 1: 138–140.

MICHAELIS DE SÁENZ, I., 1963. Authigener Sanidin. *Schweiz. Mineral. Petrog. Mitt.*, 43: 485–492.

MICHOT, J., 1963. Les feldspaths dans les sédiments dévoniens et carbonifères de la Belgique. *Acad. Roy. Belg. Classe Sci., Mém.*, 34: 55 pp.

MICHOT, P., 1961. Struktur der Mesoperthite. *Neues Jahrb. Mineral., Abhandl.*, 96: 213–216.

MILNER, H. B., 1962. *Sedimentary Petrography*, 4 ed. Allen and Unwin, London, 1: 643 pp.

MITZUTANI, VH., 1959. Clastic plagioclases in Permian Graywacke from the Mugi Area, Gifu Prefecture, C. Japan. *J. Earth Sci., Nagoya Univ.*, 7: 108–136.

MOHR, E. C. J., 1909. Ein Verwitterungsversuch in den Tropen. *Bull. Dépt. Agr. Indes Néerlandaises*, 32: 1–26.

MOORE, J. R., 1963. Bottom sediment studies, Buzzards Bay, Massachusetts. *J. Sediment. Petrol.*, 33: 511–558.

MOREY, G. W. and CHEN, W. T., 1955. The action of hot water on some feldspars. *Am. Mineralogist*, 40: 996–1000.

MORONEY, M. J., 1957. *Facts from Figures*. Penguin, Harmondsworth, 470 pp.

MUIR, I. D., 1962. The paragenesis and optical properties of some ternary feldspars. *Norsk Geol. Tidsskr.*, 42 (Feldspar Volume): 477–493.

MÜLLER, G. M., 1964. *Sediment Petrologie. 1. Methoden der Sediment-Untersuchung*. Schweizerbart, Stuttgart, 303 pp.

MUNRO, M., 1963. Errors in the measurement of 2V with the universal stage. *Am. Mineralogist*, 48: 308–324.

NABHOLZ, W. K., 1945. Geologie der Bündnerschiefergebirge zwischen Rheinwald, Valser und Safiental. *Eclogae Geol. Helv.*, 38: 1–120.

NICKEL, E., 1949. Bemerkungen zur Zwillingsbildung bei Plagioklasen. *Heidelberger Beitr. Mineral. Petrog.*, 2: 176–180.

NIEUWENKAMP, W., 1948. *Stereograms for the Determination of Plagioclase Feldspars in Random Sections*. Spectrum, Utrecht, 29 pp.

NIKITIN, W., 1936. *Die Fedorow-Methode*. Borntraeger, Berlin, 109 pp.

NIKITIN, W., 1942. On the possibility of assigning feldspars to the anorthoclase group solely on the basis of measurements of the orientation of the indicatrix with the universal stage *Raspredelit. Mat. Prirodn. Razved. Akad. Nauk Ljubljana*, 2: 269–298. (Yougosl. text, with german summary.)

NOTA, D. J. G. and BAKKER, A. M. G., 1960. Identification of soil minerals using optical characteristics and specific gravity separation. *Mededel. Landbouwhogeschool Wageningen*, 60 (11): 1–11.

NOWOCHATSKI, J. P. and KALININ, S. K., 1947. The occurrence of thallium in the silicates of the earth crust. *Doklad. Akad. Nauk S.S.S.R.*, 56: 831–832. (In Russian.)

OFTEDAHL, I., 1959. Distribution of Ba and Sr in microclines in a section across a granite pegmatite band in gneiss. *Norsk Geol. Tidsskr.*, 39: 343–349.

PARRISH, W. and MACK, M., 1963. Data for X-ray analysis. I–IV. Charts for solution of Bragg's equation. *Philips Tech. Library, Eindhoven*.

PEDRO, G., 1961. An experimental study on the geochemical weathering of crystalline rocks by water. *Clay Minerals Bull.*, 4: 266–282.

PEISER, H. S., ROOKSBY, H. P. and WILSON, A. J. C., 1960. *X-ray Diffraction by Polycrystalline Materials*. Chapman and Hall, London, 725 pp.

PETERS, TJ., 1963. Mineralogie und Petrographie des Totalserpentins bei Davos. *Schweiz. Mineral. Petrog. Mitt.*, 43: 531–685.

PETERSON, M. N. A. and GOLDBERG, E. D., 1962. Feldspar distribution in South Pacific pelagic sediments. *J. Geophys. Res.*, 67: 3477–3492.

PITTMAN, E. D., 1962. Plagioclase feldspar as an indicator of provenance in sedimentary rocks. *Geol. Soc. Am., Progr., Ann. Meeting*, 1962: 116A.

PITTMAN, E. D., 1963. Use of zoned plagioclase as an indicator of provenance. *J. Sediment. Petrol.*, 33: 380–387.

PORRENGA, D. H., 1958. Application of multiple Guinier camera in clay mineral studies. *Am. Mineralogist*, 43: 770–774.

PRIEM, H. N. A., 1956. An optical study of plagioclase feldspars in thermally metamorphosed volcanics from the southern part of the Cordillera Blanca, Peru. *Verhandel. Koninkl. Ned. Geol. Mijnbouwk. Genoot., Geol. Ser.*, 17: 81–86.

REEDER, S. W. and MCALLISTER, A. L., 1957. A staining method for the quantitative determination of feldspars in rocks and sands from soils. *Can. J. Soil Sci.*, 37: 57–59.

REINHARD, M., 1924. Données complémentaires pour la détermination des plagioclases par la méthode théodolite. *Schweiz. Mineral. Petrog. Mitt.*, 4: 2–14.

REINHARD, M., 1928. À propos de la détermination des plagioclases par la méthode de Fedoroff. *Compt. Rend. Soc. Phys. Hist. Nat.*, 40: 12–15.

REINHARD, M., 1931. *Universaldrehtischmethoden*. Wepf, Basel, 119 pp.

RETGERS, J. W., 1891. De samenstelling van het duinzand van Nederland. *Verhandel. Koninkl. Ned. Akad. Wetenschap., Afdel. Natuurk., Ser. D1*, 29: 48 pp.

REYNOLDS, R. C. and LESSING, P., 1962. The determination of dioctahedral mica and potassium feldspar in submicroscopic grain sizes. *Am. Mineralogist*, 47: 979–982.

RIBBE, P. H., 1960. An X-ray and optical investigation of the peristerite plagioclases. *Am. Mineralogist*, 45: 626–644.

RIBBE, P. H. 1962. Observations on the nature of unmixing in peristerite plagioclases. *Norsk Geol. Tidsskr.*, 42 (Feldspar Volume): 138–152.

RIBBE, P. H. and VAN COTT, H. C., 1962. Unmixing in peristerite plagioclases observed by phase-contrast and dark-field microscopy. *Can. Mineralogist*, 7: 278–290.

RITTMANN, A., 1929. Die Zonenmethode. *Schweiz. Mineral. Petrog. Mitt.*, 9: 1–46.

RITTMANN, A. and EL-HINNAWI, E., 1961. The application of the zonal method for the distinction between low- and high-temperature plagioclase feldspars. *Schweiz. Mineral. Petrog. Mitt.*, 41: 41–48.

ROBERTSON, F., 1959. Perthite formed by reorganisation of albite from plagioclase during potash feldspar metasomatism. *Am. Mineralogist*, 44: 603–620.

ROSENQVIST, I. TH., 1954. Investigations into the crystal chemistry of feldspars. *Proc. Intern. Symp. Reactivity Solids, Gothenburg, 1952*, 1 (1954): 453–461.

SAWARIZKY, A. N., SOBOLEW, W. S., KWASCHKA, L. G., KOSTJUK, W. P. and BOBRIEWITSCH, A. P., 1958. New diagrams for the determination of the composition of high-temperature plagioclases. *Zap. Vses. Mineralog. Obshchestva*, 87: 529–541. (In Russian.)

SCHAIRER, J. F., 1950. The alkali-feldspar join in the system $NaAlSiO_4$–$KAlSiO_4$–SiO_2. *J. Geol.*, 58: 512–517.

SCHAIRER, J. F., SMITH, J. R. and CHAYES, F., 1956. Refractive indices of plagioclase glasses. *Ann. Rept. Director Geophys. Lab.—Carnegie Inst. Wash., Yearbook*, 55: 195–197.

SCHIAVINATO, A. G., 1951. Sull' anorthoclasio incluso in una roccia effusiva femica de Monte Gemola (Euganei). *Periodico Mineral. (Rome)*, 20: 193–208.

SCHNEIDER, T. R. und LAVES, F., 1957. Barbierit oder Monalbit? *Z. Krist.*, 109: 241–244.

SCHÖNER, H., 1960. Ueber die Verteilung und Neubildung der nichtkarbonatischen Mineralkomponenten der Oberkreide aus der Umgebung von Hannover. *Beitr. Mineral. Petrog.*, 7: 76–103.

SCHUSTER, M., 1881. Ueber die optische Orientierung der Plagioklase. *Mineral. Petrog. Mitt.*, 3: 117–284.

SCHWARZMANN, S., 1956. Ueber die Lichtbrechung und die Achsenwinkel von Hochtemperaturplagioklasen und ihre Entstehungsbedingungen. *Heidelberger Beitr. Mineral. Petrog.*, 5 (1956): 105–112.

SCOTT MACKENZIE, H. M., 1957. The crystalline modifications of $NaAlSi_3O_8$. *Am. J. Sci.*, 255: 481–516.

SEN, S. K., 1959. Potassium content of natural plagioclases and the origin of antiperthites. *J. Geol.*, 67: 479–495.

SHAPIRO, L. and BRANNOCK, W. W., 1956. Rapid analysis of silicate rocks. *U.S., Geol. Surv., Bull.*, 1036C: 55 pp.

SIEGEL, S., 1956. *Nonparametric Statistics for the Behavioral Sciences*. MacGraw-Hill, New York, N.Y., 312 pp.

SLEMMONS, D. B., 1962a. Determination of volcanic and plutonic plagioclases using a three- or four-axis universal stage. *Geol. Soc. Am., Spec. Papers*, 69: 64.

SLEMMONS, D. B., 1962b. Observation on order–disorder relations of natural plagioclase. I. A method of evaluating order–disorder. *Norsk Geol. Tidsskr.*, 42 (Feldspar Volume): 533–554.

SMITH, J. R., 1958. The optical properties of heated plagioclases. *Am. Mineralogist*, 43: 1179–1194.

SMITH, J. V., 1956. The powder patterns and lattice parameters of plagioclase feldspars. I. The soda-rich plagioclases. *Mineral. Mag.*, 31: 47–68.

SMITH, J. V., 1958. The effect of composition and structural state on the rhombic section and pericline twins of plagioclase feldspars. *Mineral. Mag.*, 31: 914–928.

SMITH, J. V., 1962. Genetic aspects of twinning in feldspars. *Norsk Geol. Tidsskr.*, 42 (Feldspar Volume): 244–263.

SMITH, J. V. and GAY, P., 1958. The powder patterns and lattice parameters of plagioclase feldspars. II. *Mineral. Mag.*, 31: 744–762.

SMITHSON, S. B., 1962. Symmetry relations in alkali feldspars of some amphibolite facies rocks from the southern Norwegian Precambrian. *Norsk Geol. Tidsskr.*, 42 (Feldspar Volume): 586–600.

SORRELL, C. A., 1962. Solid state formation of barium, strontium and lead feldspars in clay–sulfate mixtures. *Am. Mineralogist*, 47: 291–309.

SPENCER, E., 1930. A contribution to the study of moonstones from Ceylon and other areas and of the stability relations of the alkali feldspars. *Mineral. Mag.*, 22: 291–367.

SPENCER, E., 1937. The potash-soda feldspars. I. Thermal stability. *Mineral. Mag.*, 24: 453–494.

STEFFEN, W., 1960. Geochemische Untersuchungen der Orthoklasen und Plagioklasen des Freiberger Grauen Gneisses. *Dissertation Abstr.*, 9: 941.

STIELER, A., 1955. Aus der Praxis der elektrostatischen Aufbereitung. *Proc. Intern. Congr., Ore Dressing, Goslar, 1955*, 8 pp.

STRAKHOV, N. M., 1958. *Méthodes d'Étude des Roches Sédimentaires*. Bur. Rech. Géol. Minière, Paris, 542 pp.

SUBRAMANIAM, A. P., 1956. Mineralogy and petrology of the Sittampundi complex, Salem district, Madras State, India. *Bull. Geol. Soc. Am.*, 67: 317–389.

SWINEFORD, A. and FRYE, J. C., 1951. Petrography of the Peora Loess in Kansas. *J. Geol.*, 59: 306–322.

TAYLOR, W. H., 1933. The structure of sanidine and other feldspars. *Z. Krist.*, 85: 425–443.

TEODOROVICH, G. I., 1958 (1961). *Authigenic Minerals in Sedimentary Rocks*. Consultants Bur., New York, N.Y., 120 pp.

THOM, C. and GISLER, H. J., 1954. Flotation of non-metallics. *Can. Mining Met. Bull.*, 47: 240–250.

TOBI, A. C., 1954. Use of the Berek compensator made easier. *Geol. Mijnbouw*, 16: 87–89.

TOBI, A. C., 1961a. Recognition of plagioclase twins in sections normal to the composition plane. *Am. Mineralogist*, 46: 1470–1488.

TOBI, A. C., 1961b. Pattern of plagioclase twinning as a significant rock property. *Koninkl. Ned. Akad. Wetenschap., Proc., Ser. B*, 64: 576–581.

TOBI, A. C., 1962. Characteristic patterns of plagioclase twinning. *Norsk Geol. Tidsskr.*, 42 (Feldspar Volume): 264–272.

TOBI, A. C., 1963. Plagioclase determination with the aid of the extinction angles in sections normal to (010). A critical comparison of current albite-Carlsbad charts. *Am. J. Sci.*, 261: 157–168.

TOBI, A. C., 1965. On the cause of internal optical scatter in plagioclase and the occurrence of lamelar albite–ala B twinning. *Am. J. Sci.*, in preparation.

TOPKAYA, M., 1950. Recherches sur les silicates authigènes dans les roches sédimentaires. *Bull. Lab. Géol. Minéral. Géophys. Musée Géol. Univ. Lausanne*, 97: 132 pp.

TRÖGER, W. E., 1959. *Optische Bestimmungen der Gesteinsbildenden Minerale. I. Bestimmungstabellen*, 3 Aufl. Schweizerbart, Stuttgart, 147 pp.

TSCHERMAK, G., 1865. Die Feldspath-Gruppe. *Sitz. Ber. Akad. Wiss. Wien, Math. Naturw. Kl., Abt. 1*, 50: 566–613.

TSUBOI, S., 1934. A straight-line diagram for determining plagioclases by the dispersion method. *Japan. J. Geol. Geograph., Trans*, 11: 325–327.

TURNER, F. J., 1947. Determination of plagioclase with the four-axis universal stage. *Am. Mineralogist*, 32: 389–410.

TURNER, F. J., 1951. Observations on twinning of plagioclase in metamorphic rocks. *Am. Mineralogist*, 36: 581–589.

TURNER, F. J. and VERHOOGEN, J., 1960. *Igneous and Metamorphic Petrology*. McGraw-Hill, New York, N.Y., 694 pp.

TUTTLE, O. F., 1952a. Origin of the contrasting mineralogy of extrusive and plutonic salic rocks. *J. Geol.*, 60: 107–124.

TUTTLE, O. F., 1952b. Optical studies on alkali feldspars. *Bowen Volume—Am. J. Sci.*, 2: 553–567.

TUTTLE, O. F. and BOWEN, N. L., 1950. High temperature albite and contiguous feldspars. *J. Geol.*, 58: 572–583.

TUTTLE, O. F. and BOWEN, N. L., 1958. Origin of granite in the light of experimental studies in the system $NaAlSi_3O_8$–$KAlSi_3O_8$–SiO_2–H_2O. *Geol. Soc. Am., Mem.*, 74: 153 pp.

UZAKOV, P., 1962. Carbonate salinization ($CaCO_3$ and $MgCO_3$) and its distribution in the soils of the Zeravshan Valley. *Pochvovedenie*, 1961: 49–57; *Soviet Soil Sci. (English Transl.)*, 1962: 1316–1321.

VANCE, J. A., 1961. Polysynthetic twinning in plagioclase. *Am. Mineralogist*, 46: 1097–1119.

VAN DER KAADEN, G., 1951. *Optical Studies on Natural Plagioclase Feldspars with High- and Low-Temperature Optics.* Thesis, State University Utrecht, Utrecht, 150 pp.

VAN DER MAREL, H. W., 1950. Het beschikbaar komen van kalium en magnesium voor de plant uit bodemmineralen bij verschillende grondsoorten. *Landbouwk. Tijdschr.*, 62: 178–189.

VAN DER PLAS, L., 1959. Petrology of the northern Adula Region, Switzerland. With an appendix on Wilcoxon's two-sample test by A. R. Bloemena. *Leidse Geol. Mededel.*, 24: 418–602.

VAN DER PLAS, L., 1962a. De stabiliteit van mineralen in de bodem. *Landbouwk. Tijdschr.*, 74: 949–960. With summary in English: the stability of minerals in soils, p. 959.

VAN DER PLAS, L., 1962b. Preliminary note on the granulometric analysis of sedimentary rocks. *Sedimentology*, 1: 145–157.

VAN DER PLAS, L. and TOBI, A. C., 1965. A graph for judging the reliability of point counting results. *Am. J. Sci.*, 263: 87–90.

VAN DER VEEN, A. H., 1963. A study of pyrochlore. *Verhandel. Koninkl. Ned. Geol. Mijnbouwk. Genoot., Geol. Ser.*, 22: 188 pp.

VLODAVETZ, V. I. and SHAVROVA, N. N., 1953. On orthoclase from a lava in Darigan volcanic region. *Izv. Acad. Sci. U.S.S.R., Geol. Ser.*, 1953 (2): 71. See also *Mineral. Abstr.*, 13: 480.

VOGEL, D. E., 1965. Thin sections for determining the composition of the light-mineral fraction of unconsolidated sediments. *Geol. Mijnbouw*, 44(2): 64–65.

VON GOETHE, I. W., 1807. Joseph Müllersche Sammlung. In: *Sämtliche Werke. 41. Mineralogie und Geologie*. Phillip Reclam Jr., Leipzig, pp.73–84.

WAHLSTROM, E. E., 1960. *Optical Crystallography*, 3 ed. Wiley, New York, N.Y., 356 pp.

WEIBEL, M., 1958. Chemische Untersuchungen an Albiten aus den Schweizer Alpen. *Schweiz. Mineral. Petrog. Mitt.*, 38: 61–76.

WEIGEL, O. und KRÜGER, E., 1934. Die Saphirlagerstätte von Bo Plei in Siam. 1. In: *Wissenschaftliche Ergebnisse meiner Forschungsreisen in Ostasien*. Noske, Marburg, 40 pp. See also *Mineral. Abstr.*, 7: 331.

WEISSMANN, R. C. and DIEHL, H. C., 1954. A new method utilizing Versene for determination of the calcite–dolomite ratio in carbonate rocks. *Proc. Iowa Acad. Sci.*, 60: 433–437.

WENK, E., 1945. Kritischer Vergleich von simultan nach der Drehtisch- und Immersions-Methode ausgeführte Anorthitbestimmungen an Plagioklasen. Diskussion der beiden Methoden. *Schweiz. Mineral. Petrog. Mitt.*, 25: 349–383.

WENK, E., 1960. Zur Analyse der Migrationskurven der Hochtemperatur-Plagioklase. *Schweiz. Mineral. Petrog. Mitt.*, 40: 313–323.

WICK, W., 1947. Aufbereitungsmethoden in der Mikropaläontologie. *Jahresber. Naturhist. Ges. Hannover*, 1942/1943–1946/1947, pp. 35–41.

WIESER, T., 1958. Identification of low- and high-temperature plagioclases with the universal stage method. *Bull. Acad. Polon. Sci., Sér. Sci., Chim., Géol. Géograph.*, 6: 465–468.

WILSON, A. F., 1950. Some unusual alkali-feldspars in the Central Australian charnockitic rocks. *Mineral. Mag.*, 29: 215–224.

WINCHELL, A. N., 1928. *Elements of Optical Mineralogy. 1. Principles and Methods.* Wiley, New York, N.Y., 283 pp.

WINCHELL, A. N. and WINCHELL, H., 1951. *Elements of Optical Mineralogy. 2. Description of Minerals*, 4 ed. Wiley, New York, N.Y., 551 pp.

WONES, D. R. and APPLEMAN, D. E., 1963. Properties of synthetic triclinic $KFeSi_3O_8$, iron-microcline, with some observations on the iron-microcline⇌iron-sanidine transition. *J. Petrol.*, 4: 131–137.

YOUNG, R. S., 1958. The geochemistry of cobalt. *Geochim. Cosmochim. Acta*, 13: 28–42.

ZIRKEL, F., 1873. *Die Mikroskopische Beschaffenheit der Mineralien und Gesteine*. Engelmann, Leipzig, 502 pp.

INDEX TO PROCEDURES

Bariumrhodizonate, reagent for staining, 52
—, staining thin sections or rock slabs with, 52
—, — rock slabs or thin sections with, 52
Becke line method, 140–143

Carbonate, removal of, 247–248, 256–257
Cobaltinitrite, staining feldspar grains with, 50–51
—, — rock slabs or thin sections with, 51–52
—, — thin sections or rock slabs with, 51–52
Conditioning of flotation, 70

Disaggregation procedure for argillaceous sediments, 241–242
Disintegration procedure for samples with low carbonate content, 232–233

Examples of twin identification, 159–160, 161, 164, 165

Feldspars, procedures for staining, 50–52
—, — — cobaltinitrite, 50–51
—, — — hemateine, 51
Flotation, 69–72
—, conditioning, 70
—, pre-treatment, 69–70

Hemateine, staining feldspar grains with, 51
—, — rock slabs or thin sections with, 52
—, — thin sections or rock slabs with, 52

Identification of twins, 159, 161, 164, 165

Measurement procedure, zone method, 117–128
— —, presence of cleavage, zone method, 117–121
— —, — — — and twins, zone method, 125–128
— —, — — twins, zone method, 121–125
— —, — — — and cleavage, zone method, 125–128
Method, *see* procedure
Mounting of thin section, zone method, 115–117

Organic compounds, oxidation of, 256
Oxidation of organic compounds, 256
— — — —, procedure, 256
— — — —, reagents, 256

Plagioclase determination in albite and Carlsbad twins in sections // (010), 136
— — — section ⊥ a, 133–136
— — — — showing an acute bisectrix figure, 136–137
— — — — — obtuse bisectrix figure, 136–137
—, — of structural state by axial angle of, 130
— — with less than 40% An, axial angle procedure, 130
— — — petrographic microscope only, 132–143
Pre-treatment of flotation, 69–70
Procedure after Hiemstra, 177
— — Rittmann and El-Hinnawi, 129
— for determination of plagioclases with less than 40% An, 130, 197–200
— — disaggregation of argillaceous sediments, 241–242
— — disintegration of samples with low carbonate content, 232–233
— — oxidation of organic compounds, 256
Procedure for staining, 50, 50–51, 51, 51–52, 52
— — — feldspars, 50–52
— — — with bariumrhodizonate, 52
— — — — cobaltinitrite, 50–51, 51–52
— — — — hemateine, 51, 52
— — thin section preparation, 238
Procedure of measurement, zone method, 117–128
— —, in case of presence of cleavage, 117–121
— —, — — — — — — and twins, 125–128
— —, — — — — — twins, 121–125
— —, — — — — — and cleavage, 125–128

Reagents for oxidation of organic compounds, 256

Reagents for *(continued)*
— — staining, 50, 51, 52
  bariumrhodizonate, 52
  cobaltinitrite, 50, 51
  hemateine, 51, 52
Relation between birefringence and orientation
  in plagioclases, 137–140
— — orientation and birefringence in plagioclases, 137–140
Relief of plagioclase fragments, 140–143
Removal of carbonates, 247–248, 256–257
Removal of carbonates, acid digestion, 247, 256
— — —, EDTA treatment, 256–257
— — —, exchange resins, 257
— — gypsum, 258–259
— — —, acid digestion, 258
— — —, EDTA treatment, 258
— — —, exchange resins, 258
— — —, Favejee's treatment, 258–259
— — iron oxide, 259–260
— — — —, after Mehra and Jackson, 259
— — — —, — the Wageningen Laboratory,
  259–260
— — — —, the nascent hydrogen method, 260
Rock slabs or thin sections, staining with
  bariumrhodizonate, 52
— — — — —, — — cobaltinitrite, 51–52
— — — — —, — — hemateine, 52

Staining feldspar grains with cobaltinitrite,
  50–51
— — — — hemateine, 51
— methods for feldspars, 50–52

Staining procedure, 50, 50–51, 51, 51–52, 52
— — with bariumrhodizonate, 52
— — — cobaltinitrite, 50–51, 51–52
— — — hemateine, 51, 52
— reagents, 50, 51, 52
— rock slabs or thin sections with bariumrhodizonate, 52
— — — — — — — cobaltinitrite, 51–52
— — — — — — — hemateine, 52
— techniques for carbonate determination,
  247–248
— thin sections or rock slabs with bariumrhodizonate, 52
— — — — — — —, cobaltinitrite, 50–51
— — — — — — — hemateine, 52

Thin section, mounting of, 115–117
— — of samples of sand or silt, after Vogel,
  238
— — or rock slabs, staining with bariumrhodizonate, 52
— — — — — — — cobaltinitrite, 51–52
— — — — — — — hemateine, 52
— — study, procedure, 238
Tsuboi's method, 86–90
Twin identification, 159, 161, 164, 165

Zone method, 115–128
— —, measurement procedure, 117–128
— —, mounting of thin section, 115–117

GENERAL INDEX

Numbers given in italics refer to procedures.

A-twins, *see* twins
Ab, definition of, 24–25
Abbe refractometer, 87
Acetone, 203
Acid treatment, *see* procedures
— digestion of gypsum, *see* procedures
— plagioclase, *see* plagioclase
Acline twins, *see* twins
Activation analysis, 48
ADAMSON, O. J., 76
Adularia, *see* alkali feldspar
Aerofroth-65, 71 (*see also* flotation)
Aeromine-2026 promotor, 68 (*see also* flotation)
AGAFANOVA, T. N., 41
Ala twins, *see* twins
Alaskite, 73
Albite, *see* plagioclase *and* alkali feldspar
— Ala twins, *see* twins
— Carlsbad law, *see* twinning
— — twins, *see* twins
— Esterel twinning law, *see* twinning
— fraction, *269*
— law, *see* twinning
— twins, *see* twins
Alcohol, 52, 115, 253
Alkali digestion, *see* procedures
Alkali feldspar, 1, *24*, *25*, 27, 29, 32, *33*, 35, 59, *62*, *75*, 77, *93*, *105*, 150, 180, 184, 192, 194, 203, 204, 229, 231, 235, 239, 243, 245, 249, 262, 263, 265, 267, 268, 272, 274, 275, 276
    adularia, 25, 31, 32, 60, 79, 80, 92, 93, 149, 166, 183, 239, 241
    albite, 1, 24, *34*, 35, 38, 57, 62, 64, 125, 143, 149, 158, 161, 178, 179, 185, 192, 194, 200, 203, 229, 240, 241, 248, 249, 267, 268, 269, 276 (*see also* plagioclase)
—, alpha, 35
—, amelia, 81, 164, 165
—, authigenic, 9, 96, 249 (*see also* plagioclase)
—, beta, 35
—, Bucarishuna or Alp Rischuna, 34, 170, 171, 183, 193, 201
—, gamma, 35
—, high, 38, 155, 178, 184 (*see also* plagioclase)
—, low, 43, 155, 171, 178, 183, 195 (*see also* plagioclase)
—, monoclinic, 35, 37 (*see also* plagioclase)
anorthoclase, 1, 25, 27, 44, 76, 77, 78, 80, 106, 244
—, calcium, 60
buddingtonite, 34
microcline, 1, 13, 14, 15, 22, 25, 29, 32, 60, 76, 77, 79, 80, 92, 93, 105, 153, 178, 179, 184, 185, 190, 192, 194, 231, 233, 239, 244, 249, 265, 267, 268, 278
—, intermediate, 78, 80, 185, 190
—, iron, 29
—, iso-, 93
—, maximum, 43, 185, 190, 191
—, Pontis, 185
—, perthite, 60, 77, 151, 183, 185, 192, 193, 231, 248, 249 (*see also* perthite)
orthoclase, 1, 13, 14, 24, 25, 27, 29, 32, 60, 76, 78, 80, 93, 100, 105, 166, 178, 239
—, iron, 60
— microperthite, 60, 178
sanidine, 1, 7, 13, 15, 25, 27, 30, 32, 43, 60, 76, 77, 78, 93, 106, 169, 178, 180, 185, 192, 193, 239, 244, 263, 273
—, high, 105, 166
—, low, 166, 190
— —, ammonium-rich, 34
— —, authigenic, 23, 31, 249
— —, axial angle of, 90, 93, 180 (*see also* axial angle)
— —, chemical composition of, *33*, 99, 106, 185
— —, high-temperature, 106, 178, 205
— —, low-temperature, 31, 182, 207
— —, monoclinic, 80, 178, 180, 184, 190, 267, 268
— —, pseudo monoclinic, 180, 190
— —, synthetic, 60, 180
— —, triclinic, 178, 184, 185, 190, 194, 265 (*see also* microcline)
Alkali-feldspar fraction, 23, 267, *268*
— — twins, *see* twins
Almandite–amphibole facies, 155
Alteration of feldspar, *see* feldspar
— — sediments, 241
— products, 2

Aluminium, 4, 230
— fluoride, 68
— hydroxide, 253
Amine compounds, 67, 70 (*see also* flotation)
Ammonium allun, 175 (*see also* X-ray)
— feldspar, *see* feldspar
— plagioclase, *see* plagioclase
— rich alkali feldspar, *see* alkali feldspar
Amphibole, 9, 12, 19, 64, 261
An, definition of, 24–25
Analyser, 115, 121
Andesine, *see* plagioclase
Anhydrite, 9, *251*
Anorthite, *see* plagioclase
Anorthoclase, *see* alkali feldspar
ANSILEWSKI, J., 26, 27, 32
Antiparallel twins, *see* twins
Antiperthite, *see* perthite
Apatite, 12, 241, 244, 251
Araldite, 143
Arctic environment, 4
— region, 3
— soil, 4
Arenaceous sediment, *230*, *235*, 249, 271
Argillaceous sediment, 229, *240*, *242*, 274
Armac T, 68, 70 (*see also* flotation)
Armoured relics, 133
A.S.T.M. powder-data file, 204
Asymmetrical extinction, *see* optical properties
Attrition, 70, 235 (*see also* flotation)
Authigenic albite, *see* albite
— alkali feldspar, *see* alkali feldspar
— feldspar, 9, 23, 31, 96, 153, 248, 249, 272, 273 (*see also* alkali feldspar *and* plagioclase)
— minerals, 53, 248, 249, 275, 276
— rims, 238, 249
Axial angle, *90*, 91, 92, 93, 94, 95, 96, 107, 128, 130, 180, 190, 239, 248, 268, 272, 273 (*see* optical properties, *see also* alkali feldspar *and* plagioclase)
— dispersion, *see* optical properties

BAILEY, E. H. and STEVENS, R. E., 49, 52
BALASANYAN, S. I., 132, 133
BAMBAUER, H. H. and LAVES, F., 31, 93, 149
BARABANOV, W. F., 33, 40
BARBER, C. T., 34
BARBIER, P. and PROUST, A., 35
Barbierite, 35 (*see also* plagioclase)
Barium, 33, 40
— chloride, 49, 52 (*see also* staining)
— rhodizonate, 49, 51, 52 (*see also* staining)
BARKER, D. S., 33, 34
BARTH, T. F. W., 20, 21, 34, 35
Basalt, 4, 14, 82, 234

BASKIN, Y., 31, 35, 36, 80
BASSET, H., 247
Batch flotation, *see* flotation
Bauxite, 4, 10, 230, *253*
Baveno law, *see* twins
— twins, *see* twins
Beach sand, 72
Beam catcher, *see* X-ray
BEAR, E., 33
Becke line method, 87, *140*
BELYANKINA, E. D., 49
Benzene, 253
BEREK, M., 146
Berek compensator, *see* compensator
BERG, R. R., 31
Bertrands' ocular, 119
Beryl, 59
Binary system, 23, 54
Biotite, 59, 64, 261
Birefringence, *see* optical properties
Bisectrix figure, *see* optical properties
Bituminous sediments, *253*
BLANCK, E., 14, 251
Boehmite, 253
BOLT, G. H. and FRISSEL, M. J., 257, 258
Borium, 12
Boulders, 234
BOWEN, N. L., 36
BOWEN, N. L. and TUTTLE, O. F., 27, 42, 180
BOWN, M. G. and GAY, P., 195
BRADLEY, J. E. S. and BRADLEY, O., 48
Bragg-Brentano para-focussing arrangement, 172 (*see also* X-ray)
BRETT, R., 44
BRINDLEY, G. W. and KURTOSSY, S. S., 242, 243
Bromoform, 58, 238 (*see also* separation)
BROWN, W. L., 35, 45
Brown coal, 5
BRUN, E., HARTMANN, P., STAUB, H. H., HAFNER, ST. and LAVES, F., 180
BUCKENHAM, M. H. and ROGERS, J., 67, 68, 70
Buddingtonite, 34 (*see also* alkali feldspar)
BUERGER, M. J., 145
BURRI, C., 101, 103, 105, 137, 146, 147
BURRI, C. and NIGGLI, P., 24
BURRI, C., PARKER, R. L. and WENK, E., 111
Bytownite, *see* plagioclase

C-twins, *see* twins
Calcareous rocks or sediments, 10, 202, 231, *245*, *246*, 248, *249*, 250
Calcic plagioclase, *see* plagioclase
— — fraction, *270*
Calcite, 59, 63, 143, 243, 245, 246, 247, 250 (*see also* carbonates)
Calcium, 4, 5, 9, 33, 99, 198, 228

Calcium *(continued)*
— anorthoclase, *see* alkali feldspar
— gluconolacto bionate, 50
Camera radius, *see* X-ray
Canada balsam, 140, 143, 243
Carbonaceous sediments, 230, *253*
Carbonate content, 231
— rich soils, *249, 275*
— sediment, 229, *245, 246, 249*, 257, *275*
Carbonates, 9, 230, 233, 245, 246, 247, 249, 253, 256, 258, 275
    calcite, 59, 63, 143, 243, 245, 246, 247, 250, 257, 258
    dolomite, 59, 245, 246, 247, 248, 257
    magnesite, 245, 247, 250
    rhodochrosite, 245
    siderite, 245, 247
    sodium carbonate solution, 258
Carbonatite, 246
Cardanian suspension system, 108, 109
Cargile set of index liquid, 87
CARL, J. D., 33
Carlsbad law, *see* twinning
— twins, *see* twins
Cartesian coordinates, 100, 101
Cationic collector, *see* flotation
— flotation, *see* flotation
Celsian, 23
Central plate of U-stage, 115
Centrifuge methods, 59 (*see also* separation)
CHAISSON, U., 31, 39
Chalcedony, 159
CHANDRASEKHAR, S., FLEET, S. G. and MEGAW, H. D., 36
CHAO, S. H. and TAYLOR, W. H., 38
Chaos phase, 26
Charnockite, 45
CHAYES, F., 49, 81, 82, 83, 90, 264
Chemical composition of alkali feldspar, *33*, 99, 106, 185, *272*
— — — feldspar, 16, 54, 272
— — — plagioclases, *38*, 95, 99, 130, 137, *272*
Chlorite, 59, 64, 242, 251, 253, 261
Chloroform, 254
Classification of feldspars, *23, 25, 26,* 32
— — feldspar twins, *see* twins
Clastic plagioclase, *see* plagioclase
— rocks, 53, 132, *227*, 230
Clay, 230, 233, 240, 242, 249, 275
— fraction, 12, 40, 56, 229, 244, 245, 248, 255
— minerals, 9,10,177,250,253,254,258,260,261
    glauconite, 251
    hydrous mica, 240, 241, 242, 245
    illite, 243, 249
    kaolinite, 62, 240, 242, 243, 245, 250
    montmorillonite, 242, 243, 244

— rich soil, *240, 242, 274*
— stone, 240
Cleavage flake, 86, 89
— plane, 107, 111, 112, *114*, 117, 118, 120, 121, 125, 128, 133, 137, 173, 233
— trace, 113, *117*, 122, 137
Clevelandite, 165, 166 (*see also* plagioclase)
Climate, 3, 5
Coal-bearing sediments, 254
Coarse fraction, 245, 260, *261, 262*
— grained samples, *234*
Coatings, 259
Cobalt, 40
— radiation, *see* X-ray
Cobaltinitrite, 49, 50, 51, 143, 232, 267, 269 (*see also* staining)
Cobbles, 234
COLE, W. F., SÖRUM, H. and KENNARD, O., 30
Collector, *see* flotation
Collimating system, *see* X-ray
Colorimetric analysis, 48
Compensator, 111, 133, 135
—, Berek, 111, 137
—, Bertrands ocular, 119
—, Ehringhaus, 111, 135, 137
—, gypsum plate, 111, 118, 119, 157
—, mica plate, 111
—, quartz wedge, 119, 137
—, Wright's biquartz wedge, 119
Complex twins, *see* twins
Complexometric titration, 49
Component, 16
Composition plane of twins, *see* twins
Concentrate, *see* procedures
Concentration methods, 55, 57, 203, 230, 262 (*see also* procedures)
    electrostatical concentration, 55
    flotation, 55, 57, 203, 255, 261, 262, 263, 268, 269
    handpicking of minerals, 57, 203, 272, 273
    high-grade concentrates, 66, 72
    magnetic separation, 55, 73, 251, 261, 262
    vibrating glass-plate method, 73
Condensor, 116
Conditioning, *see* flotation
Conglomerate, 234
Conoscopical observation, 92, 108, 111, *116*, 121, 124, 133, 166
Consolidated sediments, 202, 234, *240*
Contact angle, *see* flotation
— metamorphic rocks, 155
Coordinate geometry, 105
Copper, 12, 33, 40
Correction of tilt for U-stage measurements, 110
CORRENS, C. W., 13, 15
Corticosteroid, 50

Counters, *see* X-ray diffractometer
Counting methods, 72, 232, 238, *263*, 271
— —, accuracy of, 264
— —, line, 234, 271
— —, point, 72, 234, 264, 271
— —, reliability of, 264, 265
— —, reproducibility of, 264
— —, ribbon, 72, 234, 264, 271
— results, *264*
Cross-hatched twins, *see* twins
Cryptoperthite, *see* perthite
Crystal lattice,
— monochromation, *see* X-ray
— structure, 54
Crystalline phase, 99, 276
Crystallographic axis, 99, 104, 117, 121, 128
Cyanamid aero promotor-800, 73 (*see also* flotation)

Data processing, 100
DAVIS, G. L. and TUTTLE, O. F., 36
DAVIS, T. E. and SLEMMONS, D. B., 107
DEB, B. C., 259
Debye-Scherrer camera, 170, 171, 176, 177, 178 (*see also* X-ray)
Decalcification, 250
Decaline, 58
DEER, W. A., HOWIE, R. A. and ZUSSMANN, J., 32, 33, 38, 56, 60, 90, 132, 146
Defect structures, 242
Deficiency of trace elements, *see* trace elements
Degree of order, *see* obliquity
De-ironing, 255, 259, 260 (*see also* procedures)
DE JONG, W. F., 105, 109
DES CLOIZEAUX, A., 30
Desert region, 4
Detrital feldspars, *see* feldspar
— minerals, 227, 248
— rocks, 47
DE WOLFF, P. M., 173
Diadochy, 19
Diagenesis, 241
Diamagnetic, 55
DIETRICH, R. V., 97
Diffraction lines, *see* X-ray
Diffractogram, *see* X-ray
Diffractometer, *see* X-ray
Diffusion of ions, 31
Direction cosinus, 101, 102, 105
Disaggregation or disintegration, *232*, 235, *241*, 271
Diseases in crops, 33
Disordered, 32, 184
— feldspar, *see* feldspar
— structure or phase, 93, 129, *180*, 229 (*see also* obliquity)

Dispersion, *see* optical properties
Dithionite, *see* sodium dithionite
DIXON, W. J. and MASSEY, F. J., 264
Dodecylamine compounds, 67, 68, 70 (*see also* flotation)
DOEGLAS, D. J., FAVEJEE, J. CH. L., NOTA, D. J. G. and VAN DER PLAS, L., 50, 58, 62, 267
DOLAR MANTUANI, L., 106, 149, 151, 153
Dolomite, 59, 245, 246, 247, 248, 257
DOMAN, R. CH., 36, 95
DONNAY, G. and DONNAY, J. H. D., 175, 179, 180, 181, 182, 206, 208, 209, 210
DONNAY, J. H. D., 155
Dowfroth-250, 71 (*see also* flotation)
Dune sand, 227

EDTA, 247, 248, *256*
Efficiency of flotation, 72,
— — methods, 72, 203, 239
EHRINGHAUS, A., 137
Ehringhaus compensator, *see* compensator
EISINGER, V. J., SWINDERMAN, J. N. and SLEMMONS, D. B., 107
Electron probe microanalysis, 48
Electrostatic neutrality, 19, 23
Electrostatical concentration, *see* concentration methods
Ellipsoid, triaxial, 91, 99
Elongation, *see* optical properties
Emergency chest, 50
EMERSON, D. O., 48
EMMONS, R. C., 38, 55, 81, 90, 107, 112, 221, 223, 225
EMMONS, R. C. and GATES, R. M., 87, 88, 155
EMMONS, R. C., CRUMP, R. M. and KETNER, K. B., 95
Enclosed minerals, 63
Entropy, 15
Eolian, 243
Epidote, 63, 232, 261
Equal area projection, 109
— extinction, *see* optical properties
Equilibrium assemblage, 16
Equivalent-norm mineral, 24
— weight, 24
ERD, R. C., WHITE, D. E., FAHEY, J. J. and LEE, D. E., 34
Erosion, 4, 9, 10
ESKOLA, P., 45
Esterel law, *see* twinning
Ethanol, *see* alcohol
Euler angles, 101–103, 104, 105
Exchange resin, 257, 258, 259 (*see also* procedures)
Exposure time, *see* X-ray

Exsolution phenomena, 16, 44, 271 (*see also* perthite)
Extinction angle, *see* optical properties
— conditions of X-rays, *see* X-ray
Extraordinary sections, 159

FAIRBAIRN, H. W., 109
FAVEJEE, J. CH. L., 50, 58, 62, 172, 177, 258
Favejee camera, 172 (*see also* X-ray)
— funnel, 58, 262 (*see also* separation)
— treatment for removal of gypsum, *see* procedures
FEDOROV, E., 36
Fedorov-Nikitin-Reinhard method, 108, *112*, 113, 121, 125
Fedorov's system of notation, 104
Feldspar, *19*, 40, 55, 57, 75, 143, 169, 202, 229, 230, 241, 243, 246, 254, 255, 261, 263, 271, 272, 274 (*see also* alkali feldspar *and* plagioclase)
—, alteration of, 3, 4, 62, 154, 231, 273
—, ammonium, 34
—, authigenic, *see* authigenic feldspar
—, chemical composition of, 16, 54, *274*
—, concentrate, 229, 267, 268
—, detrital, 8, 9, 16, *229*, 234, 248, 251, 254, 255, 263, 272, 273, 276
—, disordered, 21
—, lattice parameter of, 178, *182*
—, morphology of, 6, 271, *273*, *275*
—, optical properties of, 27, 30, 34, 36, 55, 56, 101
—, qualitative analysis of, *271*
—, quantitative analysis of, *228*
—, structure of, 178, 192
—, twinning of, *see* twinning
—, high-temperature, 179
—, low-temperature, 100, 179
—, ordered, 21
—, potassium, 23, 57
—, synthetic, *see* alkali feldspar *or* plagioclase
—, ternary, 24
— fraction, 59, 203, 231, 240, 267, 268
— glasses, 56 (*see also* plagioclase)
— identification, 19, 99, 177, *227*
FERGUSON, R. B., 22
Ferro-manganese minerals, 244
Ferruginous sediments, 230, 250, *251*
Fertility, soil, 10, 11, 13, 33, 228, 235
Fertilizers, 10, 11, 14
Fine fraction, 233, 255, *260*, *261*, 264, 270, 275
FINNEY, J. J. and BAILEY, S. W., 206
FISHER, D. J., 175
Flame photometry, 48
— spectroscopy, 48
Flint fragments, 268
Float, 257, 258, 261, 263, 267, 268, 272

Flotation, 55, *57*, *66*, *70*, 203, 255, 261, *262*, 263, 268, 269 (*see also* concentration methods)
—, Aerofroth-65, 71
—, Aeromine-2026 promotor, 68
—, amine compounds, 67, 70
—, Armac T, 68, 70
—, attrition, 235
—, batch, 70
—, cationic, 66
—, cell, 71, 268
—, conditioning, *70*
—, contact angle, 67
—, Cyanamid aero promotor-800, 73
—, dodecylamine compounds, 67, 68, 70
—, Dow Froth-250, 71
—, efficiency of, *72*
—, float, 257, 258, 261, 263, 267, 268, 272
—, froth, 69, 71
—, frother, 71
—, Hallimond tube, 69, *71*
—, hexadecylacetate, 68
—, hydrofluoric acid, 67, 70
—, hydrophobic film, 66
—, interface tension, 66
—, non-polar group, 66
—, octadecenylacetate, 68
—, octadecylacetate, 68
—, petroleum sulphonate, 73
—, physico-chemical aspects of, *66*
—, polar group, 66
—, pre-treatment, *69*
—, pulp, 69, 70
—, quartz depressant, 68
—, selectivity of, 67
—, sulphuric acid, 73
—, surface properties, 66
—, tailing, 72, 263, 267, 268
—, tetradecylacetate, 68
— collector, 67, 73
— —, cationic, 67
Flow meter, 71
— sheet, 72, *236*, *252*, *254*, *265*, *267*, 270
Fluorescent radiation, *see* X-ray
Focussing arrangement, *see* X-ray
FOSTER, W. R., 56
FOUQUÉ, F., 121, 125
Fouqué method, 121, 125, 133, 136
Four la Brouque law, *see* twinning
FRANCO, R. R. and SCHAIRER, J. F., 24
FRIEDMAN, G. M., 247, 276
Froth flotation, *see* flotation
Frother, *see* flotation
Frequency of twinning, 151, 232 (*see also* twinning)
FÜCHTBAUER, H., 31, 96, 249

Funnel, *see* separation
FÜRSTENAU, D. W., METZGER, P. H. and
    SEELE, G. D., 71
FYFE, W. S., TURNER, F. J. and VERHOOGEN, J.,
    47

GABRIEL, A. and COX, P., 49, 50
Gallium, 33
Garnet, 47, 64, 261
Gasoline, 203
GAUDIN, A. M., 66
GAY, P., 36, 37, 38, 195
GAY, P. and BOWN, M. G., 195
GAY, P. and TAYLOR, W. H., 36
Gem stones, 23
Genesis of plagioclase, *see* plagioclase
— — rocks, 235, 245
Geomorphology, 6
Geosyncline, 231
GERHARD, D., 34, 42
Gibbsite, 251, 253
Glacial acetic acid, 51, 52 (*see also* staining)
— drift, 234
Glaciers, 4
Glass hemispheres of U-stage, 115
— sand, 5, 66, 73
— spar, 73
Glauconite, *see* clay minerals
Glide twins, *see* twins
Glycerine, 115
Gneiss, 82, 153
Goethite, 242, 251
GOLDSMITH, J. R. and LAVES, F., 27, 173, 178,
    179, 180, 181, 182, 184, 185, 191, 192, 205, 206
GOODYEAR, J. and DUFFIN, W. J., 172, 179,
    199, 215, 217, 219, 221, 223, 225
GORAI, M., 154
GORBUNOV, N. T., 251
GOTTARDI, G., 105
GRADWELL, R., 56
Grain morphology, 227
— size, 13, 195, 203, 255
— — frequency distribution, 233
— slide, 143, 156, 231, 235, 238, 239, 264
Granite, 4, 5, 82, 153, 234
Granulite, 45, 231
Granulometric analysis, 233
Graywacke, 113, 230, 231, 274
Greenschist facies, 149, 153, 155, 264, 270
Growth twins, *see* twins
Gypsum, 9, 10, 59, 230, 250, 251, 253, 255, 257,
    258
— and anhydrite-bearing samples, *251*
— plate, *see* compensators
— rich sediments, 230, *251*
GYSIN, M., 149

HAFNER, ST. and LAVES, F., 23, 29, 93, 180, 194
Hair perthite, *see* perthite
Hallimond tube, 69, *71* (*see also* flotation)
Handpicking of minerals, 57, 203, 272, 273
Harmonic X-rays, *see* X-ray
HAY, R. L., 31
HAY, R. L. and MOIOLA, R. J., 31
HAYES, J. R. and KLUGMAN, R., 49
HEALD, M. T., 76
Heat treatment, 82
Heavy fraction, *see* separation
— liquid, *see* separation
— — separations, *see* separation
— minerals, 9, 12, 33, 40, 47, 57, 70, 131, 231,
    232, 253, 254, *261*, 262, 264, 270
HEIER, K. S., 33, 40
HEIER, K. S. and TAYLOR, S. R., 33
Hemateine, 49, 51, 52, 72, 232, 263, 267, 268,
    269, 270 (*see also* staining)
Hematite, 242, 251
Heulandite, 242, 248, 249
Hexadecylacetate, 68 (*see also* flotation)
HIEMSTRA, S. A., 177, 203, 268
Hiemstra method, *177*, 203, 268, 272 (*see also*
    X-ray)
High albite, *see* albite
— sanidine, *see* alkali feldspar
— temperature alkali feldspar, *see* alkali feld-
    spar
— — feldspar, *see* feldspar
— — phase, 13, 32, 76, 107, 197, 198, 270, 271
— — plagioclase, *see* plagioclase
— — structure, 36, 150
HILL, D. E. and TEDROW, J. C. F., 244
HILL, W. E. and GOEBEL, E. D., 247, 257
HOEKSEMA, K. J., 10
HOOGENDAM, I. and VAN DIJK, M. C., 50
H_2O_2 procedure, *see* procedures
HOWIE, R. A., 33, 40
HUANG, C. K., 31, 93
Humid tropical regions, 3, 4
Hydrofluoric acid, 49, 50, 51, 52, 67, 70 (*see
    also* staining *or* flotation)
— — burns, *50*
Hydrolysis, 49
Hydrophobic film, *see* flotation
Hydrous mica, *see* clay minerals

Identification of feldspars, 19, 99, 177 (*see also*
    feldspar)
— — twins, *see* twins
Igneous rocks, 1, 2, 5, 7, 9, 12, 16, 29, 32, 42,
    47, 53, 56, 106, 108, 132, 150, 153, 166, 197,
    202, 203, 273
Illite, *see* clay minerals
Immersion liquid, 115, 235

— method, 86, 90, 92, 272
Impregnation, 140
Incident light, 232
Inclination, 104
Index liquid, 86, 239, 240, 254, 265, 270
— of refraction, *see* optical properties
Indicatrix, 99, 100, 132, 165 (*see also* optical properties)
— orientation, *see* optical properties
Induration, 230, 233, 240, 241
Infrared pattern, 194
— spectroscopy, 48
INGERSON, E., 151
Initial fertility, 11
Integration ocular, 232
Intensity of diffraction lines, *see* X-ray
Interface tension, *see* flotation
Interference colours, 157
Intermediacy index, 96, 190 (*see also* obliquity)
"Intermediate", 29, 30, 31, 32, 35, 198
— microcline, *see* alkali feldspar
— plagioclase, *see* plagioclase
— structure, 29, 30, 32, 38, 80, 95, 179, 198
Ionic structures, 22
Iron, 12, 33, 40, 251, 255, 259
— microcline, *see* alkali feldspar
— orthoclase, *see* alkali feldspar
— oxide, 62
Iso-microcline, *see* alkali feldspar
Isotope geology, 73

JEFFRIES, C. D., 62
JEFFRIES, C. D. and JACKSON, M. L., 62
Joined angle technique, 83, 108, 113
JONES, J. B. and TAYLOR, W. H., 76

Kainite, 14
KANO, H., 81
Kantennormalengesetz, *see* twinning
Kaolinite, *see* clay minerals
KARL, F., 36, 80
Kataklastic phenomena, 238
Keesom capillaries, 172, 177 (*see also* X-ray)
KEMPSTER, C. J. E., MEGAW, H. D. and RADO-SLOVICH, E. W., 36, 178
Kerosine, 203
KHADR, M., 62, 235
KIRCHBERG, H., 66, 69
KLOCKMANN, F., 35
KÖHLER, A., 35, 45, 83, 113, 121
Kosmo-phase, 26
KRACEK, F. C. and NEUVONEN, K. J., 93, 225
KRUMBEIN, W. C. and PETTIJOHN, F. J., 59, 62, 251, 255
KUELLMER, F. J., 43, 192

Labradorite, *see* plagioclase

Lakeside thermoplastic cement, 143, 238
Lamellar twinning, *see* twinning
LARSSON, W., 35
Laser technology, 48
Laterite, 250, *253*
Latite, 151
Lattice defect, 242
— parameters of feldspars, 178, *182*, 196, 198
— type C, 178
— — P, 178
Lava, 81, 274
LAVES, F., 20, 21, 31, 35, 36, 41, 45, 150, 155, 173
LAVES, F. and GOLDSMITH, J. R., 21, 22, 23, 194
LAVES, F. and SCHNEIDER, T., 153
Leaching, 3, 8, 13, 15, 250
Lead, 12, 33, 40
— nitrate, 175 (*see also* X-ray)
LEAVITT, F. G. and SLEMMONS, D. B., 107
LEBEDSINSKIJ, W. T. and TSCHU, Z., 76
LEDENT, D., PATTERSON, C. and TILTON, G. R., 22
Leucite, 242
Leuko granite, 73
LEWIS, C. C. and EISENMENGER, W. S., 14
LiF monochromator, *see* X-ray
Light fraction, *see* separation
— minerals, 9, 47, 131, 253, *261*, 265
Lignite, 5
Limestone, 7, 231, 245, 246, 247, 249, 250, 255
Lindemann glass capillary, *see* X-ray
Line counting, *see* counting methods
— focus, *see* X-ray
Lithium, 40
Loam, 242, 244
Loess, 239, 250
Low albite, *see* albite
— grade metamorphite, 150, 151
— sanidine, *see* alkali feldspar
— temperature alkali feldspar, *see* alkali feldspar
— — feldspar, *see* feldspar
— — phase, 13, 76, 107, 198, 270
— — plagioclase, *see* plagioclase
— — state, 31, 150
LUNDEGÅRDH, P. H., 35
LÜTHY, H., MATTER, A. and NABHOLZ, W. K., 231
LUTJEN, G. P., 73

M-twins, *see* twinning
MACKENZIE, W. S., 35, 191
MACKENZIE, W. S. and SMITH, J. V., 43, 44
Macro elements, 10, *11*
Magma, 8, 16
Magnesite, *see* carbonates
Magnesium, 12, 33, 40, 245

Magnetic fraction, *see* separation
— separation, 55, 73, 251, 261, 262 (*see also* separation, *see also* concentration)
— susceptibility, 54
Magnetite, 261
MALLARD, F., 31
Manebach acline-A law, *see* twinning
— law, *see* twinning
— pericline law, *see* twins
— twins, *see* twinning
Manganese, 251, 255, 259
MARFUNIN, A., 27, 29, 31, 32, 56, 76, 77, 81, 83, 90, 92, 93, 94, 100, 105, 106, 149, 150, 180
Marine environment, 8
— sediments, 5, 6, 250
Marl, 245
Marlaceous slates, 231
MARSHALL, C. E., 15, 34, 49
MARSHALL, C. E. and JEFFRIES, C. D., 59
Matrix of rocks, 202, 234
Maximum extinction angle method, *see* method of Michel Levy
— microcline, *see* alkali feldspar
MAXWELL, J. A., 49
MCANDREW, J., 91
MEGAW, H. D., 36, 178
MEGAW, H. D., KEMPSTER, C. J. E. and RADOSLOVICH, E. W., 178
MEHRA, O. P. and JACKSON, M. L., 259, 260
Melinex, *see* X-ray
MELLOR, J. W., 101, 105
MERWIN, H. E., 34
Mesoperthite, *see* perthite
MESSNER, W. E., 69
Metabolic disorder, 33
Metamorphic processes, 8, 241
— rocks, 1, 2, 7, 9, 12, 16, 19, 32, 41, 47, 53, 56, 57, 106, 108, 132, 150, 155, 166, 197, 202, 203, 270, 273, 274
Metasomatism, 133
Method of graphical construction, 105
— — Michel-Lévy, 132, 137, 138
— — Rittman and El Hinnawi, 129
Mica, 9, 12, 14, 19, 40, 62, 63, 73, 177, 233, 240, 241, 249, 261, 262
— plate, *see* compensator
MICHOT, J., 7, 45, 230, 274
Micro elements, *12*
— fossils, 248
Microcline, *see* alkali feldspar
— perthite, *see* alkali feldspar *and* perthite
Microperthite, *see* perthite
MILNER, H. B., 251
Mineral assemblage, 53, 133
Mineralogical composition, 11, *12*, 13, 14, 244, 270

Minor elements, 12, 33, 75
Mitscherlich pots, 14
MITZUTANI, VH., 155, 232, 274
Mixed crystals, 23, 38, 54, 75
Modification, 31
MOHR, E. C. J., 14
Monochromatic light, 87, 111
— X-rays, *see* X-ray
Monoclinic alkali feldspar, *see* alkali feldspar
— phase, 94
Montmorillonite, *see* clay minerals
Monzonite, 151
Moonstone, 36, 75
MOORE, J. R., 238
MOREY, G. W. and CHEN, W. T., 15
MORONEY, M. J., 264
Morphology of feldspars, *see* feldspar
Moulding sand, 72
MUIR, I. D., 24
MÜLLER, G. M., 241, 251, 253, 255, 257, 260, 264, 276
Multiple twins, *see* twins
MUNRO, M., 92, 108, 110
Muscovite, 59, 261
Myrmekite, 238

NABHOLZ, W. K., 149, 153
Natural fertility, 11
— plagioclase, *see* plagioclase
NICKEL, E., 113
NIEUWENKAMP, W., 56
Niggli classification of nomenclature, 240
NIKITIN, W., 106
Nitrate, 253
Nitrogen, 12
Non-crystallonomic plane, 153
— magnetic fraction, *see* separation
— polar groups, *see* flotation
Normal twinning law, *see* twinning
— twins, *see* twins
NOTA, D. J. G. and BAKKER, A. M. G., 62, 235, 237, 265
NOWOCHATSKI, J. P. and KALININ, S. K., 33
Nuclear magnetic resonance technique, 29
Nutation, 104
Nutrient elements, 10, 15
Nutritional disorder, 33

(010)-twin ratio, *see* twinning
Obliquity, 30, 175, 180, 184, *190*, 191, 192, 194
— index, 95, 97, 190, 191
Octadecenylacetate, 68 (*see also* flotation)
Octadecylacetate, 68 (*see also* flotation)
OFTEDAHL, I., 33
Oligoclase, *see* plagioclase
Opal, 253

Opaque minerals, 248
Optic axis, *see* optical properties
— — figure, *see* optical properties
— sign, *see* optical properties
Optical methods, *see* procedures
Optical properties, *see also* feldspar
    axial angle, *90–94*, 96, 107, 128, 130, 180, 190, 239, 248, 268, 272, 273
    — dispersion, 86
    birefringence, 115, 120, 121, 124, 128, 133, 136, *137*, 156, 158, 160, 238
    elongation, 120, 121, 123, 136
    —, negative, 119, 121, 124, 133, 160
    extinction, 99, 105, 119, 123, 124, 126, 128, 129, 136, 157, 158, 159, 160, 238
    —, agree, 157
    —, asymmetrical, 123, 124, 157
    —, equal, 124, 128, 159
    —, extraordinary, 158
    —, opposite, 157
    —, straight, 128
    —, symmetrical, 123, 124, 128, 157, 158, 159, 160
    —, undular, 238
    — angle, 99, 105, 119, 124, 126, 128, 129, 136, 157
    — position, 156
    index of refraction, 54, *75*, 76, 77, 78, 79, 80, *81*, *82*, 83, 84, *91*, 93, 99, 107, 143, 197, 198, 238, 246, 247, 249, 270
    indicatrix, *99*, 100, 132, 165
    —, orientation of, *99*, 100, 106, 107, 165
    optic axis figure, 111
    — sign, 91
    optical axis, 111, 112, 124
    — bisectrix, 121, 124, 125, 133, *136*, 143
    relief, 132, *140*
    schiller, 36, 41, 75
Or, definition of, 24–25
Order–disorder relation, 21, 22, 31, 35, 36, 96
Ordered, 31, 150
— feldspar, *see* feldspar
— structure or phase, 93, 129, 180, *184*, 229
Ore-dressing techniques, 66
Organic material, 4, 230, 256
Orthoclase, *see* alkali feldspar
— microperthite, *see* alkali feldspar
Orthogneisses, 153
Orthoscopical observation, 91, 108, *116*
Oslo Feldspar Symposium, 154
Outcrop, 234
Oxidation of organic compounds, *see* procedures

Para-focussing arrangement, *see* X-ray
Parallel law, *see* twinning

— twins, *see* twins
Parent material, 5, 9, 11, 12, 250
Particle size, 274, 275 (*see also* separation)
Partly ordered phase, 3?, *184*
Pebbles, 234
Pedology, 33, 106
PEDRO, G., 15
Pegmatite, 82
PEISER, H. S., ROOKSBY, H. P. and WILSON, A. J. C., 172
Percolation, 249
Pericline, 35 (*see also* plagioclase)
— law, *see* twinning
— twins, *see* twins
Peristerite, *see* plagioclase
Perthite, 1, 6, 7, 24, 30, 41, *42*, 44, 45, 56, 60, 77, 151, 180, 183, 185, 190, 192, 193, 194, 229, 231, 239, 249, 267, 268, 269, *274*, *275*
    antiperthite, 41, *44*, 45, 180
    cryptoperthite, 41, 42, 43, 92, 94, 106, 239, 269
    hair perthite, *45*, 231
    mesoperthite, 7, 41, *44*, 45, 231, 274
    microcline perthite, 60, 77, 157, 183, 185, 192, 193, 231, 248, 249 (*see also* alkali feldspar)
    microperthite, 42, 48, 60, 79, 80, 178, 231
    orthoclase microperthite, 60, 178
    peristerite, 6, 24, 36, 38, 41, 43, *45*, 83, 84, 199
—, exsolution phenomena of, 16, 44, 271
—, powder pattern of, 191
—, specific gravity of, 63
—, submicroscopic, 75, 100, 190
—, sub-X-ray, 42, 100, 190
—, X-ray, 42, 239
PETERS, TJ. J., 48
PETERSON, M. N. A. and GOLDBERG, E. D., 8
Petrofabric studies, 108
Petrographic microscope, 107, *132*, 240, 268, 269, 275
Petroleum sulphonate, 73 (*see also* flotation)
Phase-contrast microscopy, 249, 275
Phenocryst, 81, 164
Phenol, 254
Phillipsite, 242, 244
Phonolite, 14
Phosphorus, 12
Phyllosilicates, 230
Physical properties, 54
PITTMAN, E. D., 155, 273
Plagioclase, 1, *24*, *34*, 59, 62, *63*, 64, *80*, 82, 84, *95*, *106*, 107, 111, 113, 119, 122, 128, 137, 143, 149, 150, *153*, 156, 179, 185, 186, 194–200, 229, 232, 238, 239, 244, 245, 248, 262, 265, 267, 269, 270, 272, 273, 274

Plagioclase *(continued)*
    albite, 1, 24, *34*, *35*, 38, 57, 62, 64, 125, 143, 149, 158, 161, 178, 179, 185, 192, 194, 200, 203, 229, 240, 241, 248, 249, 267, 268, 269, 276 (*see also* alkali feldspar)
    —, alpha, 35
    —, Amelia, 81, 164, 165, 198
    —, authigenic, 9, 96, 249 (*see also* alkali feldspar)
    —, beta, 35
    —, Bucarischuna, 34, 170, 171, 183, 185, 193, 201
    —, gamma, 35
    —, high, 38, 155, 178, 184 (*see also* alkali feldspar)
    — low, 43, 155, 171, 178, 183, 195 (*see also* alkali feldspar)
    andesine, 1, 38, 59, 96, 143, 238, 244, 270
    anorthite, 1, 34, *35*, 38, 57, 143, 178, 195, 200, 201
    —, hexagonal, 24, 36
    —, orthorhombic, 36
    barbierite, 35
    bytownite, 1, 38, 96, 143, 178
    clevelandite, 165, 166
    labradorite, 1, 38, 41, 96, 143, 201, 267
    oligoclase, 1, 38, 54, 59, 143, 185, 203, 233, 238, 244, 248, 267, 268
    pericline, 35
    peristerite, 6, 24, 36, 38, 41, 43, *45*, 83, 84, 199 (*see also* perthite)
  —, acid, 229, 231, 267
  —, ammonium, 38
  —, axial angle of, *90*, 95
  —, calcic, 120, 267, 268, *270*
  —, calcium-rich, 197, 203, 229
  —, chemical composition of, *38*, 95, 99, 130, 137, 272
  —, clastic, 113
  —, genesis of, 7
  — glasses, 56
  —, high-temperature, 82, 83, 84, 195, 196, 197, 229, 235
  — in between 20% and 40% *An, 197*
  —, intermediate (chem.), *36*, 96, 197, 229, 235
  —, low-temperature, 195, 196, 197, 198, 199, 200
  —, natural, 64
  —, powder pattern of, 186, 190, *195*, 197, 199, 210–225
  —, sodium-rich, 197
  — stereogram, *see* stereogram
  —, structural state of, 129
  —, synthetic, 64
  — with less than 20% *An, 197*

— — more than 40% *An, 200*
—, zonal, 273
Poikiloblastic structure, 64
Point counting, *see* counting methods
— focus, *see* X-ray
Polar groups, *see* flotation
Polarizers, 118, 122, 160
Pole of cleavage or composition plane, 112
Polycrystalline material, 169, 176
Polymetamorphic, 53
Polysynthetic twins, *see* twins
Potassium, 4, 5, 12, 14, 99, 228
— cobaltinitrite, 49 (*see also* staining)
— feldspar, *see* feldspar
— rhodizonate, 49 (*see also* staining)
Pot experiments, 13
Pottery spar, 73
Powder pattern of albite, 210–213
— — — —, Amelia, heated, 212, 213
— — — —, —, natural, 211
— — — —, synthetic, 214
— — — —, —, high-temperature, 210
— — — alkali feldspar, 205–209
— — — — —, natural low-temperature, 207
— — — — — —. synthetic high-temperature, 205, 206, 208, 209
— — — andesine, 215–216, 220–221
— — — —, calcic, 220, 221
— — — —, synthetic, 215, 216
— — — anorthite, 218–219, 225
— — — —, natural, 225
— — — —, synthetic, 218, 219
— — — bytownite, 217–218, 223–224
— — — —, acid, 223
— — — —, calcic, 224
— — — —, synthetic, 217, 218
— — — labradorite, 216–218, 222
— — — —, calcic, 222
— — — —, synthetic, 216, 217, 218
— — — microcline, 207
— — — —, authigenic maximum. 207
— — — oligoclase , 214–215, 220
— — — —, synthetic, 214, 215, 220
— — — perthite, 191
— photograph, *see* X-ray
— sample, *see* X-ray
Precession, 104
Preferred orientation, *see* X-ray
Prehnite, 59
Preparation of thin sections, *see* procedures
Pre-treatment, *69*, 229, 235, 245, 256, 258
Priem, H. N. A., 36, 80
Primary twinning, *see* twinning
— X-ray beam, *see* X-ray
Prism law, *see* twinning
Probable error, 265

Procedures, *115*, 129
    acid digestion of gypsum, 258
    — treatment, *232*, *247*, 256
    alkali digestion, 233
    concentration, 203
    flotation, *68*
    H₂O₂ procedure, 233, *256*
    optical methods, 106, 270
    oxydation of organic compounds, 256
    preparation of thin sections from grain
        samples, *238*
    removal of carbonates, *246*, *256*
    — — — with EDTA, *256*, 257
    — — — — exchange resins, 257, 258, 259
    — — gypsum, 258
    — — — with EDTA, 258
    — — — — exchange resins, *257*, 258
    — — —, Favejee's treatment, *258*
    — — iron, nascent hydrogen method, *260*
    — — —, Wageningen procedure, *259*
    — — — oxide, *259*
    — — — —, method of Mehra and Jack-
        son, *259*
Provenance, 9, 41, 53, 56, 150, 153, 155, 203,
    228, 231, 235, 273
Pseudo monoclinic alkali feldspar, *see* alkali
    feldspar
Pulp, *see* flotation
Pyridine, 254
Pyrite, 258
Pyroxene, 9, 12, 19, 33, 261

Quadruple Guinier de Wolff camera, 43, 172
    (*see also* X-ray)
Quantitative feldspar analysis, 228
Quartz, 5, 10, 12, 54, 55, 59, 62, 63, 64, 133,
    143, 151, 227, 229, 230, 231, 238, 239, 241,
    242, 243, 244, 245, 246, 248, 249, 261, 268,
    269, 271
— depressant, *see* flotation
— feldspar fraction, 230, 234
— monochromator, *see* X-ray
— plagioclase fraction, 269
— wedge, *see* compensator
Quartzite, 230, 255, 272

Radiation, *see* X-ray
Random orientation, *see* X-ray
REEDER, S. W. and MCALLISTER, A. L., 49, 50
Refractive index, *see* optical properties
REINHARD, M., 112
Reliability of counts, *see* counting
Relief, *see* optical properties
Removal of carbonates, *see* procedures
— — gypsum, *see* procedures
— — iron oxide, *see* procedures

RETGERS, J. W., 9, 227, 229
Rhodizonic acid potassium salt, 52 (*see also*
    staining)
Rhodochrosite, *see* carbonates
Rhombic section, 122, 137, 158, 160 (*see also*
    twinning)
RIBBE, P. H., 36, 41, 45, 81, 83, 90
RIBBE, P. H. and VAN COTT, H. C., 45
Ribbon counting, *see* counting methods
RITTMANN, A., 83, 113, 114, 119, 128
RITTMANN, A. and EL-HINNAWI, E., 128, 129,
    130
Rittmann-Ebert method, 114
ROBERTSON, F., 44, 45
Rock fragments, 231
— salt, 9
— slabs, 51, 52, 232, 234, 235, 241, 264, 276
Roc-Tourné law, *see* twinning
ROSENQVIST, I. TH., 35
Rotation, 103
Rubidium, 12, 33, 40

Sample holder, *see* X-ray
— preparation, *see* X-ray
Sampling model, 73
Sandstone, 7, 202, 229, 230, 231, 232, 250, 272,
    273, 274
Sandy soil, 229, *235*
Sanidine, *see* alkali feldspar
Saussuritization, 238
SCHAIRER, J. F., SMITH, J. R. and CHAYES, F.,
    56
SCHIAVINATO, A. G., 76
Schiller, *see* optical properties
Schmidt net, *see* equal area projection
SCHNEIDER, T. R. and LAVES, F., 35
SCHÖNER, H., 248
SCHUSTER, M., 83
Schuster's convention, *119*, 121, 157
SCHWARZMANN, S., 81, 82, 83, 92
Scopi law, *see* twinning
Sea floor, 5, 6
Section ⊥ *a*, *118*, 120, 123, 124, 126, *133*, 143,
    157, *158*, *160*, 166
— ⊥ *b*, 121, *122*, 160
— ⊥ *c*, *120*, 121, 124, 128, 166
— ⊥ (001), *126*, 138, *158*, 166
— ⊥ (010), 138, 153, *158*, 166
— normal to the composition plane, *158*, 159
— — — — rhombic section, 140, *158*
— — — — twin axis, *159*
— parallel to the twin axis, *159*
Sediment, 6, 57, 143, 150, 178, 194, 203, 234,
    240, 241, 249, 250, 253, 254, 274
Sedimentary rocks, 202, 274
— structure, 109

Sedimentology, 33, 106, 108, 227, 274, 276
Seeman-Bohlin true focussing arrangement, 172 (see also X-ray)
Selectivity of flotation, see flotation
SEN, S. K., 40, 44
Separation, 59, 255, 263
    bromoform, 58, 238
    centrifuge methods, 59
    decaline, 58
    Favejee funnel, 58, 262
    funnel, 14, 58, 257
    heavy fraction, 232, 248
    — liquids, 57, 73, 203, 235, 268
    — liquid separation, 54, 57, 254, 263, 267
    light fraction, 47, 178, 229, 232, 233, 235, 262
    magnetic fraction, 261
    — separation, 55, 73, 251, 261, 262
    non-magnetic fraction, 55, 261
    particle size, 274, 275
    silt fraction, 56, 255
Serpentinite, 59
Shale, 240, 246
SHAPIRO, L. and BRANNOCK, W. W., 48
Shell deposits, 245
Siderite, see carbonates
SIEGEL, S., 264
Sieve analysis, 233, 249, 260
Silicium, 4
— tetrahedron, 20
Silicon, 4, 230
— fluoride, 68
Sillimanite, 261
Silt, 242, 245
— fraction, 56, 255, 274, 275 (see also separation)
Silver nitrate, 175 (see also X-ray)
Simple twins, see twins
Single crystal X-ray method, see X-ray
Size fraction, 260, 265
Skin ointment, 50
Slate, 240
SLEMMONS, D. B., 83, 92, 95, 96, 107, 108, 112
SMITH, J. R., 8, 82, 83, 95, 96
SMITH, J. V., 36, 80, 154, 175, 179, 180, 196, 197, 198, 199, 202, 212, 213, 244
SMITH, J. V. and GAY, P., 36, 80, 179, 195, 196, 197, 200, 244
SMITH, J. V. and MACKENZIE, W. S., 150
SMITHSON, S. B., 97
Sodalite, 59
Sodium, 45, 99, 192, 194
— acetate, 51
— carbonate, 258
— dithionite, 251, 259
— hypochlorite, 254

— rich plagioclase, see plagioclase
Soil, 57, 194, 249
— erosion, 4
— fertility, 10, 11, 13, 33, 228, 235
— formation, 9, 10, 244
— forming process, 4, 5, 12, 245
— micromorphology, 239
— monolith, 239
— type, 12
Solid solution, 19, 27, 36, 106
Source area, 6, 231, 235
Soxhlet, 253
Space group, 178
— — C$\bar{1}$, 178, 195
— — C 2/m, 178
— — P$\bar{1}$, 178, 195
Specific density, 54
— gravity, 54, 56, 57, 59, 60, 197, 240, 258, 261, 262, 264, 270, 271
— — separation, 57, 235, 261, 267, 268, 275
SPENCER, E., 23, 29, 30, 55, 75, 76, 77, 80, 93, 105, 192
Stability field, 21, 31
Stable phases, 22
Staining, 49, 50, 72, 143, 239, 241, 254, 263, 267, 268, 271, 276
    barium chloride, 49, 52
    — rhodizonate, 49, 51, 52
    cobaltinitrite, 49, 50, 51, 143, 232, 267, 269
    glacial acetic acid, 51, 52
    hemateine, 49, 51, 52, 232, 263, 267, 268, 269, 270
    hydrofluoric acid, 49–52
    potassium cobaltinitrite, 49
    — rhodizonate, 49
    rhodizonic acid potassium salt, 52
    sodium acetate, 51
Staurolite, 261
STEFFEN, W., 33, 40
Stereo microscope, 203
Stereogram, 103, 111, 112, 113, 114, 118, 119, 120, 122
Stereographic net, 103, 109, 112
— projection, 104, 105, 112, 114, 118, 120, 121, 122
STIELER, A., 55
Stilpnomelane, 59
STRAKHOV, N. M., 251
Strontium, 33, 40
Structural phenomena, 27
— state, 7, 75, 86, 92, 94, 99, 105, 128, 179, 198, 270, 271, 272, 273, 275
Structure of feldspars, see feldspar
Submicroscopic perthites, see perthite
Submicroscopical twins, see twinning

Sub-X-ray perthite, *see* perthite
— twinning, *see* twinning
Sulfates, 9, 25, 255, 259
Sulfide ores, 66
Sulphuric acid, 73 (*see also* flotation)
Superstructure, 100
Surface properties, *see* flotation
— tension, 69
SWINEFORD, A. and FRYE, J. C., 239
Symmetrical extinction, *see* optical properties
Symmetry, 99
— plane of twins, *see* twinning
Synthetic alkali feldspar, *see* alkali feldspar
— feldspar, *see* alkali feldspar *or* plagioclase
— plagioclase, *see* plagioclase
System of coordinates, 101

Tailing, 72, 263, 267, 268 (*see also* flotation)
Target of X-ray tubes, *see* X-ray
TAYLOR, W. H., 20, 21, 27, 169
Tectonites, 150
Tenability of liquids, 58
TEODOROVICH, G. I., 31
Ternary feldspars, *see* feldspar
— system, 23, 24
Terrestrial environment, 3
— influence, *3*
Tetradecylacetate, 68 (*see also* flotation)
Thermodynamical properties, 3, 13, 15, 47
Thin section, 51, 52, 107, *115*, 117, 136, 143,
    156, 230, 231, 234, 235, 238, 239, 240, 241,
    246, 253, 254, 264, 268, 272, 273, 274, 275
— — study, *232, 238, 246*
THOM, C. and GISLER, H. J., 73
TOBI, A. C., 112, 119, 124, 126, 134, 135, 137,
    138, 140, 143, 146, 154, 156, 159, 160, 165,
    167
Tourmaline, 12, 33, 248, 249
Trace elements, 12, 33, 40, 228
Trachyte, 161
Traditional fertility, 10, 11
Transformation twins, *see* twins
Triclinic alkali feldspar, *see* alkali feldspar
Triclinicity, 96, 97 (*see also* obliquity)
TRÖGER, W. E., 56, 90, 110, 111, 112, 113, 121,
    125, 126, 128, 130, 153
TSCHERMAK, G., 42
TSUBOI, S., 86, 87, 89
Tsuboi's method, *86, 88, 89*
Tube axis of microscope, 117
Tuff, 82, 274
TURNER, F. J., 112
TUTTLE, O. F., 42, 75, 76, 93, 106
TUTTLE, O. F. and BOWEN, N. L., 35, 81
Twinning, 56, 107, 117, 121, 124, 125, 132,
    145, 165, 232, 239, 271, 273, *275*

(010)-twin ratio, 155
    composition plane, 107, 112, 113, 121, 122,
        123, 124, 125, 133, 136, 145, 146, 156
    Kantennormalengesetz, 146, 147
    rhombic section, 122, 137, 158, 160
    Roc-Tourné quadruplet, 249
— axis, 121, 123, 145, 150
—, classification of, *145*, 146
—, definition of, 145
—, frequency of, 151, 232
—, identification of, *156*, 161
— law, 112, 114, 145, 148, 271
— —, Ala, 146
— —, albite, 104, 146, 147, 150, 274
— —, — Carlsbad, 146
— —, — Esterel, 146
— —, Baveno, 146, 147, 158
— —, — left, 146, 147, 151
— —, — right, 146, 147, 151
— —, Carlsbad, 104, 146, 148, 166, 274
— —, — B, 146
— —, Esterel, 146
— —, Four la Brouque (Manebach), 146, 147,
    158
— —, Manebach (Four la Brouque), 146, 147,
    158
— —, — acline-A, 146
— —, — pericline, 146
— —, normal, 147
— —, parallel, 147
— —, pericline, 146, 148, 150, 166
— —, prism, 146, 153
— —, Roc-Tourné, 146
— —, Scopi, 146
— —, X-, 146
— —, X-Carlsbad, 146
— —, X-pericline, 146
— pattern, 7, 153, 229, 271, 272, *273, 275*
— record or inventory, 151
—, Sub-X-ray, 94, 190
—, symmetry plane of, 121, 137
—, type of, 7, 151, 160
Twins, *see also* twinning
—, A-, 123, 154
—, acline, 123, 125, 155, 160, 161
—, acline-A, 123, 124, 128, 146
—, Ala, 125
—, Ala-A, 123, 124, 128, 146
—, Ala-B, 123, 146, 274
—, albite, 121, 122, 123, 124, 126, 128,
    136, 149, 154, 155, 160
—, — Carlsbad, 122, 123, 124, *136*, 148, 161
—, alkali-feldspar, 165
—, antiparallel, 147
—, Baveno, 122, 123, 148, 150, 151, 152,
    153, 158

Twins *(continued)*
—, C-, 154
—, Carlsbad, 121, 122, 123, 124, 128, 133, 136, 137, 142, 147, 151, 153, 160, 248
—, characteristic, 6, 7
—, complex, 123, 124, 146, 147, 158, *159*
—, cross-hatched or M-, 25, 94, 149, 150, 180, 248, 267, 268, 275
—, glide, 150, 152, 155
—, growth, 149
—, lamellar, 113, 126, 146, 148, 149, 155, 160
—, M-, 150
—, Manebach, 123, 124, 128, 147, 148, 150, 151, 153, 158, 161
—, microcline, *see* cross-hatched twins
—, multiple, 124, 148, 249, 274
—, normal, 121, 123, 132, 146, 147, *158*
—, parallel, 121, 123, 124, 128, 132, 146, 147, 149, 158, *159*
—, pericline, 122, 123, 124, 137, 150, 153, 155, 160, 161
—, polysynthetic, 148, 153, 155
—, primary, 155
—, simple, 148, 153, 154, 274
—, submicroscopical, 75, 94, 100
—, transformation, 100, 150, 151

UAC triangle, 154
Ultrasonic cleaner, 241, 253, 275
Unconsolidated sediments, *242*, 249, 250
Unit cell, 29, 30, 100, 179
— — parameters, 62, 94, 150, 170, *178*, 180
Universal stage, 86, 92, 104, 107, *108*, 109, 111, 115, *116*, 117, 118, 119, 121, 122, 123, 128, 131, 132, 156, 159, 165, 238, 239, 240, 248, 269, 270, 272, 274
— —, five-axes stage, 108
— —, four-axes stage, 108, 116
— —, three-axes stage (Cooke and Throughton), 108
Uzakov, P., 250

Valency, 19
Vance. J. A., 155
Van der Kaaden, G., 83, 92, 96, 107, 112, 113, 163, 164
Van der Marel, H. W., 14
Van der Plas, L., 72, 154, 234, 264, 267, 269
Van der Veen, A. H., 48
Vapour pressure, 58
Vestopal, 143, 239
Vicinal forms. 112
Viscosity of heavy liquids, 58
Vogel, D. E., 238
Volcanic rocks, 7, 27, 35, 82, 245, 270, 273

Von Goethe, J. W., 145

Wahlstrom, E. E., 93, 105, 109, 112, 117, 137
Wavelength, *see* X-ray
Weathering, 3, 4, 9, 10, 11, 34, 244, 245
— experiments, *14*
Weibel, M., 38
Weissman, R. C. and Diehl, H. C., 257
Wenk, E., 36, 86
Wetting properties of heavy liquids, 58
Wick, W., 241
Wilson, A. F., 76, 93
Winchell, A. N., 91
Winchell, A. N. and Winchell, H., 56, 146
Wones, D. R. and Appleman, D. E., 28
Wright's biquartz wedge, 119
Wulff's net or stereographic net, 105, 109, 118

Xenolith, 82
X-law, *see* twinning
X-ray, 36, 170, 244
    beam catcher, 176
    calibration, 170, *174*, 175
    camera, 42, 43, 170–178, 184, 193, 203, 204, 242, 243, 272
    —, Debye-Scherrer, 170, 171, 176, 177, 178
    —, Favejee, 172
    —, quadruple Guinier-de Wolff, 43, 171, 172, *173*, *174*, 175, 176, 177, 178, 184, 193, 203, 204, 242, 243, 272
    camera radius, 170
    capillary, Keesom, 172, 177
    —, Lindemann glass, 177
    collimating system, 170
    crystal monochromation, 172, 173
    diaphragm, 173
    diffractogram, 169, 170, 172, 204, 261
    exposure time, 170, 172, 176
    focussing arrangement, *172*, 173, 174
    intensity of diffraction lines, 175
    Melinex film, 176
    methods, 107, 203, 268, 272
    —, Hiemstra's, 177, 203, 268, 272
    —, single crystal, 43, 169, 196
    monochromator, 173
    —, LiF, 172
    —, quartz, 172
    parafocussing arrangement, 172
    preferred orientation, 172, 177, 242, 243
    radiation, cobalt, 175, 176, 183, 197, 199, 200, 270
    —, copper, 175, 176, 200, 242
    —, fluorescent, 175, 176
    —, iron, 270
    random orientation, 243

X-ray *(continued)*
    resolving power of instruments, 170, 172
    sample, powder, 170
    — holder, 176
    — preparation, *176*
    standard substances, 175
    —, ammonium allun, 175
    —, lead nitrate, 175
    —, silver nitrate, 175
    target, *175*
    true-focussing arrangement, 172
—, analysis, 176, 202, 233, 235, 255, 267, 268, 270, 272
— diffraction lines, 170, 172, 174, 179, 194, 272
— diffractometer, 43, 172, 173, 174, 175, 177, 178, 242, 243, 244
— extinction conditions, 178
— film, 172, 175
— fluorescence, 175
—, harmonic, 172
— line focus, 176
—, monochromatic, 170, 172
— perthite, *see* perthite

— primary beam, 243
— point focus, 176
— powder data, 56
— — pattern, *169*, 170, *180*, 183, 191, 203, 238, 240, 241, 261, 267, 270, 272, 275
— — photograph, 171, 173, 175, 203, 204
— cobalt tube, 176, 242
— copper tube, 175
— tube, 172
— —, focus of, 172, 176

YOUNG, R. S., 40
Yttrium, 33

Zeolite, 241, 242
Zircon, 47, 55, 241, 261
ZIRKEL, F., 42
Zonal plagioclase, *273* (*see also* plagioclase)
— structure, 53, 86, 133
Zone method, 108, 114, *115*, 124, 130, 167
— normal to (001), 121, 140, 141
— — — (010), 138, 139
— — — rhombic section, 142, 143